PENGUIN BOOKS

THE DICK TRACY CASEBOOK

Max Allan Collins brings his contemporary crime-novelist's touch to the classic comic strip that was his own childhood favorite. Taking over from creator Chester Gould in 1977, Collins is only the second person ever to write *Dick Tracy*. He has also written the *Batman* comic book and strip, and his historical detective novel *True Detective* won the Private Eye Writers of America "Shamus" for best novel of 1983. He, his wife Barb and their son Nathan live in Muscatine, Iowa.

Dick Locher brings his own uniquely comic flair to *Dick Tracy*, while maintaining the strip's traditional look as only a former Chester Gould assistant could. Locher's ability to capture the absurdities of life in his political cartoons earned him a Pulitzer Prize in 1983; his *Chicago Tribune* panels have been reprinted in *Time*, *Newsweek*, *Forbes*, *Playboy* and hundreds of newspapers around the world. He, his wife Mary and their family live in Naperville, Illinois.

Chester Gould, the creator of Dick Tracy, was born in 1900. He grew up in Oklahoma, where his newspaper-publisher father encouraged his artistic abilities. After ten years of struggling as a journeyman cartoonist, he created the innovative *Dick Tracy* comic strip in 1931, virtually inventing the tough American detective. *Dick Tracy* has been adapted for radio, TV and movies and has generated toys, games, clothing, books and much more. Gould died at his home in Woodstock, Illinois, in 1985, and is survived by his wife Edna and their daughter Jean Gould O'Connell.

THE DICK TRACY CASEBOOK

Favorite Adventures, 1931–1990

Selected by

Max Allan Collins and Dick Locher

PENGUIN BOOKS

PENGUIN BOOKS

Published by the Penguin Group
Penguin Books Ltd, 27 Wrights Lane, London W8 5TZ, England
Viking Penguin, a division of Penguin Books USA Inc.
375 Hudson Street, New York, New York 10014, USA
Penguin Books Australia Ltd, Ringwood, Victoria, Australia
Penguin Books Canada Ltd, 2801 John Street, Markham, Ontario, Canada L3R 1B4
Penguin Books (NZ) Ltd, 182-190 Wairau Road, Auckland 10, New Zealand

Penguin Books Ltd, Registered Offices: Harmondsworth, Middlesex, England

This selection first published in the USA by St Martin's Press, New York 1990
Published in Great Britain in Penguin Books 1990
1 3 5 7 9 10 8 6 4 2

Printed in England by Clays Ltd, St Ives plc

CONTENTS

"THIS BOOK IS DEDICATED TO THE MEMORY OF GOOD FRIENDS, STILL WITH US IN SPIRIT."
CHESTER GOULD
DICK MOORES
JOHN LOCHER
RICK FLETCHER
GA

INTRODUCTION

I remember a conversation with my father, many years back. It was on one of our special father-son fishing trips. He said to me, "You know, I grew up in the golden age of everything!"

I was taken aback. I knew that his years were the years of America's great Depression. "C'mon, Dad, how could it have been the golden years when there was joblessness, hunger, suffering, and loss of purpose in the country?"

"That's just it—Americans were desperate. They wanted work! They worked furiously to keep whatever they had and I figure they made the best of everything just to hang on."

I had no idea where my dad was going with this, but I listened intently because my father had some sly observations on life. "Analyze it," he said. "We had the golden age of sports, the golden age of movies, automobiles, literature, and aviation. We had the Lou Gehrigs, Babe Ruths, the Cords, and Duesenbergs, Clark Gable, Jimmy Doolittle, Hemingway, and F. Scott Fitzgerald."

My father continued, "I don't think we recognized it then, but it was the golden age. If we could sidestep the suffering I mentioned, it was a high point in America's acknowledgment of quality and pride. It was America's renaissance." I nodded approvingly. My father was all wise.

As I think about my father's words today, I would have added one more category to his list. His youth was the golden age of cartooning.

In the 1920s and 1930s, giants reigned in the comic industry. I'm sure you remember *Krazy Kat*, *Li'l Abner*, *Terry and the Pirates*, and *Buck Rogers*. It's a world in which I am deeply immersed, for . . . I draw *Dick Tracy*.

I was asked to become Chester Gould's assistant in the late 1950s, and I had the opportunity to observe and admire the workings of one of the true masters of the golden age of comics. I watched his drawing unfold. I saw his kaleidoscope of villains come and then go to their untimely demises. In the likes of B.O. Plenty and Gravel Gertie, I saw humor as it had never been delivered before. I heard people call to see what would happen to Tracy because they couldn't wait till his "Perils of Pauline" type of adventure came to a conclusion.

Today, America's comic pages are not the same. In some ways they are better. The pages of our newspapers now have more gag-type strips. Who, today, could not smile with Charlie Brown and his clan, the everyday traumas of *For Better or for Worse*, with Calvin the mischievous, or *Hagar the Horrible*? These are classics in their own right.

However, we still retain a cord to the past. We have comics today born of dedication and inspiration—strips that have such entertainment value that they still flourish. *Orphan Annie* and *Dick Tracy* are two of these strips. They continue to enhance the comic pages because they possess a key ingredient of today's popular strips—humor.

When Chet needed me, I agreed to do the strip because I was fond of him. When I worked with him on *Tracy* he insisted on using a humorous tone from time to time. It wasn't all blood and guts. He did this because he possessed a fine sense of humor of his own. I can remember vividly one practical joke that he took great delight in executing.

One Friday evening we were finishing up a week's worth of the Tracy strip. Chet asked me to draw a machine gun in panel three of the Sunday page. Since it was late in the day, he suggested that I take it home to finish it up, and—in keeping with his policy of strict authenticity—that I use a machine gun I would find on the top shelf of our closet. "Wrap it up and take it home," he said as he stepped out the door.

I investigated, with the help of a stool, and, sure enough, there on the shelf—way back behind some paper supplies—was a true-to-life German Schmeisser, a World War II machine gun. I rolled it in brown kraft paper and, with my drawing case and strips, started out the door of the Tribune Tower to catch my 5:40 train at Union Station, a mile away.

I wasn't twenty feet out the door when I heard a stern voice say, "Sir, may I speak with

you?" I glimpsed a figure out of the corner of my eye. It was one of Chicago's finest. I thought, "My God, I'm carrying a machine gun and a Chicago policeman wants to converse!" My first reaction was to quicken the pace and put some distance between us.

A hand on my shoulder destroyed that notion immediately. As he stared into my frightened face, the policeman said, "Would you step over to my squad car, please!" Panic had now set in. I would never see my wife and son again, except in Joliet prison. I was carrying an automatic weapon through the streets of Chicago—and the police knew it! "What have you got in the package?" the cop asked, gently seating me in the back of his blue-and-white police cruiser.

"Leftover pizza," was the best I could come up with, as sweat appeared all over my body.

"Let's see the pizza!" came a firm reply.

"Now wait a minute, Officer, there's a story behind this. . . ." I unwrapped the blue-steel instrument of destruction.

"I know there is," the cop replied. "Chester Gould called us and told us to give you a ride to Union Station!"

I call this mega-humor. Chet could make anyone laugh—including Chicago cops.

The Dick Tracy strip continued after Chet retired. It was handed down to two exceptional comic strip practitioners, Max Allan Collins and Rick Fletcher. The humor remained, as well as sparkling art, and Tracy was catapulted into new adventures.

Life sometimes imitates art, where personalities come and go. The strip suddenly lost its artist when Rick Fletcher died. I was called in to take his place. A challenge, to be sure. There had been many Tracy scenarios since I'd last worked with Chet, but Allan and I forged ahead.

I was elated at this point to be joined by my son John, who had just completed his art studies at Northern Illinois University. The three of us took Tracy into some uncharted waters with great gusto. We toyed with toxic wastes and cryogenics, and schemed with the KGB, sending Tracy to the Soviet Union.

But just as suddenly as before, we lost another Tracy man—John. I grieved for many reasons, but losing someone so close, who I had thought would some day do Tracy, haunts me today.

Many of America's strips are gone now—gone like the Clark Gables, the Humphrey Bogarts, the Packards and the Auburns. Can we see their likes now? Can we see the Li'l Abners, Offissa Pupp, Pruneface, B-B Eyes, Pat Ryan, and Terry? Not really, but then maybe we don't have to. . . . I still remember the best, as did my father. It truly was a unique age of everything. He was right, and he was lucky.

Let's hope the generations of today start their own list of greats. I have mine and I revel in them. My son, Steve, and his son, Michael, have theirs, and they are great. I can hear them now: "Dad, did you see what Putty Puss did today?" And I know some things are still golden.

DICK LOCHER

THE 1930s

THE HOTEL MURDERS

by Chester Gould

3/9/36–4/27/36

Chester Gould introduced his square-jawed sleuth in late 1931, causing a sensation in the comic-strip world. While soap-opera continuities such as Harold Grey's *Little Orphan Annie* and Sidney Smith's *The Gumps* preceded *Dick Tracy*, as did a few adventure strips (notably Roy Crane's *Wash Tubbs* and Hal Foster's *Tarzan*), it was *Tracy* that set the tone and the standard for fast-paced, violently melodramatic story-strip fare.

In the opening days of the strip, the murder of Tess Trueheart's father by minions of the Al Capone-like Big Boy led to Tracy swearing vengeance and joining the police force of a major unnamed city that might be Chicago. His single-minded, meet-violence-with-violence war on crime continues unabated to this day.

That the first villain, Big Boy, was patterned on Capone is of course no accident; Gould, a Chicagoan (by way of Oklahoma), shared the frustration of the local citizenry when Capone brazenly shot down reporter Jake Lingle (who proved to be dirty himself, but never mind) and apparently ordained the brutal St. Valentine's Day massacre. Partially inspired by the publicized successes of a handful of federal men (notably the young, handsome Eliot Ness), Gould—by instinct a "bigfoot" humor cartoonist—turned his pen to the creation of a modern-day American Sherlock Holmes who might take on the Capones of the urban jungle.

Gould patterned Tracy rather directly on Holmes, a snap-brim fedora substituting for the deerstalker cap, the yellow topcoat taking the place of the Inverness cape, and a loyal but not brilliant Watson in Pat Patton (replaced later by the more street-smart Sam Catchem). But Gould mixed realism with his fantasy; he was always concerned with matters of police procedure and criminology—lie detectors, ballistic tests, and fingerprints were part of Tracy's police-science arsenal from day one.

In the 1930s, Tracy most frequently fought villains who might have crawled off the front page: Big Boy was Capone, Boris Arson escaped jail in a Dillinger-like fashion, and other Gould baddies invoked Bonnie and Clyde, Baby-Face Nelson, Legs Diamond, and other outlaws and gangsters of the day. Movie stars provided the pattern for some characters: Edward G. Robinson inspired both Stooge Viller and Dan Mucelli; Marlene Dietrich was Marrow; Boris Karloff was Karpse. Larger-than-life villains like Flattop and the Brow were not yet part of Tracy's world.

Also characterizing the thirties *Tracy* was a strong element of soap opera, always present in the strip (even today) but never more so than during the Depression years. Much of this derived from Tracy's ongoing, sometimes stormy relationship with his fiancée Tess Trueheart; but drama also characterized Tracy's relationship with his adoptive son Junior, whose dead-end kid background provided heartache, particularly when his real parents turned up. Sequences in hospitals, where sympathetic characters fight for their lives (and sometimes lose) while Tracy and others pray for their recovery, are common throughout the run of the strip.

"The Hotel Murders" is a rarity in *Dick Tracy*—a mystery. Tracy, America's most famous fictional detective, has hardly ever tackled mysteries in the true Agatha Christie/Ellery Queen or even Hammett/Chandler sense. The day-to-day nature of story strips, with continuities lasting months, makes it difficult if not impossible for readers to keep track of clues, red herrings, and the various details necessary to keep a whodunit afloat. (The only other whodunit to appear in Tracy was a 1982–83 Collins/Fletcher continuity, reprinted in 1987 by Dragon Lady Press as "Who Shot Pat Patton?") Consequently, this is a short continuity, by Gould standards. But the solution is a memorable one, and would be prominently referred to, decades later, in the Sydney Pollack/Robert Redford film *Three Days of the Condor.*

This tale is also unusual in that the perpetrator is sympathetic; Gould rarely had sympathy for his bad guys, despite his uncanny ability to make even the most evil villains interesting and human.

THAT'S WHAT I SAID, FOLKS, THE TRIP IS OFF- THAT TELEPHONE CALL WAS FOR ME.
OH! OHH!
NO KIDDING, DICK!

GOTHORN SHOT! DYING
KING OF GAMBLE AND CONFIDENC MEN DISCOVERE IN HOTEL, BULL WOUND IN STO
ADDIE GOTHORN

WE KNOW ALL ABOUT IT, DICK. THE NEWSBOY CAME ALONG WITH THIS PAPER WHILE YOU WERE IN THE HOUSE.

CHIEF BRANDON BEGGED ME TO CALL THE TRIP OFF AND GO TO WORK ON THE CASE. I MUST REPORT TO HEADQUARTERS IMMEDIATELY.
CHESTER GOULD

TO THE EMERGENCY HOSPITAL, DRIVER!
YES SIR.
TAXI

TRACY, TOO BAD TO CALL OFF YOUR TRIP SOUTH — BUT THIS IS THE BIGGEST UNDERWORLD BLOW-OFF WE'VE EVER HAD!

ADDIE GOTHORN IS DEAD! HE DIED 3 MINUTES AFTER I TALKED TO YOU ON THE TELEPHONE.

AT LEAST A THOUSAND PEOPLE COULD HAVE COMMITTED THIS MURDER. -GOTHORN WAS THAT HATED!
HM-M- TWO BULLETS THROUGH THE STOMACH.

THAT'S THE SERVANTS' ENTRANCE TO THE HOTEL. JUST INSIDE THE DOOR IS WHERE GOTHORN WAS DISCOVERED.

HERE'S THE DAY DOORMAN AND THE JANITOR THAT DISCOVERED HIM.
ALL I KNOW IS— OTTO AND I HEARD GROANS AS WE CAME BACK TO CHANGE OUR CLOTHES AND GO OFF DUTY—

AND LYING RIGHT THERE IN THAT SPOT WAS MR. GOTHORN. SEE THE BLOODSTAINS?

IS THAT THE FIRST TIME YOU HAD SEEN HIM THAT DAY?
NO. FROM MY STATION OUT FRONT, I SAW HIM COME OUT OF BINDIE'S RESTAURANT, JUST ACROSS THE STREET, AND ENTER THE HOTEL 10 MINUTES BEFORE HE WAS FOUND.
CHESTER

NOW, CHIEF, LET'S GET THIS STRAIGHT: GOTHORN'S CROWD HAD A BIG POKER GAME ABOUT THREE WEEKS AGO - AND GOTHORN LOST!

YES, HE LOST ABOUT $200,000 — OR MORE -AND REFUSED TO PAY, CLAIMING THE GAME WAS A FRAME-UP.

HEY! I'VE JUST FOUND OUT THAT THE NIGHT GOTHORN WAS KILLED "LIPS" MANLUS, THE BIGGEST WINNER IN THE POKER GAME WAS OCCUPYING A ROOM IN THAT SAME HOTEL!

GOOD! NOW I WANT YOU BOYS NOT ONLY TO BRING IN MANLUS BUT ALSO ROUND UP EVERY PLAYER IN THAT POKER GAME!

LET'S SEE- THE CASHIER'S NAME IN. HERE IS.. FRANE. THAT'S IT.. FRANE.
Bindie's RESTAURANT

HELLO TRACY. WHAT CAN I DO FOR YOU?
HELLO, FRANE CAN YOU DROP OVER TO HEADQUARTERS WITH ME FOR A FEW MINUTES?
CASHIER

I UNDERSTAND ADDIE GOTHORN WAS IN HERE ABOUT 15 MINUTES BEFORE HE WAS SHOT -AND THE CHIEF WAS THINKING THAT IF-
GOSH- I DON'T KNOW MUCH -BUT ANYTHING I CAN DO TO HELP-

MEANWHILE
LISTEN, PIERRE- GET ME THE BELLHOP THAT WAITED ON ROOM 404 THE DAY GOTHORN WAS PLUGGED, WILL YOU?
CERTAINLY! LET'S SEE, THAT WAS NO. 28- LORIMOR IS HIS NAME.
CHESTER

HERE HE IS, MR. PATTON. -BELLHOP LORIMOR.
HELLO LORIMOR. DID YOU WAIT ON ROOM 404 THE DAY GOTHORN WAS KILLED?

WHY YES. I DID.
GREAT! THEN YOU'LL BE ABLE TO GIVE US A LOT OF DOPE. WAIT DOWN IN THE LOCKER ROOM- I'LL BE RIGHT BACK.

WOW! THIS WILL BE OUR FIRST REAL INFORMATION! NOW TO GET DICK!
HOTEL CENTER SHORE

I GO OFF DUTY IN 10 MINUTES- MIGHT AS WELL CHANGE MY CLOTHES.
CHESTER GOULD

ALL RIGHT, FRANE, YOU'RE CASHIER IN BINDIE'S RESTAURANT! NOW REPEAT AGAIN JUST WHAT YOU KNOW ABOUT THIS CAGE.

A CALL CAME IN OVER THE TELEPHONE AT THE CASHIER'S DESK ABOUT NINE O'CLOCK OF THE EVENING GOTHORN WAS SHOT.
YES.

THE VOICE ASKED IF GOTHORN WAS IN THE RESTAURANT. I SAID NO, AND THE PARTY ASKED ME IF I WOULD TELL GOTHORN TO CALL ROOM 404 AT THE CENTER SHORE HOTEL WHEN HE CAME IN.

I DELIVERED THE MESSAGE. HE CALLED AND THEN WALKED OUT.
AND IT WAS JUST TEN MINUTES AFTER GOTHORN WALKED OUT OF THERE THAT HE WAS FOUND IN THE HOTEL'S SERVANTS' ENTRANCE SHOT.

TRACY! I JUST CALLED THE CENTER SHORE HOTEL, AND—
DID YOU GET THE BELLBOY WHO WAITED ON THE OCCUPANTS OF ROOM 404 THE NIGHT GOTHORN WAS SHOT?

THE MANAGER SAID THE BELL HOP IS THERE NOW, AND FOR US TO COME OVER AND GET HIM.
OKAY- LET'S GO.

HELLO, PIERRE.
OH YES, MR. TRACY. THE BELL HOP YOU WISH TO SEE IS LORIMOR. HE'S DOWN IN THE LOCKER ROOM CHANGING HIS CLOTHES AND WAITING FOR YOU.

OH, LORIMOR! HEY, LORIMOR!

THAT'S FUNNY.. HE CAME DOWN HERE JUST A MINUTE AGO TO CHANGE.
HE'S NOT IN THE WASH ROOM, DICK!

WELL - I'LL BE..? YES, THAT'S HIS LOCKER ALL RIGHT- NUMBER 12.
H'M! LOCKED TIGHT, I GUESS.
11
12
13

OW-W! LOOK!
11
13

IT'S YOUR BELL HOP, PIERRE. SHOT - DEAD!
11
13

COMING BACK TO THE CENTER SHORE HOTEL TO QUESTION THE BELL HOP- OUR FRIENDS MAKE A GRIM DISCOVERY.
GREAT SCOTT!!
YES, PIERRE, YOUR BELL HOP, LORIMOR, IS DEAD.
SHOT THROUGH THE HEAD!

BUT HOW COULD IT HAVE HAPPENED? HE CAME DOWN HERE ONLY TEN MINUTES AGO TO CHANGE CLOTHES!

HM- VICTIM OF A .38 CALIBER LEAD SLUG- I WOULD SAY!
BUT WHY? HE'S.. HE'S ONLY A BOY!

THE MURDERERS OF ADDIE GOTHORN HAVE DEFINITELY ASSURED THEMSELVES- BELL HOP LORIMOR WONT BE TALKING!!

WELL TRACY- HOW DO YOU EXPLAIN THIS BELLHOP MURDER?
THERE'S ONLY ONE EXPLANATION, CHIEF!

THIS BELLHOP WAITED ON THE OCCUPANTS OF ROOM 404 THE DAY GOTHORN WAS MURDERED- AND THE BELLHOP WAS SLAIN TO KEEP HIM SILENT.

THEN NAB WHOEVER OCCUPIED ROOM 404 THAT DAY! WHO WERE THEY?
THE PARTY WHO RENTED THAT ROOM, UNDER AN ALIAS, WAS "LIPS" MANLIS, THE HOODLUM!

I'VE ESTABLISHED HIS IDENTITY THROUGH FINGER PRINTS FOUND IN THE ROOM. ALSO, MANLIS WAS THE BIGGEST WINNER IN THAT POKER GAME WHERE GOTHORN LOST AND "WELSHED".

WELL OUR NEXT MOVE IS TO NAB "LIPS" MANLIS. DID YOU LOCATE HIS APARTMENT, PAT?

NO, BUT I CANVASSED THE PUBLIC GARAGES IN THE NEIGHBORHOOD WHERE HE'S SUPPOSED TO LIVE AND I LOCATED HIS BIG YELLOW SEDAN.

GOOD! WE'RE MAKING A BEE LINE FOR THAT GARAGE!
POLICE

WE'RE FROM POLICE HEADQUARTERS, BUD. WANT TO HANG AROUND TILL THE OWNER OF THAT BIG YELLOW CAR SENDS HIS CHAUFFEUR OVER.
YOU WON'T HAVE TO WAIT LONG-HE GETS HIS CAR EVERY EVENING ABOUT THIS TIME.

THERE'S MANLIS' CHAUFFEUR, DICK! LOOK!
GOOD! THERE'S A CAB WAITING OUTSIDE. COME ON!

FOLLOW THAT BIG YELLOW CAR, DRIVER
OKE!
TAXI

COME ON PAT!!
TEA ROOM

HEY! WHAT ARE YOU ~~!!xxx! COPS DOING HERE!
TAKE IT EASY, BUD. AND CALL UP THROUGH THAT SPEAKING TUBE. TELL MANLIS HIS CAR'S HERE!

UNSUSPECTING, "LIPS" MANLIS STEPS FROM THE ELEVATOR IN HIS APARTMENT BUILDING, TAKES ONE GLANCE AND REALIZES A TRAP—
WHAT IN THE—

COPS, EH? COME ON JOCKO - OUT TO THE CAR!

TAKE IT EASY, MANLIS!

GRAB THE SKY - YOU! AND BACK THE DOOR UP. I'D LIKE TO GET MY FOOT OUT, IF YOU DON'T MIND.

NOW, MR. MANLIS, JUST. RELAX AND TELL US ALL YOU KNOW ABOUT THE MURDER OF ADDIE GOTHORN.
IS THAT WHAT YOU WANT?

WE KNOW GOTHORN OWED YOU 100 GRAND ON A POKER DEBT AND HE WELSHED. NOW JUST TELL US HOW YOU KILLED HIM.

LISTEN, COPPER- I DID NOTHING AND I KNOW NOTHING!
TRACY! THE CORONER IS HERE AND WANTS TO SEE YOU IMMEDIATELY.

YES, MR. CORONER?
TRACY, I'VE MADE AN IMPORTANT DISCOVERY! THE BULLET WOUNDS IN GOTHORN'S STOMACH WERE NOT WHAT KILLED HIM. LOOK AT THIS DIAGRAM!

BUT I DIDN'T SHOOT HIM! -AND I DIDN'T SHOOT THAT BELLHOP!
THAT'S WHAT YOU SAY, MANLIS!

NOW GET THIS! WE KNOW THAT YOU ARE ONE OF THE TEN MEN THAT SAT IN A POKER GAME WITH ADDIE GOTHORN ABOUT FOUR WEEKS AGO.
22

WE ALSO KNOW THAT GOTHORN LOST ABOUT THREE HUNDRED GRAND, AND THAT YOU WERE THE BIGGEST WINNER!
SO WHAT?

WE ALSO KNOW THAT GOTHORN WELSHED ON THAT GAMBLING DEBT! .... THAT HE OWED YOU ALMOST A HUNDRED THOUSAND DOLLARS WHICH HE REFUSED TO PAY!
RING

TRACY-IT'S THE CORONER'S OFFICE! EVERYTHING'S READY.
OKAY, CHIEF. LOCK UP THE PRISONER, PAT – AND COME ALONG WITH ME.

TRACY, WHY ALL THIS FUSS TO FIND OUT WHO KILLED ADDIE GOTHORN? IT SEEMS TO ME THAT WHOEVER DID IT RENDERED HUMANITY A REAL SERVICE.
PAT- THAT'S NO WAY TO LOOK AT MURDER.

IN MY OPINION, THE SOLUTION TO GOTHORN'S KILLING WILL INVOLVE AT LEAST THREE OF THE BIGGEST AND MOST POWERFUL NAMES IN THIS CITY! WELL, HERE WE ARE.

WHY-THIS IS THE CEMETERY!
YOU'RE RIGHT, PAT. IT IS THE CEMETERY.

YOU DON'T MEAN-
YES-THE BODY OF ADDIE GOTHORN IS GOING TO BE EXHUMED- AT MY REQUEST.

LOOK AT THIS CORONER'S DIAGRAM. IT SHOWS THAT THE TWO BULLETS ENTERING GOTHORN'S STOMACH WERE IN REALITY QUITE SUPERFICIAL.

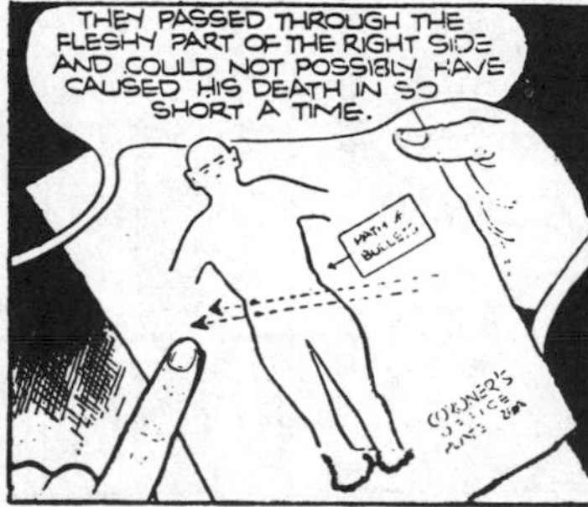
THEY PASSED THROUGH THE FLESHY PART OF THE RIGHT SIDE AND COULD NOT POSSIBLY HAVE CAUSED HIS DEATH IN SO SHORT A TIME.

YOU MEAN-
I MEAN DEATH RESULTED FROM SOME OTHER CAUSE. AND THAT CAUSE IS WHAT I INTEND TO UNCOVER!

SCENE: CEMETERY–
YES PAT, ACCORDING TO THIS CORONER'S REPORT THE TWO BULLETS THAT PASSED THROUGH GOTHORN'S BODY WERE MERELY FLESH WOUNDS.
PATH OF BULLETS
CORONERS OFFICE PLATE 26 A

DO YOU MEAN TO SAY, MR CORONER, THAT GOTHORN DIED OF SOMETHING ELSE?
EXACTLY!

THAT'S WHY I HURRIED TO HEADQUARTERS AND ASKED TRACY TO HAVE THE BODY EXHUMED.
IN OTHER WORDS, YOUR ORIGINAL VERDICT WAS WRONG.

YES, AFTER EXAMINING THE PAPERS AND CHARTS ON THIS CASE – I'M CONVINCED THE DEATH OF ADDIE GOTHORN WILL PROVE A MORE KNOTTY MYSTERY THAN YOU DETECTIVES SUSPECT.
CHESTER

EASY, BOYS!
EVEN IN DEATH ADDIE GOTHORN KNOWS NO REST!

TRACY, THE CORONER'S CRAZY WHEN HE SAYS THOSE BULLET HOLES DIDN'T KILL GOTHORN.
I DON'T THINK SO, PAT! I HAVE A GREAT DEAL OF RESPECT FOR THE CORONER'S JUDGEMENT.

IT WOULDN'T HAVE BEEN POISON?
HARDLY! OUR GANGSTERS OF TO-DAY DON'T BOTHER WITH SUCH HOMELY METHODS AS FATAL POTIONS AND POWDERS.

THEN WHAT DID CAUSE HIS DEATH?
I'M QUITE SURE, PAT, I CAN ANSWER THAT QUESTION WITHIN 24 HOURS!
HM-M-
?
CHESTER

NEW ANALYSES SHOW ABSOLUTELY NO TRACES OF POISON IN GOTHORN'S BODY!
I FELT SURE OF THAT, CORONER

LET'S CONTINUE WITH THE EXAMINATION. THE JOB'S GOING TO BE DONE THOROUGHLY THIS TIME!

AHA!
WHAT IS IT?

TAKE A CLOSE LOOK AT THE BACK OF GOTHORN'S HEAD.
WHAT IN–?

HOW COULD WE HAVE OVERLOOKED IT BEFORE! A BULLET HOLE IN THE BACK OF THE HEAD.
UNDER A LOCK OF HAIR!

HM..! BUT THERE'S SOMETHING PECULIAR HERE, CORONER!

WHAT DO YOU MEAN?
I DON'T THINK THAT'S A BULLET HOLE!

LISTEN! DON'T TELL ME! I KNOW A BULLET HOLE WHEN I SEE ONE.
ALL RIGHT! THERE'S ONE WAY TO SETTLE THAT..PROBE -PRODUCE THE BULLET!
CHESTER

YOU'RE RIGHT TRACY! THERE IS NO BULLET THERE!
I THOUGHT SO! THAT WOUND IN THE BACK OF THE HEAD IS NOT A BULLET HOLE.

HELLO, CHIEF? GET DOWN HERE RIGHT AWAY– WE'VE RUN INTO A MYSTERY THAT'LL TIE THE WHOLE DEPARTMENT IN KNOTS!

JUNIOR! HIKE ACROSS THE STREET AND GET ME A SANDWICH AND A POT OF COFFEE.
SURE MIKE, TRACY!

AND ALL ALONG I THOUGHT WE HAD JUST ANOTHER ORDINARY GANG SLAYING.
THIS CASE WILL KEEP YOU DETECTIVES BUSY! YOU DONT WANT SET-UPS ALL THE TIME DO YOU?
CHESTER

TRACY'S INSIDE WAITING FOR YOU. I'M JUST GOING ACROSS THE STREET TO GET HIM COFFEE AND A SANDWICH.
COUNTY MORGUE

A HAM ON WHITE TO GO OUT AND A POT OF JAVA.
OKAY!

HI THERE, POLLY.
NICE A BIRD, HEY, KEED?

WHILE THE COUNTER MAN DRAWS THE COFFEE--- AND JUNIOR WATCHES THE PARROT-A PAIR OF DEFT HANDS MOVE TOWARD TRACY'S SANDWICH-AND-
CHESTER

I WOULDN'T CALL IT A BULLET HOLE, CHIEF, ALTHOUGH IT LOOKS LIKE ONE.

BUT DEATH WAS DEFINITELY DUE TO A WOUND IN THE BACK OF THE SKULL HERE, COME INTO THIS NEXT ROOM.

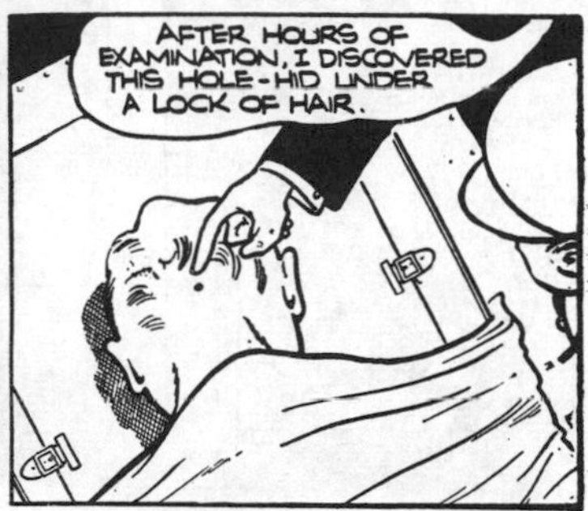
AFTER HOURS OF EXAMINATION, I DISCOVERED THIS HOLE-HID UNDER A LOCK OF HAIR.

THE WOUND EXTENDS ABOUT AN INCH INSIDE THE SKULL AND APPEARS TO BE A BULLET HOLE-EXCEPT THAT NO BULLET CAN BE FOUND INSIDE THE SKULL.

BESIDES THAT, THE WOUND SHOWS NO EVIDENCE OF PARTICLES OF BURNED POWDER OR GREASE LUBRICANT FROM THE BULLET, USUALLY FOUND ABOUT THE EDGE OF ANY WOUND MADE BY A REVOLVER SLUG.

FURTHERMORE, THERE IS NO HOLE OF EXIT WHERE A BULLET LEFT THE HEAD!
IN OTHER WORDS, WHATEVER IT WAS THAT ENTERED GOTHORN'S HEAD DID NOT COME OUT!

EXACTLY! AND SINCE IT DID NOT COME OUT-IT SHOULD STILL BE IN THERE, BUT IT ISN'T!
ALL OF WHICH IS TOO MUCH OF A MYSTERY FOR ME-I GIVE UP.

PERHAPS GOTHORN WAS PUNCHED-ER.. ..WITH AN IRON ROD OR SOMETHING.
IMPOSSIBLE! BECAUSE THE HAIR AROUND THE WOUND ALL POINTS IN! IF AN OBJECT HAD BEEN WITHDRAWN, SOME OF THE HAIR WOULD POINT OUT.

TRACY-HERE'S THE SANDWICHES AND COFFEE YOU ASKED ME TO BRING YOU FROM ACROSS THE STREET.

AS I SEE IT, THERE'S-WELL-WHAT IN-?
MORGU

A PIECE OF PAPER!
IN THE SANDWICH!

LAY OFF

LAY OFF

IT CAN'T BE!
BUT IT IS! A PIECE OF PAPER RIGHT IN MY SANDWICH! -WITH A WARNING ON IT!

JUNIOR, WHERE DID YOU GET THIS SANDWICH?
IN THE COZY CAFE - JUST ACROSS THE STREET!

WE'RE GOING ACROSS THE STREET!

MAYBE SOMEONE PUT THAT WARNING IN THE SANDWICH FOR A GAG. TRACY.
MAYBE SO! MAYBE NOT! WE'VE GOT TO FIND OUT!

GO TO THE REAR OF THE PLACE, PAT! TRACY WILL GO INSIDE AND I'LL KEEP MY EYES ON THE SIDE DOOR!

TONY, IS THIS YOUR ONLY CUSTOMER?
WHY-YES, MEESTER TRACY- WHAT'S OPP?

WHO ELSE HAS BEEN IN HERE IN THE LAST TEN MINUTES? QUICK!
LET ME THINK- OH YES- YOUR BOY AND ONE OTHER MAN. -HE'S A CAB DRIVER.

THE IDEA IS THIS, TONY JUNIOR BOUGHT A SANDWICH IN HERE FOR ME AND THERE WAS A NOTE TUCKED IN BETWEEN THE SLICES OF BREAD
YOU DONT A SAY!

CALL THE CAB DRIVER YOU SAY WAS IN HERE WHEN JUNIOR WAS
YES SIR- YOU BET!

I'M SORRY, OLD TIMER, BUT I'VE GOT TO SEARCH YOU TO SEE IF YOU'VE GOT A PENCIL OR A PIECE OF PAPER LIKE THIS.
OH- POLICE, EH?
BUNS

MY BOY- YOU'LL FIND MANY PENCILS ON ME.. I SELL THEM FOR A LIVING.
THERE'S NOBODY IN THE KITCHEN, TRACY, BUT THE COOK.
PENCILS 5¢

WELL, TRACY... WE'RE SURE OF ONE THING! WHOEVER SLIPPED THAT NOTE INTO YOUR SANDWICH WAS SLICK ENOUGH TO KEEP HIMSELF FROM BEING DISCOVERED

BEAUTIFUL HEADWAY WE'RE MAKING, I MUST SAY- IN SOLVING THE MURDER OF ADDIE GOTHORN! WHY-
GO AHEAD, CHIEF I'VE GOT IT COMING

WELL! WHOM DO WE SEE IN THIS NEXT SCENE BUT TRACY'S G-MAN PAL, JIM TRAILER.
...AND I'D LIKE YOU TO IDENTIFY THESE GLASSES FOR ME, IF YOU CAN.
HM! I'LL DO MY BEST, MR TRAILER
GHI
EFZL

I'VE BEEN TO EXACTLY 21 OTHER OPTOMETRISTS TO FIND THEIR OWNER
AND IN JUST WHAT CASE, MAY I ASK, ARE THE SPECTACLES FIGURING?

HERE WE ARE, MR TRAILER! THOSE GLASSES WERE GROUND AND FITTED HERE-FOR A MR ATHNEL JONES.
JONES, EH! NOW THATS A NAME THAT STANDS OUT!

HIS ADDRESS AT THE TIME THE GLASSES WERE SOLD WAS THE SKYCREST APARTMENTS.
THANK YOU! THAT'S ALL I WANT TO KNOW.

NO TRAILER DON'T COME HERE! I DONT WANT ANYONE TO KNOW THAT YOU'RE WORKING ON THIS CASE WITH ME.

THOSE GLASSES YOU FOUND NEAR WHERE GOTHORN WAS SHOT BELONG TO ONE ATHNEL JONES OF THE SKY-CREST APARTMENTS I'M GOING THERE NOW!!

SKYCREST APARTMENTS! THIS IS THE PLACE.

CLERK, I'M TRYING TO LOCATE A MAN NAMED JONES - MR ATHNEL JONES. DOES HE STAY HERE?
YES, HE DOES. -HE'S-

-HE'S STANDING OVER THERE NOW AT THE CIGAR COUNTER!
SSH-SH-

AHA! I MUST SEE TRACY IMMEDIATELY! THE FIRST REAL HEADWAY IN THIS CASE IS NOW IN THE MAKING!

SAY, BY THE WAY, CHIEF - WHAT WAS THE TEMPERATURE THE DAY GOTHORN WAS SHOT?
WHAT WAS THE TEMPERATURE? YE GODS, TRACY - HAVE YOU GONE MAD?

WE'RE DEALING WITH MURDER - AND YOU ASK THE TEMPERATURE!
I'LL CALL THE WEATHER BUREAU, DICK.

THE DAY GOTHORN WAS SHOT WE WERE IN THE GRIP OF OUR COLD WAVE. THE TEMPERATURE THAT DAY DROPPED TO TEN DEGREES BELOW ZERO!
THANKS, PAT.

WHO'S THAT?
JIM TRAILER! COME IN, FELLOW. I'VE BEEN ANXIOUSLY WAITING FOR YOU.

CHIEF, JIM TRAILER'S BEEN WORKING ON A PIECE OF EVIDENCE THAT EVEN YOU DIDN'T KNOW ABOUT. A PAIR OF GLASSES!
GLASSES?

THESE SPECTACLES WERE PICKED UP BACK OF THE DOOR TO THE SERVANTS' QUARTERS OF THE HOTEL ABOUT 12 FEET FROM WHERE GOTHORN WAS FOUND WOUNDED!

TRACY FOUND THEM - AND ASKED ME TO KEEP THEIR DISCOVERY A SECRET WHILE I RAN DOWN THEIR OWNERSHIP. I VISITED 22 OPTOMETRISTS BEFORE I MET WITH SUCCESS.

WHOSE SPECS WERE THEY, JIM?
THOSE GLASSES BELONGED TO ONE ATHNEL JONES, RETIRED MANUFACTURER.

ATHNEL JONES? NEVER HEARD OF HIM.
HE DID QUITE A BIT OF RESEARCH IN MECHANICAL REFRIGERATION IN HIS DAY - AND WAS THE INVENTOR OF SEVERAL DEVICES NOW USED IN ARTIFICIAL COOLING.

ARTIFICIAL REFRIGERATION - HM-M.. NATURALLY THAT BRINGS TO MIND THE SUBJECT OF ICE - UH HUH.. ICE! -ER.. WHERE DOES THIS JONES LIVE, TRAILER?
IN THE ARISTOCRATIC SKYCREST HOTEL.

ATHNEL JONES? WHY BOYS - THAT'S THE SAME JONES WHO HAD GOTHORN ARRESTED ABOUT TWO YEARS AGO FOR BLACKMAIL! BUT WHEN THE CASE CAME TO COURT, IT WAS THROWN OUT.
YOU'RE RIGHT, CHIEF.
SNAP

WHAT? YOU WANT ME TO TELEPHONE JUNIOR TO COME HERE?
YES. HE DOESN'T KNOW IT - BUT HE'S GOING TO BECOME A BELLHOP IN THE SKYCREST HOTEL.

YES, THIS IS JUNIOR! OH, IT'S YOU, PAT! YOU'RE TALKING FROM HEADQUARTERS EH?

LISTEN KID! COME DOWN HERE RIGHT AWAY-TRACY'S ORDERS! WE WANT YOU TO HELP US ON THE GOTHORN CASE.

HOT DOG! WELL IT'S TIME THEY LET ME IN ON A CASE! I WONDER WHAT THEY'RE GOING TO HAVE ME DO?

YOU MEAN-YOU'LL GET JUNIOR A JOB AS BELLHOP IN ATHNEL JONES' HOTEL? BUT HOW WILL THAT HELP?

A BELLHOP CAN LEARN MORE ABOUT A HOTEL ROOM OCCUPANT IN ONE DAY THAN A DETECTIVE CAN LEARN IN A WEEK.

CHESTER GOULD

WELL HERE I AM TRACY- WHAT DO YOU WANT ME TO DO?

JUNIOR, IN YOUR LONG AND COLORFUL CAREER AS A DETECTIVE'S ASSISTANT YOU'VE NEVER HAD ANY EXPERIENCE AS A BELLHOP, HAVE YOU?

WELL, -NO- BUT I CAN LEARN.

GET THIS, KID! WE BELIEVE WE'VE LOCATED THE KILLER OF ADDIE GOTHORN. AND IT'S UP TO YOU TO HELP US GET THE GOODS ON HIM!

RIGHT DOWN MY ALLEY, DICK.

PAT, CALL THE MANAGER OF THE SKYCREST HOTEL- TELL HIM TO COME TO HEADQUARTERS IMMEDIATELY!

CHESTER GOULD

AND AS MANAGER OF THE SKYCREST HOTEL YOU ARE IN POSITION TO LEND US A LOT OF HELP, MR BROWN.

GOOD! WHAT CAN I DO?

ALL WE WANT YOU TO DO, MR. BROWN, IS LET JUNIOR GO IN THERE AS A BELL HOP-WITHOUT PAY-AND LET HIM HANDLE ALL CALLS TO THE ROOM OF ATHNEL JONES

GLADLY!

TREAT HIM LIKE ANY OTHER BELLHOP- AND BY ALL MEANS KEEP YOUR LIPS SEALED AS TO HIS REAL IDENTITY.

I UNDERSTAND.

HAVE HIM REPORT TO THE BELLHOP CAPTAIN IN THE LOCKER ROOM TO MORROW MORNING.

THANK YOU

CHESTER GOULD

SCENE: THE BASEMENT LOCKER ROOM OF THE SKYCREST HOTEL

NEW BOY. EH? YOU LOOK KINDA YOUNG TO ME.

YES, SIR! BUT I KNOW THE ROPES. I'LL BE RIGHT ON THE JOB.

YOU KNOW THE RULES, DON'T YOU? WHEN THERE'S THREE COMPLAINTS LODGED AGAINST YOU, YOU'RE FINED A DOLLAR.

YES, SIR.

THIS IS ROOM 310. SEND UP A BOTTLE OF SELTZER WATER- AND TELL YOUR CONFOUNDED BELLHOP TO MOVE LIVELY!

FRONT! BOTTLE OF SELTZER TO 310.

YES, SIR!

OH! -OH! 310! THAT'S ATHNEL JONES' ROOM!

CHESTER GOULD

SOME BELLHOP YOU ARE! HAVE THEY STARTED ROBBING THE CRADLE? THE SERVICE IS ROTTEN!

WILL YOU SIGN FOR IT, PLEASE, SIR?

SIGN FOR IT? WHY THIS IS A BLANK CARD.

OH, EXCUSE ME, SIR. THIS IS THE SLIP.

NOW TO HURRY DOWN TO THE BOILER ROOM WHERE TRACY AND TRAILER ARE WAITING.

I GOT HIS FINGER PRINTS ON THIS CARD! BOY! HE LOOKS LIKE SATAN HIMSELF

GOOD WORK, KID!

CHESTER GOULD

SCENE: THE BOILER ROOM OF THE SKYCREST HOTEL.
WHILE TRAILER TAKES THESE FINGER PRINTS BACK TO HEADQUARTERS TO COMPARE THEM WITH THE RECORDS, I'VE GOT ANOTHER JOB FOR YOU, JUNIOR.

THIS IS A TINY BUTTON HOLE CAMERA. IT FASTENS RIGHT INSIDE YOUR JACKET. THERE'S ROOM FOR 3 EXPOSURES ON EACH FILM.

THE LENS PROJECTS THROUGH A HOLE IN THE BRASS BUTTON- AND THAT BULB FITS IN YOUR POCKET.

NEXT TIME YOU'RE IN ATHNEL JONES' ROOM GET A SNAP SHOT OF HIS FACE---- AND--- ANYTHING IN THE ROOM THAT LOOKS SUSPICIOUS!
OKAY, DICK!
CHESTER GOULD

GOSH! PLAYING BELLHOP IN A RITZY HOTEL JUST TO GET THE DOPE ON A MURDER SUSPECT IS NO SNAP. THIS FELLOW JONES DEMANDS SERVICE.
312

HUMPH! YOU FINALLY GOT HERE WITH THAT BOTTLE OF SODA, DID YOU? HAH! OF ALL THE ROTTEN SERVICE!
311

I'M GOING TO REPORT YOU TO THE MANAGER AND DEMAND THAT A NEW BOY BE PUT ON MY CALLS!
YES SIR.
CLICK

WHAT WAS THAT CLICK?
ER... I'M SORRY, SIR... ..I GUESS IT WAS JUST THE KEYS IN MY POCKET.

WILL THAT BE ALL, SIR?
GET OUT- GET OUT OF HERE!

OH BOY! THAT WAS A CLOSE CALL! NOW TO GET DOWN TO THE BOILER ROOM WHERE TRACY AND JIM TRAILER ARE WAITING FOR ME.
SLAM

HERE'S THE BUTTON-HOLE CAMERA! I GOT A GOOD PICTURE OF HIS FACE. AND HIS FINGER-PRINTS ARE ON THIS TRAY.
WE'LL TAKE THEM BOTH. I'M ANXIOUS TO DEVELOP THE SNAP SHOT. NOW GET BACK UPSTAIRS!

WELL, MR. ATHNEL JONES, TRACY WILL SOON HAVE YOUR PEDIGREE . . . OW-W! WHAT WAS THAT?
ZING

GREAT GOVERNOR! SOMEBODY SENT A BULLET RIGHT THROUGH MY CAP!

THAT'S WHERE THE BULLET HIT THE WALL- BUT IT DIDN'T MAKE A HOLE---WELL FOR...

THERE WAS NO BULLET- OR ELSE IT DISAPPEARED! WHAT'S THIS.... ON THE FLOOR..?

LITTLE PIECES OF ICE! YES SIR! - ICE! HOLY SMOKES! I MUST CATCH TRACY BEFORE HE LEAVES THE HOTEL.

WHERE'S TRACY?
HE AND JIM TRAILER ARE DEVELOPING A PICTURE. I'M FIXING SOME HYPO FOR THEM.

WE'RE JUST COMPLETING AN ENLARGEMENT, CHIEF— A SNAP JUNIOR TOOK WITH HIS BUTTON-HOLE CAMERA.

WHO IN TH—?
WHAT A FACE!
PLEASANT OLD DUCK, EH?

HEY, TRACY! WHERE ARE YOU? OH, TRACY!
IT'S JUNIOR'S VOICE!
BUT—WE LEFT HIM AT THE HOTEL!

TRACY—SOMETHING'S HAPPENED!
WHAT'S ON YOUR MIND, KID? I THOUGHT YOU WERE AT THE HOTEL!

SOMEBODY SHOT AT ME!
JUST AFTER I LEFT YOU IN THE HOTEL BOILER ROOM AND STARTED UPSTAIRS.

SEE THOSE HOLES IN MY CAP?
I DON'T KNOW WHO DID IT—BUT....
THE BULLET WAS MADE OUT OF ICE!

I PICKED UP THE PIECES THAT HIT THE WALL AND PUT THEM IN THIS CAN--- LOOK! THEY'RE WATER NOW!
KID, WAS A FOOL TO RISK YOUR LIFE! WE'RE DEALING WITH A MANIAC, BOYS, AND IT'S OUR MOVE.

SCENE: LOBBY OF THE SKYCREST HOTEL.
PATTON AND MYSELF ARE GOING TO BE WINDOW WASHERS AROUND YOUR PREMISES FOR A COUPLE OF HOURS, BROWN. OFFICIAL BUSINESS!
I GET YOU, TRACY.

ANYTHING I CAN DO FOR YOU BOYS, LET ME KNOW.
JUST KEEP YOUR FINGERS CROSSED, BROWN—WE NEED LUCK!

IT'S BEEN SOME TIME SINCE I'VE TRIED ANY HUMAN-FLY TRICKS—BUT HERE GOES.

JUST WASHING YOUR TRANSOM, SIR.
ATHNEL JONES HIMSELF! DOES HE SUSPECT HE IS BEING SPIED ON?

WHY TH'—

CLERK! I OBJECT TO THESE CONFOUNDED WINDOW WASHERS ANNOYING ME THIS TIME OF DAY! THEY—WHAT?

HM-M-M! I MIGHT HAVE SUSPECTED AS MUCH—

GREAT SCOTT! WHAT HAVE I DONE? I SLIPPED! I TOLD HIM THE WINDOW WASHERS AREN'T ON DUTY TODAY—THEN I REMEMBERED—TRACY!

TRACY, JUST AS I CAME DOWN THE CORRIDOR I SAW ATHNEL JONES LEAVE HIS ROOM. HE WENT OUT!
GOOD! GET ON YOUR STREET CLOTHES, PAT!

SAW ENOUGH THROUGH THAT WINDOW TO CONVINCE ME A SEARCH OF JONES' APARTMENT IS OUR NEXT MOVE.

MEANWHILE THE HOTEL MANAGER—
I'VE GOT TO FIND TRACY AND PUT HIM ON HIS GUARD, AFTER FORGETTING MYSELF AND TELLING JONES THE WINDOW WASHERS WERE OFF DUTY!

JUST A MOMENT, MR. MANAGER—BACK INTO THAT FIRE-HOSE CLOSET—AND TURN AROUND!

SPARRING FOR TIME, TRACY SEES TINY TRICKLES OF WATER COME TO THE MOUTHS OF THE SINGLE SHOT PISTOLS AND DROP TO THE FLOOR. HE REALIZES HIS SEARCH FOR THE MURDERER OF ADDIE GOTHORN IS OVER.

YES-MY LITTLE "WINDOW-WASHER" FRIENDS. **YOU HAVE DONE YOUR LAST SNOOPING!**

TURN YOUR FACES TO THE WALL SO THAT I CAN GET TO THE BACK OF YOUR HEADS. I WILL MAKE THIS JUST AS PAINLESS AS POSSIBLE!

PRETENDING TO TRIP OVER THE RUG-**TRACY FALLS SUDDENLY TO THE FLOOR.**

IT WORKS! AS ATHNEL JONES POINTS ONE OF HIS SINGLE SHOT PISTOLS DOWNWARD- **A SMALL PELLET OF ICE SLIDES FROM THE BARREL.**

YOU ARE LOSING SOMETHING FROM YOUR GUN-**ARENT YOU, MR. JONES?**

AN ICE BULLET IS QUITE HARMLESS AFTER IT HAS SLIPPED FROM THE GUN BARREL, DON'T YOU THINK?

-OR HAS MELTED SO MUCH THAT IT IS SHOT OUT AS WATER!

GRAB THAT ARM, PAT-HE MAY HAVE A REAL GUN IN HIS POCKET!

JONES, YOU'RE A RATHER TOUGH CUSTOMER-FOR AN OLD DUCK!

GOLLY, TRACY, THAT ONE PUT HIM TO SLEEP.

SET HIM IN THAT CHAIR AND PUT THE CUFFS ON HIM.

WHILE HE'S NAPPING LET'S EXAMINE THIS CASE HE WAS CARRYING —ONCE MORE.

HM-HM-CAKES OF FROZEN CARBONIC ACID GAS-ONE OF THE COLDEST REFRIGERANTS KNOWN! AND WHAT'S THIS? LOOKS LIKE A BULB FOR PUTTING WATER IN A BATTERY!

HEY TRACY LOOK!

THESE BLANK CARTRIDGES WERE IN HIS POCKETS. AND IT LOOKS LIKE THERE'S PARAFFINE ON TOP OF THE POWDER.

ALL RIGHT, PAT! BRING ALONG THE REFRIGERATOR BOX, WATER BULB, CARTRIGES AND ALL-WE'RE GOING!

JONES, YOU'RE UNDER ARREST FOR THE MURDER OF ADDIE GOTHORN!

AND WHY NOT? **I MURDERED HIM!**

LIKE ALL OTHER CRIMINALS WHO THOUGHT THEY COULD COMMIT THE PERFECT CRIME, **ATHNEL JONES REACHES THE END OF HIS ROW.**

CHIEF, MEET MR. ATHNEL JONES- THE MAN WHO MURDERS WITH ICE.

LOCK HIM UP, PAT.

COME INTO THE NEXT ROOM, CHIEF. I WANT TO SHOW YOU ONE OF THE MOST VICIOUS CONTRAPTIONS THAT EVER CAME FROM A TWISTED MIND.

YOU SEE BEFORE YOU A MACHINE FOR KILLING PEOPLE WITH ICE! GUNS THAT SHOOT-WITHOUT LEAVING BALLISTICS EVIDENCE.

GREAT SCOTT!

BUT I WANT A STENOGRAPHER... AND WITNESSES...... I WANT TO MAKE A FULL CONFESSION... AND GET THIS THING OFF MY MIND!

TRACY! JONES IS GOING NUTS... HE WANTS A COURT STENO TO TAKE DOWN A CONFESSION.

GOTHORN BLACKMAILED ME FOR 50 THOUSAND DOLLARS..HE CAUSED MY WIFE TO COMMIT SUICIDE!

THAT'S WHY I KILLED HIM... WRITE IT DOWN.... IT'S THE TRUTH... I'LL SIGN IT...
LISTEN, MR. JONES.. NOW TAKE IT EASY.
CHESTER GOULD

GOTHORN BLACKMAILED ME OUT OF FIFTY THOUSAND DOLLARS- HE WRECKED MY HOME - MY FORTUNE.

AND HERE IS THE WAY JONES MADE HIS "ICE BULLETS" TO FOOL BALLISTICS EXPERTS.

THIS LITTLE REFRIGERATOR FILLED WITH FROZEN CARBONIC ACID GAS, CAPABLE OF CREATING TEMPERATURES WELL BELOW ZERO, HAS TWO SMALL RACKS INSIDE.

THESE RACKS SUPPORTED IN AN UPRIGHT POSITION, TWO SINGLE SHOT PISTOLS, WITH SPECIALLY DESIGNED BARRELLS THAT WERE "LEAK PROOF."

THESE BLANK 38 SHELLS HAD A COATING OF PARAFFINE ON TOP OF THE POWDER SO THAT WATER COULD NOT GET TO THE EXPLOSIVE.

MR. JONES WOULD PUT THE LOADED PISTOLS IN HIS ICE BOX THUS.

THEN HE WOULD DEPOSIT ONE DROPPER FULL OF WATER IN EACH BARREL- JUST LIKE THIS -

15 MINUTES LATER
NOW GENTLEMEN, OUR GUNS HAVE BEEN COOLING FOR FIFTEEN MINUTES-LET US SEE THE RESULTS.

HOLDING EACH GUN IN THE HAND FOR A FEW SECONDS ALLOWED THE ICE PELLET TO MELT LOOSE FROM THE SIDES OF THE BARREL

AND WE HAVE A BULLET THAT WILL KILL AT FAIRLY CLOSE RANGE -YET LEAVE NO EVIDENCE FOR THE BALLISTICS EXPERT TO TOY WITH.

YES SIR- LITTLE PIECES OF ICE.
GAD! WHAT A VICIOUSLY CLEVER WEAPON.
YES CHIEF- SO CLEVER THAT ITS OWN CLEVERNESS GAVE IT AWAY.

THEN YOU CALL THE GOTHORN MURDER SOLVED, EH, TRACY.
BY NO MEANS, CHIEF! ATHNEL JONES HAD ACCOMPLICES. IN FACT JONES WAS MERELY THE TOOL. OUR JOB IS JUST HALF OVER!

YOU SEE, TRAILER, AFTER DROPPING WATER DOWN THE PISTOL BARRELS ON TOP OF THE BLANK SHELLS-AND ALLOWING IT TO FREEZE—

JONES HAD A PISTOL THAT SHOT ICE-LEAVING NO BALLISTICS EVIDENCE WHATSOEVER.
WELL, I'LL BE-

AND IT WAS DUE TO YOUR TRACING THE OWNERSHIP OF THOSE GLASSES THAT WE CAUGHT UP WITH JONES.
THANKS, TRACY! I'M GOING TO WASHINGTON TO DAY-THE BOSS WANTS TO SEE THIS LITTLE BOX.

GIVE ME THE KEYS TO YOUR CABINETS AND DRAWERS, THEN WE WON'T HAVE TO SMASH THEM OPEN TO DAY WHEN WE SEARCH YOUR PLACE.
OKAY! THERE YOU ARE
CHESTER GOULD

THE 1940s

THE BROW

by Chester Gould

5/22/44–9/26/44

As the outlaw era of Dillinger, Bonnie and Clyde, and Baby-Face Nelson drew to a close, and as organized crime began to shun publicity and retreat behind respectable fronts, newspaper headlines were filled with a new kind of "gangster," a larger-than-life international villain who robbed not banks but entire countries, who didn't kidnap individuals but occupied nations.

Gould always saw himself in competition with the front page, and when Hitler and Mussolini rose to power, *Dick Tracy*'s creator upped the home-grown criminal ante. A succession of vivid grotesques, their names often echoing their physiognomies, began squaring off with Tracy, and in 1941 the first two of the great "crazy villains" appeared: Little Face Finny and the Mole. In 1942 and '43, B-B Eyes, Pruneface, and 88 Keyes joined the ever-growing Rogues' Gallery.

By just about any critical yardstick, however, 1944 was Gould's golden year. During a time of personal problems—his beloved wife Edna was ill during this period—Gould threw himself into his work and came up with three of his most enduring villains in one blazing twelve-month run: Flattop, the Brow, and Shaky.

As popular as Tracy was throughout the thirties (spinning off into toys, radio series, and movie serials), the 1940s—with 1944 the point of critical mass—were the pinnacle. Radio comedians included *Tracy* references in their gags; Daffy Duck parodied the shovel-jawed sleuth as "Duck Twacy" in *The Great Piggy Bank Robbery*; a new series of feature films was launched at RKO. Gould was at his creative peak, and not just in the villainy department: B.O. Plenty, Gravel Gertie, Sparkle Plenty, Vitamin Flintheart, and Diet Smith all made their first appearances in the 1940s.

With the exception of "leetle" Sparkle, that listing of sympathetic characters must be clarified: both Vitamin and Diet came aboard under somewhat suspicious circumstances; and the lovable, rustic hillbilly characters B.O. Plenty and Gravel Gertie—comic creations that harked back to Gould's "big-foot" roots—entered, essentially, as villains.

Gertie, in fact, makes her entrance in this story—not so much as a villain, but as an eccentric soul, a physical witch with a heavenly voice (a typical Gould irony) who aids and abets the Brow.

And though the Brow may not have quite achieved the household name status of Flattop, Pruneface, and the Mole, he is inarguably the quintessential Gould grotesque villain. Physically hideous yet sauve, sadistic yet capable of love, the Brow is a Nazi spy whose cunning, whose unending resourcefulness, whose twisted courage allows him to lead Tracy on a grand extended chase reminiscent of the outlaw days of Bonnie and Clyde.

Also memorable are the Summer Sisters, who are not bad girls, really—more like naughty. What becomes of them is a lesson in Gould morality (more of this in the Afterword; we don't want to spoil one of Gould's greatest yarns).

"The Case of the Brow" (as a 1946 reprint volume dubbed it) was gathered in *The Celebrated Cases of Dick Tracy* (Chelsea House, 1970). The editors of this volume have tried to avoid using much-reprinted stories here, but (a) we are assembling personal favorites and the Brow falls into that category for both editors, and (b) in *Celebrated Cases*, the Brow tale was savagely edited (the Sunday pages were omitted) and the brutal ending was censored. As you will see, the fate this Nazi spy meets represents Gould at his most pointedly ironic.

Since it has been over forty years since the complete Brow story was collected, we are proud to present here what may well be the best tale from Gould's finest year.

CHIEF BRANDON, THIS IS CAPTAIN BOWLINE. I WANT TO INFORM YOU, DICK TRACY HAS JUST BEEN COMMISSIONED LIEUTENANT, SENIOR GRADE, IN THE NAVAL INTELLIGENCE.

HE'LL OPERATE IN PLAIN CLOTHES. IT WON'T INTERFERE WITH HIS REGULAR WORK WITH YOU, AND IT WILL MEAN MUCH TO US.

SO YOU'RE MEETING YOUR BROTHER AT THE SERVICE CENTER, EH? WELL, YOU GO 3 BLOCKS THAT WAY, AND TWO BLOCKS OVER-

YES. WE'RE LOST, MISTER

—THEN YOU GO 3 FURTHER AND THEN ONE BLOCK TO THE RIGHT— AND THAT BRINGS YOU RIGHT TO **HEADQUARTERS. AND THAT'S WHERE WE'RE GOING.**

CHESTER GOULD

AH-AH-AH-AH—!! **PUT IT BACK!**

SO THAT'S YOUR GAME! THE SERVICE CENTER STUFF IS JUST A GAG, EH? OKAY. NOW, **WHO ARE YOU?**

OH, SIR, WE REALLY ARE THE SUMMER SISTERS. I'M MAY AND SHE'S JUNE.

WELL, YOU'LL PROBABLY SPEND THE REST OF MAY AND ALL OF JUNE IN THE JUG. YOU'RE **PICKPOCKETS**.

BUT, MISTER, I WAS ONLY REACHING FOR YOUR HANDKERCHIEF. YOU SEE, WE ALL ARE STRANGERS IN TOWN.

WE MUST GET BETTER ACQUAINTED.

HELP KEEP THE CITY CLEAN

CHESTER GOULD

COME, LADIES. WE'RE GOING TO HAVE A NICE LONG TALK.

POLICE

OH, SIR, YOU'RE MAKING A TERRIBLE MISTAKE BRINGING US TO THE JAIL HOUSE THIS WAY.

JUST A PAIR OF LITTLE PICKPOCKETS.

OKAY, NOW, **SIT DOWN** THERE, YOU TWO.

AND, MURPHY, CALL THE MATRON.

WELL! WHO ARE YOUR FRIENDS??

THE SUMMER SISTERS. SHE'S MAY. AND SHE'S JUNE. H'M!

I'M **TIRED**

AND I'M **HUNGRY**

CHESTER GOULD

I SEARCHED THEM, MR. TRACY. THEY HAVE NO WEAPONS.

H'M. THE SUMMER SISTERS??

WE MIGHT AS WELL TELL THE TRUTH, MISTER. WE WEREN'T HEADED FOR THE SERVICE CENTER. WE WERE JUST HUNGRY AND BROKE.

WE'RE FROM HOMETON. WE CAME TO THE CITY TO GET A JOB **ON THE RADIO**.

DON'T SWEETHEART ME

COME ON. **CUT IT!**

OH, BOO HOO HOO!

SAY, THAT'S **MY** HANDKERCHIEF. WHY, SHE PICKED MY POCKET!

CHESTER GOULD

SUMMER SISTERS, YOU TOLD ME YOU HAD A BROTHER IN THE NAVY. HOW ABOUT IT?

WELL, THAT'S A FIB, TOO, SIR.

DO YOUR FOLKS IN HOMETON **KNOW** YOU CAME TO THE CITY?

OH, NO, SIR. I DON'T THINK SO.

HEY, DICK, LOOK! I OPENED THEIR BAG. **IT'S EMPTY!**

WELL, I'LL BE DARNED! CAME TO THE CITY WITH NO MONEY—NO BAGGAGE! DID YOU EXPECT TO GO RIGHT INTO **BIG TIME** RADIO?

OH, YES, SIR, **OR THE STAGE**. YOU SEE, WE **ACT**, TOO.

BESSY MAY BESSY MAY MUCHO
HEY, MURPHY!

GO DOWN TO THE RAILWAY TICKET OFFICE AND BUY TWO TICKETS TO HOMETON. THE SUMMER SISTERS ARE GOING HOME.

HELLO, VITAMIN
GREETINGS, AND THE TOP OF THE MORNING TO YOU, OFFICER MURPHY. IS THE GREAT DETECTIVE WITHIN?

TEARS OF SHEER JOY WILL WELL UP IN HIS MANLY EYES WHEN I TELL HIM I'VE LANDED A STARRING ROLE IN "LOVES AFIRE." YES, SIR, A STARRING ROLE!

WE'RE THE SUMMER SISTERS — I'M MAY AND SHE'S JUNE.
OH, I KNOW THAT. BUT YOU'RE ALSO A PAIR OF PICKPOCKETS, AREN'T YOU?

YOU SEE, WE REALLY WEREN'T GOING TO MEET OUR BROTHER AT THE SERVICE CENTER. WE HAVE NO BROTHER BUT WE WERE JUST BROKE AND—
WELL, YOU MADE A GREAT START TRYING TO PICK THE POCKET OF A DETECTIVE.

LISTEN, SUMMER SISTERS. LET'S CUT OUT THE BUNK. WHAT DID YOU COME TO THE BIG CITY FOR? WHAT'S YOUR GAG?

WE WANT TO BE ACTRESSES, MR. TRACY. WE CAME TO THE BIG TOWN TO GET ON THE STAGE.
THE STAGE? DID SOMEBODY SAY STAGE?

VITAMIN FLINTHEART WOULD BE GLAD TO LEND HIS TALENTS TOWARDS COACHING TWO LOVELY CREATURES IN THE ART OF THE DRAYMA.

EASY, VITAMIN.
MERE CHILDREN. BABES IN SWADDLING CLOTHES. LOVELY THINGS!
SUMMER SISTERS, I'VE BOUGHT TWO RAILROAD TICKETS! YOU TWO ARE GOING HOME.

PAT, TAKE THEM DOWN TO THE COAST FLIER! AND SEE THAT THEY GET ABOARD
BOO! HOO! HOO!
OH, BOO! HOO!

COME ON. YOU HEARD HIM. IT'S FOR YOUR OWN GOOD.

MY DEAR BOY, YOU'VE MADE A GRAVE MISTAKE. I'VE JUST LANDED A PART IN THE MUSICAL "LOVES-AFIRE." I-I COULD DO WONDERS FOR THEM.
THAT I DOUBT.

30 MINUTES LATER
WELL, HERE YOU ARE! TRACY EVEN GOT YOU A COMPARTMENT.
OH, MR PATTON. YOU'RE SO NICE.

BUT YOU'RE THE ONLY ONE WHO IS NICE. (SOB) NOBODY UNDERSTANDS US. WE HAVE TALENT, MR. PATTON. LOTS OF TALENT. (SOB)

HEY!
TEAR UP THAT SHEET AND TIE HIM, MAY. WHEN THIS TRAIN PULLS OUT WE WON'T BE ON IT BUT MR. PATTON WILL!

SCENE: TRAIN COMPARTMENT TO WHICH PAT HAS ESCORTED THE SUMMER SISTERS.

YOU **GRABBED MY GUN**, **YOU**—

TEAR UP THAT SHEET, MAY.

THEN YOU REALLY **ARE** LITTLE **CROOKS**! TRACY WAS **RIGHT**.

TIE HIM **GOOD**!

WE CAME TO THE BIG CITY TO **STAY** AND NO POLICE OR DETECTIVES ARE GOING TO SEND US **BACK**.

WELL, THAT'S THE END OF THE SUMMER SISTERS, MAY AND JUNE! THEY'RE SAFELY ON THEIR WAY BACK TO HOMETON BY NOW.

YES, PAT PROBABLY SIGHED WITH RELIEF WHEN THE TRAIN PULLED OUT.

WELL, THERE HE IS, TIED GOOD AND TIGHT.

BUT WHAT WILL WE DO, JUNE? THE TRAIN'S ALREADY ON ITS WAY.

I MADE THIS TRIP ONCE BEFORE. THIS TRAIN STOPS AT QUINLAN AVENUE. WE'LL GET OFF THERE!

I THINK THE TRAIN'S SLOWING DOWN. LET'S GO.

WAIT A MINUTE, JUNE.

WE'LL NEED MONEY.

MAY—YOU **SHOULDN'T** HAVE TAKEN HIS WALLET! IT-IT'S—

LET'S GO. OBOY! —ALL THE MONEY!

THE VESTIBULE DOOR ISN'T OPEN.

WAIT! I'LL PUSH THIS LITTLE LEVER. WE'LL GET OUT OKAY.

THE STATION'S ON THE OTHER SIDE. NO ONE WILL SEE US.

YOU KNOW, TRACY, MY LAD—I'VE BEEN THINKING OF THOSE SUMMER SISTERS! PERHAPS AT HEART THEY WERE LITTLE ANGELS. AND BESIDES, MY SHOW NEEDS TWO GIRLS

VITAMIN, THE SUMMER SISTERS ARE A CLOSED CHAPTER! THEY'VE GONE HOME!

TICKETS! **TICKETS**!

HUH? WH—?

STOP THE TRAIN! WIRE HEADQUARTERS! NAB THOSE **SUMMER SISTERS! WHY, I'LL** —!!★!

WHAT **IS** THIS?

MAY, I JUST COUNTED THE MONEY IN HIS POCKETBOOK— **FIFTY DOLLARS**. WE'RE RICH!

LET'S EAT. I'M **HUNGRY**. OH-H- -AND I'M SCARED

WE-WE'VE GOT TO BUY NEW COSTUMES, MAY. WE'RE FUGITIVES, YOU KNOW. WE'LL BE RECOGNIZED TOO EASILY IN THESE THINGS.

WE'LL EAT FIRST, SIS.

WE'LL FEEL BETTER AFTER SOME FOOD. WE CAN THINK BETTER, TOO

GREETINGS, LADIES, LEAVE US NOT BE HASTY, BUT CAN I TAKE YOUR ORDER?

EGAD! I CAN'T GET THOSE SUMMER SISTERS OFF MY MIND IT WAS MERELY A GLIMPSE OF THEM I HAD IN HEADQUARTERS THAT DAY— BUT I COULD SEE THEY HAD TALENT.

WELL! WHERE HAVE—?? **WHAT** HAPPENED TO YOU?

SUMMER SISTERS! **PHOOEY!**

AHA, IT'S OVER AN HOUR TILL MATINEE TIME. METHINKS I'LL WATCH THE FISHERMAN BENEATH THE BOULEVARD BRIDGE—AND DAY DREAM.

GONNA TRY YOUR LUCK, MISTER?
LUCK? AHA, MY BOY, I HAVE TRIED MY LUCK—IN LIFE'S MAD WHIRLPOOL, LO, THESE MANY YEARS.

I MERELY WISH TO SIT HERE IN SWEET REPOSE AND DREAM — THAT'S ALL. JUST DREAM.

AFTER WE EAT WE WANT TO BUY SOME CLOTHES. WHERE IS THE NEAREST SHOP?
THE SHOPS ARE ALL ON THE OTHER SIDE OF THE BRIDGE, MA'M, A BLOCK DOWN. YOU JUST CROSS THE BRIDGE.
CAN THAT BE THE SAME BRIDGE VITAMIN IS SITTING UNDER?

I TELL YOU, THEY'RE VICIOUS! AFTER SEIZING MY GUN, THEY TIED ME UP IN THE TRAIN COMPARTMENT AND TOOK FIFTY DOLLARS OUT OF MY POCKET.

TRACY, HOW DO YOU FIGURE THOSE SUMMER SISTERS?
I HARDLY KNOW, CHIEF. SOMETIMES I THINK THEIR SISTER ACT, AS STAGE-STRUCK KIDS, IS MERELY A FRONT FOR SOMETHING MORE SINISTER.

DO YOU MEAN THAT, TRACY?
JOE, TELL THE RADIO OPERATOR TO SEND OUT THIS FLASH ON THE SUMMER SISTERS. WE'VE GOT TO PICK THEM UP.

MEANWHILE
THERE! I FEEL BETTER THAT'S THE FIRST SQUARE MEAL WE'VE HAD IN OVER A WEEK.
LET'S GO.

WE'VE GOT TO BUY NEW CLOTHES—AND CHANGE OUR APPEARANCE. THE COPS WILL BE AFTER US NOW, FOR SURE.

JUNE, I DON'T LIKE THIS. LET'S GO BACK HOME AND FORGET TRYING TO BE SINGERS AND RADIO ACTRESSES AND—
BACK HOME? WELL, I SHOULD SAY NOT, MAY! WE'VE GOT MONEY NOW —WE CAN—
DRESS SHOPPE

WE'LL TAKE THEM. AND WOULD YOU WRAP UP THE OLD ONES, PLEASE?

LOOK, TRACY! I CONTACTED THE CHIEF OF POLICE IN THAT LITTLE TOWN WHERE THOSE SISTERS SAID THEY LIVED. HE NEVER HEARD OF 'EM.
JUST AS WE FIGURED, PAT. THEY LIED ALL ALONG.

AND NOW, LET US LOOK IN ON THE WANDERING VITAMIN FLINTHEART
SO YOU'RE AN ACTOR, EH? WHAT ARE YOU DOING DOWN HERE?
JUST DAY DREAMING, MY LAD, JUST DAY DREAMING.

YEAH? DON'T YOU LIKE TO FISH?
DREAMING OF THE DAYS GONE BY. WOMEN BEAUTIFUL WOMEN THAT CAME AND WENT. WHY, ONLY YESTERDAY, I MET TWO SISTERS-

AND ON THE BRIDGE ABOVE
THERE! NOW WE'RE RID OF THOSE OLD COSTUMES FOR GOOD.

WHAT'S THIS?
EGAD! THE PETTICOAT INFLUENCE FOLLOWS ME LIKE MY SHADOW— MAN THE NET, BOYS! HERE IT COMES.

THERE THEY **GO**, JUNE! THAT'S THE END OF THOSE FRILLY DRESSES OF OURS.

I FEEL MUCH BETTER IN THIS SLACK OUTFIT.

—WELL, I'LL BE DARNED! A **DRESS** —COMMITTING SUICIDE!

TWO DRESSES!

I TELL YOU, MY LAD, THE PETTICOAT INFLUENCE FOLLOWS ME LIKE A SHADOW! GIVE ME YOUR **FISHING ROD**!

IS THAT YOUR DRESS—ER I MEAN DO YOU KNOW **WHOSE** IT IS?

HOLD TIGHT, SON. THE GARMENT LOOKS STRANGELY FAMILIAR!

HEY! DON'T **BREAK MY ROD**!

TUT, TUT! I'VE ALMOST GOT IT!

THERE WERE TWO OF 'EM! I RECOVERED ONE! THAT MEANS JUST ONE THING —**THE SUMMER SISTERS**!

MY DREAM GIRLS! THE POLICE MAY THINK THEY'RE CROOKS—BUT TO ME—AH, THEY'RE TWO DELICATE FLOWERS! I MUST FIND THEM.

THERE'S A NEWSSTAND! LET'S BUY A PAPER AND LOOK IN THE WANT ADS FOR A ROOM BEFORE THE POLICE SPOT US.

YES, EVEN NOW I HAVE A FEELING WE'RE BEING FOLLOWED.

ATTENTION—ALL SQUADS. WATCH FOR TWO GIRLS ABOUT NINETEEN YEARS OLD—BLONDE HAIR KNOWN AS THE SUMMER SISTERS. DRESSED ALIKE—WANTED FOR LARCENY—THEY ARE ARMED.

WHY, THOSE LITTLE CRIMINALS! THAT GUN THEY TOOK FROM ME WAS MY PET. I CARRIED IT FOR EIGHT YEARS.

H'M! TWO LITTLE DAMES! I CAN'T GET OVER IT.

IT'S **THEM**! I'VE **FOUND** THEM! HEY—**MY DARLINGS**! WAIT—WAIT!

IT'S THAT EX-ACTOR, VITAMIN FLINTHEART. WE MET HIM IN THE POLICE STATION. I'LL BET HE'S A **STOOL PIGEON FOR THE COPS**. WHAT'LL WE DO?

STAND STILL. I'LL HANDLE VITAMIN FLINTHEART.

LADIES, **LOOK**. I WAS BENEATH THE BRIDGE WHEN YOU THREW YOUR OLD DRESSES OVER. I WANT TO TALK TO YOU.

HAIL A CAB AND HAVE THE DOOR OPEN.

I HAVE A **JOB** FOR YOU. I'M GOING TO PUT YOU ON THE **STAGE**—I

MIND YOUR OWN BUSINESS, YOU EX-HAM! WE KNOW **YOU'RE WORKING FOR THE POLICE**! YOU—★!!¢

VICIOUS! THAT, IS THE WORD! —VICIOUS!

AFTER THEIR ENCOUNTER WITH VITAMIN FLINTHEART, THE SUMMER SISTERS CONTINUE THEIR SEARCH FOR A ROOM.

THE RENT IS TWELVE DOLLARS A WEEK. IT'S A NICE AIRY ROOM.

AFTER BUYING THE SLACK SUITS, WE HAVE JUST THIRTEEN-FIFTY LEFT. WHAT'LL WE DO?

PAY HER. WE'LL HAVE A ROOM FOR A WEEK, ANYWAY.

AHA! I SHALL WRITE DOWN THE ADDRESS. LITTLE DO THEY DREAM I TOOK THE NEXT CAB AND FOLLOWED THEM. THE LITTLE CRIMINALS.

IT'S VITAMIN FLINTHEART. HE SAYS HE HAS SOMETHING IMPORTANT TO TELL YOU.

CAN'T TALK TO HIM NOW, PAT. I HAVE AN APPOINTMENT WITH THE NAVY INTELLIGENCE DEPARTMENT.

YOU WILL GO TO THIS ADDRESS AT NINE O'CLOCK, LIEUTENANT. TWO MEN WILL JOIN YOU THERE. YOU'RE TO INVESTIGATE A SUSPECT WHO IS USING FIELD GLASSES TO WATCH THE HARBOR.
AYE, AYE, SIR.

THIS REALLY IS A SECLUDED ROOM, MAY. NO ONE WOULD EVER LOOK FOR US HERE.
RIGHT, JUNE.

BUT WE'VE GOT TO GET SOME KIND OF A JOB. WE CAN'T EAT LONG ON A DOLLAR AND A HALF.

I TELL YOU, PATTON, OLD BOY, I'VE LOCATED THE SUMMER SISTERS. WHERE'S DICK TRACY? THIS IS A HOT TIP.
GOOD FOR YOU. TRACY WILL BE HERE IN A FEW MINUTES, VITAMIN.

THIS IS A HONEY OF A ROOM, MAY. JUST LOOK AT THE VIEW. WE CAN SEE RIGHT DOWN TO THE DOCKS.
YES. LOOK AT ALL THE SHIPS.

I'LL BET THOSE ARE TROOP SHIPS. YOU KNOW, I SAW A LOT OF SAILORS AND SOLDIERS MARCHING DOWN THAT OTHER STREET.
TROOP SHIPS?

GEE, THE SCENERY FROM HERE IS WONDERFUL! I BET IF WE HAD FIELD GLASSES—WE COULD SEE EVERY LITTLE DETAIL.

YOU KNOW, JUNE, I THINK WE'LL FORGET ABOUT OUR STAGE CAREERS TEMPORARILY AND GET JUST ANY KIND OF A JOB. WE'VE GOT TO EAT.
I'LL SAY! I'M HUNGRY!

I TELL YOU, MY LAD, THE DRESS CAME FLUTTERING DOWN FROM THE BRIDGE. I THOUGHT I RECOGNIZED IT AND I RAN UP THE STAIRS TO THE BRIDGE.
YEAH?

SURE ENOUGH. IT WAS THE SUMMER SISTERS. THEY DIDN'T SEE ME. I FOLLOWED THEM. I KNOW WHERE THEY'RE STAYING.
THAT'S GREAT, VITAMIN, BUT I'LL SEE YOU LATER. I'VE GOT TO BEAT IT NOW!

KEEP THAT ACTOR HERE TILL I GET BACK, PAT. I'VE GOT A RUSH ASSIGNMENT WITH THE NAVY INTELLIGENCE DEPARTMENT.

TWENTY MINUTES LATER
WHAT WAS THAT?
WHO IN-??
CRASH

EASY, CHUMP.
NAB HIS PAPERS AND GET THE FIELD GLASSES.
CAN'T FIND ANY FIELD GLASSES.

LOOK! WHY, JUNE, WHERE DID THOSE COME FROM?

SEARCH THE SHRUBBERY BELOW HIS WINDOW. WE WON'T LEAVE HERE TILL WE FIND THOSE GLASSES.

SO–YOU'VE BEEN WATCHING THE HARBOR WITH FIELD GLASSES, EH? WE'LL, WE'RE TAKING YOU IN.
THE NAVY'S INTERESTED IN YOU, BUD.

THERE ARE NO FIELD GLASSES IN THE SHRUBBERY. HE **DIDN'T** THROW THEM DOWN HERE

YOU'VE GOT NOTHING ON ME.
WHEN WE FIND THOSE FIELD GLASSES, WE'LL HAVE **PLENTY** ON YOU.

BUT, MAY, THEY JUST SUDDENLY APPEARED ON THE WINDOW SILL OUT OF NOWHERE. WHAT'LL WE **DO** WITH THEM?
WE'LL **KEEP** 'EM. THAT'S WHAT. SH– SH– LISTEN!

COME ALONG, BROTHER, THE HEAD OF THE NAVY INTELLIGENCE WANTS TO TALK TO YOU.

CONTINUE SEARCHING THE ROOM FOR THOSE FIELD GLASSES. I'LL BE WAITING TO HEAR FROM YOU AT POLICE HEADQUARTERS.

MAY, THOSE WERE **COPS** NEXT DOOR. I HEARD SOMEONE MENTION POLICE HEADQUARTERS.
WHAT?

AND IN ANOTHER PART OF TOWN

WELL, HANTZ, WHAT **IS** IT? YOU SEEM EXCITED!
BROW. I'VE GOT **BAD** NEWS.

HERE'S YOUR SPY, CAPTAIN.
GOOD! BRING HIM INTO THE NEXT ROOM. WE'RE GOING TO HAVE A LONG TALK.

IT'S THIS WAY, **BROW**. SHIP SPOTTER 26, IN THE OLD ROOMING HOUSE, HAS BEEN PICKED UP BY NAVAL INTELLIGENCE.
WHAT? WHY, THAT STUPID PIG!

WHAT ABOUT HIS FIELD GLASSES? THEY ARE THE MOST DAMNING EVIDENCE. DID POLICE GET **THEM**?
THE FIELD GLASSES HAVE FALLEN INTO THE HANDS OF TWO GIDDY GIRLS ROOMING NEXT TO HIM.

MAY, THESE ARE **WONDERFUL** GLASSES! WHY, I CAN SEE A GOLD TOOTH IN THE MOUTH OF THAT POLICEMAN DOWN THERE.
JUNE, **GET BACK FROM THAT WINDOW**!

YOU SAY THOSE FIELD GLASSES ARE IN THE HANDS OF TWO GIRLS.
YES, BROW.

I **WANT** THOSE GLASSES AND **WANT THEM NOW**.
BUT, BROW, THE PLACE IS UNDER SURVEILLANCE BY **NAVY MEN**.

DID I ASK YOU FOR A LITERARY DESCRIPTION OF THE PLACE? I **WANT THOSE GLASSES!**
NO, BROW, **NOT THAT**! I'LL GET THE GLASSES!

YOUR FINGERPRINT RECORD SHOWS YOUR NAME IS NOFFEL. YOU WERE CONVICTED OF ESPIONAGE DURING THE LAST WAR AND YOU ENTERED THIS COUNTRY ILLEGALLY IN 1938! NOW, DO YOU CARE TO CARRY ON FROM THERE?

MAY, **WHERE ARE YOU GOING**?
I'VE GOT TO GET RID OF THIS GUN WE TOOK FROM MR. PATTON.

WE DON'T WANT THE POLICE TO **FIND** IT ON US! YOU STAY THERE, I'LL BE RIGHT BACK.

AH! THE BATHROOM LINEN CLOSET! I'LL PUT IT UNDER THESE WINTER BEDCLOTHES.

PAT, GO TO THAT ROOMING HOUSE AND GET THE LANDLADY TO GIVE YOU A LIST OF NAMES OF ALL HER ROOMERS. ALSO KEYS TO EVERY ROOM IN HER HOUSE.

SHIP 29 ON CHART DEPARTED N.E. TOWARD NEWFOUNDLAND 12. A.M. CONVOY FORMING OFF CAPE NESS THAT IS ALL—BROW

HAS 12 RECOVERED THOSE FIELD GLASSES FROM THE TWO SISTERS
I DON'T KNOW, BROW. HE'S SUPPOSED TO REPORT BACK HERE IN ONE HOUR

VITAMIN! WHAT ARE YOU DOING HERE?
AH! "WHAT AM I DOING?" HE SAYS! WHY, I'VE BEEN WAITING DAYS TO SEE MR. TRACY.

I KNOW WHERE THE SUMMER SISTERS ARE LIVING. BUT IS ANYONE INTERESTED? THEY ARE NOT. EGAD! I'M IGNORED!

THE ENTIRE ROOMING HOUSE IS UNDER SURVEILLANCE, CAPTAIN, AND WE EXPECT TO FIND OUT MORE AND GET THE FIELD GLASSES BEFORE LONG.
H'M! SPYING ON TROOPS AND SUPPLY SHIPS, EH?

I TELL YOU, MAY, SOMETHING'S HAPPENING IN THIS BUILDING. THOSE WERE COPS NEXT DOOR. WE'VE GOT TO GET OUT OF HERE!
BUT WE HAVEN'T ENOUGH MONEY TO RENT ANOTHER ROOM.

YOU'RE RIGHT WE'RE — SAY, WE COULD ROCK THOSE FIELD GLASSES.
BUT THEY'RE NOT OUR FIELD GLASSES. SOMEBODY PUT THEM ON THE WINDOW SILL.

WE HAVEN'T EATEN IN TWO DAYS. WE CAN'T JUST ROT UP IN THAT ROOM. COME ON. LET'S GO!
BUT IF WE HOCK THOSE GLASSES WE'LL BE MIXED UP IN WHATEVER IT IS THAT'S GOING ON HERE.

BUT MY TIME, SIR, IS VALUABLE. I TOLD MR. TRACY I'D SHOW HIM THE LOCATION OF THE SUMMER SISTERS' ROOM LAST WEEK. WHAT ARE WE WAITING FOR?
EASY, VITAMIN.

TRACY'S BUSY THIS MORNING WITH THE NAVAL INTELLIGENCE DEPARTMENT. HE'LL BE HERE LATER.
LATER, HE SAYS. BAH! TEMPUS FUGITS AND HE SAYS LATER!

SCENE: ABOUT FIVE BLOCKS FROM THE SUMMER SISTERS' ROOMING HOUSE.
HELLO, GIRLS. YOU'RE A LITTLE LATE. I'VE BEEN WAITING FOR YOU.
LATE? WHO ARE YOU?

WE HAVE NO DATE WITH YOU! WHERE ARE—
KEEP YOUR TRAPS SHUT OR I'LL CHOKE THE LIFE OUT OF BOTH OF YOU— AND I'LL TAKE THAT PACKAGE.

AND ABOUT TWENTY MINUTES LATER IN ANOTHER PART OF TOWN
HE'S HERE, BROW.
GOOD. SEND HIM IN.

I RETRIEVED OUR FIELD GLASSES, BROW, AND I ALSO BROUGHT ALONG THE TWO CHARMING GIRLS WHO HAD THEM.
WE'RE THE SUMMER SISTERS. I'M MAY AND SHE'S JUNE.

CHARMED! CHARMED, INDEED SIT DOWN, LADIES. THE BROW WELCOMES YOU.

THAT'S THEIR ROOM, MY LAD. THE WINDOW ON THE LEFT
YE GODS! THAT'S THE BUILDING WHERE WE JUST PICKED UP THE SPY!

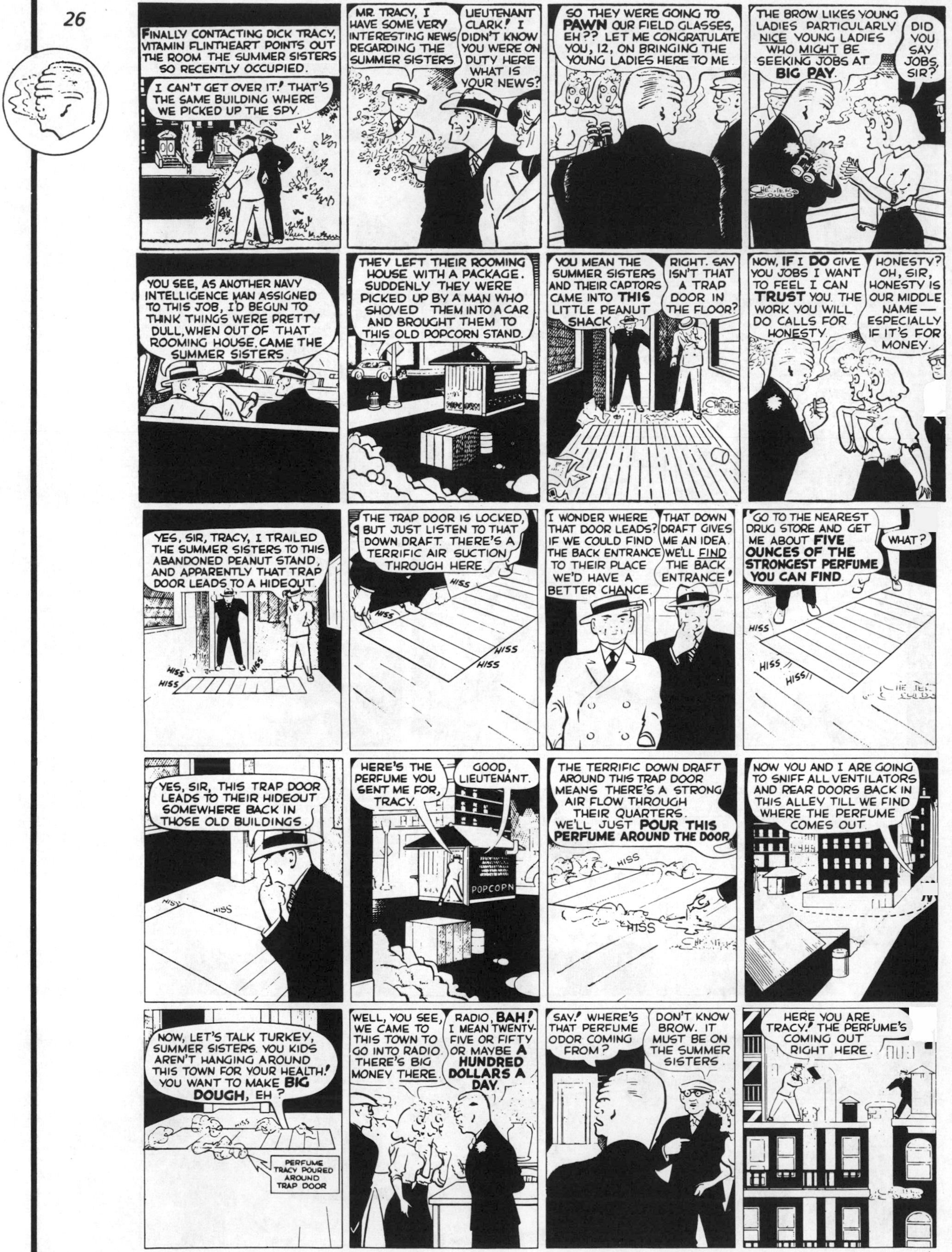

FINALLY CONTACTING DICK TRACY, VITAMIN FLINTHEART POINTS OUT THE ROOM THE SUMMER SISTERS SO RECENTLY OCCUPIED.

I CAN'T GET OVER IT! THAT'S THE SAME BUILDING WHERE WE PICKED UP THE SPY.

MR. TRACY, I HAVE SOME VERY INTERESTING NEWS REGARDING THE SUMMER SISTERS.

LIEUTENANT CLARK! I DIDN'T KNOW YOU WERE ON DUTY HERE. WHAT IS YOUR NEWS?

SO THEY WERE GOING TO **PAWN** OUR FIELD GLASSES, EH?? LET ME CONGRATULATE YOU, 12, ON BRINGING THE YOUNG LADIES HERE TO ME.

THE BROW LIKES YOUNG LADIES PARTICULARLY NICE YOUNG LADIES WHO MIGHT BE SEEKING JOBS AT **BIG PAY**.

DID YOU SAY JOBS, SIR?

YOU SEE, AS ANOTHER NAVY INTELLIGENCE MAN ASSIGNED TO THIS JOB, I'D BEGUN TO THINK THINGS WERE PRETTY DULL, WHEN OUT OF THAT ROOMING HOUSE, CAME THE SUMMER SISTERS.

THEY LEFT THEIR ROOMING HOUSE WITH A PACKAGE. SUDDENLY THEY WERE PICKED UP BY A MAN WHO SHOVED THEM INTO A CAR AND BROUGHT THEM TO THIS OLD POPCORN STAND.

YOU MEAN THE SUMMER SISTERS AND THEIR CAPTORS CAME INTO **THIS** LITTLE PEANUT SHACK.

RIGHT. SAY ISN'T THAT A TRAP DOOR IN THE FLOOR?

NOW, **IF** I **DO** GIVE YOU JOBS I WANT TO FEEL I CAN **TRUST** YOU. THE WORK YOU WILL DO CALLS FOR HONESTY.

HONESTY? OH, SIR, HONESTY IS OUR MIDDLE NAME— ESPECIALLY IF IT'S FOR MONEY.

YES, SIR, TRACY, I TRAILED THE SUMMER SISTERS TO THIS ABANDONED PEANUT STAND, AND APPARENTLY THAT TRAP DOOR LEADS TO A HIDEOUT.

HISS HISS HISS

THE TRAP DOOR IS LOCKED, BUT JUST LISTEN TO THAT DOWN DRAFT. THERE'S A TERRIFIC AIR SUCTION THROUGH HERE.

HISS HISS HISS HISS

I WONDER WHERE THAT DOOR LEADS? IF WE COULD FIND THE BACK ENTRANCE TO THEIR PLACE WE'D HAVE A BETTER CHANCE.

THAT DOWN DRAFT GIVES ME AN IDEA. WE'LL FIND THE BACK ENTRANCE!

GO TO THE NEAREST DRUG STORE AND GET ME ABOUT **FIVE OUNCES OF THE STRONGEST PERFUME YOU CAN FIND**.

WHAT?

HISS HISS HISS

YES, SIR, THIS TRAP DOOR LEADS TO THEIR HIDEOUT SOMEWHERE BACK IN THOSE OLD BUILDINGS.

HISS HISS

HERE'S THE PERFUME YOU SENT ME FOR, TRACY.

GOOD, LIEUTENANT.

POPCORN

THE TERRIFIC DOWN DRAFT AROUND THIS TRAP DOOR MEANS THERE'S A STRONG AIR FLOW THROUGH THEIR QUARTERS. WE'LL JUST **POUR THIS PERFUME AROUND THE DOOR**.

HISS HISS

NOW YOU AND I ARE GOING TO SNIFF ALL VENTILATORS AND REAR DOORS BACK IN THIS ALLEY TILL WE FIND WHERE THE PERFUME COMES OUT.

NOW, LET'S TALK TURKEY, SUMMER SISTERS. YOU KIDS AREN'T HANGING AROUND THIS TOWN FOR YOUR HEALTH! YOU WANT TO MAKE **BIG DOUGH**, EH?

PERFUME TRACY POURED AROUND TRAP DOOR

WELL, YOU SEE, WE CAME TO THIS TOWN TO GO INTO RADIO. THERE'S BIG MONEY THERE.

RADIO, **BAH!** I MEAN TWENTY-FIVE OR FIFTY OR MAYBE **A HUNDRED DOLLARS A DAY**.

SAY! WHERE'S THAT PERFUME ODOR COMING FROM?

DON'T KNOW BROW. IT MUST BE ON THE SUMMER SISTERS.

HERE YOU ARE, TRACY! THE PERFUME'S COMING OUT RIGHT HERE.

YOU'RE RIGHT, LIEUTENANT. THE PERFUME'S COMING FROM THIS VENTILATOR.
3 FLOORS DOWN

IT GOES INTO THE BUILDING AT THIS POINT. THAT WOULD BE THE CEILING OF THE BASEMENT.

FIRST, WE'LL UNCOUPLE THIS JOINT. WATCH IT. THIS USED TO BE AN OLD RESTAURANT. THERE'S PROBABLY GREASE ON THE PIPES.

SH-SH- EASY, LIEUTENANT. I HEAR VOICES — WOMEN'S VOICES
OH **THANK YOU**, SIR! YOU'RE **WONDERFUL**

WHY- YES, WE'D LIKE A **STEADY** JOB.
FINE. YOUR WORK WILL CONSIST OF SHIP SPOTTING AND OTHER DUTIES. THE PAY WILL BE TWENTY-FIVE DOLLARS A DAY.

TWENTY-FIVE DOLLARS A DAY! WHOEE!!
ALL WORK IS CONFIDENTIAL, OF COURSE. LET ME HAVE YOUR HANDS, PLEASE.

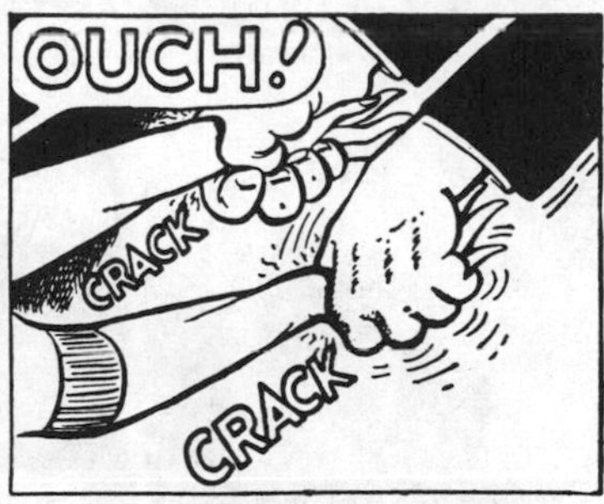
OUCH!
CRACK
CRACK

MY **WRIST! YOU BROKE MY WRIST.**
YOU **BROKE IT**. I HEARD THE BONE **CRACK!**
YOU BELONG TO ME, NOW, SUMMER SISTERS!

YOU HAVE NOT LIVED TILL YOU HAVE BEEN BRANDED BY THE **BROW**. HAVE THE DOC FIX THEM UP, TURTLE.

HALF AN HOUR LATER
YOU WILL REST IN HERE THE REMAINDER OF THE DAY. WE WILL GO INTO DETAILS OF YOUR WORK, TOMORROW.
OH-H-H MY WRIST. **OHOH OHOH!**

I HEARD THE DOOR CLOSE. I'M GOING IN.

SH-SH! EASY, SUMMER SISTERS! YOU DIDN'T EXPECT COMPANY THROUGH THIS OLD VENTILATOR SHAFT, DID YOU?
YOU SEE, THIS USED TO BE A FAMOUS RESTAURANT.

OH, MR. TRACY, WE'LL **NEVER** DO ANYTHING **BAD** AGAIN IF ONLY YOU'LL GET US OUT OF HERE
SH-SH

PLEASE HELP US, MR. TRACY. **PLEASE!**
HOW DID YOU KNOW WHERE WE WERE?
A NAVY MAN SAW YOU LEAVE YOUR ROOM WITH THOSE FIELD GLASSES. HE SAW YOU ENTER THE CAR. HE FOLLOWED.

WE'VE BEEN BAD — BUT PLEASE HELP US. **PLEASE!**
GIRLS, YOU CAN SQUARE YOURSELVES WITH ME IF YOU'LL JUST SIT TIGHT AND DO AS I SAY. PLAY THEIR GAME WITH THEM. PRETEND NOTHING'S WRONG AND BE PATIENT.

SHIP 26 LOADED WITH AMMUNITION HEADED N.E. TO JOIN CONVOY OFF CAPE SABLE. SHIP 4, ON CHART STILL IN PORT —— BROW.

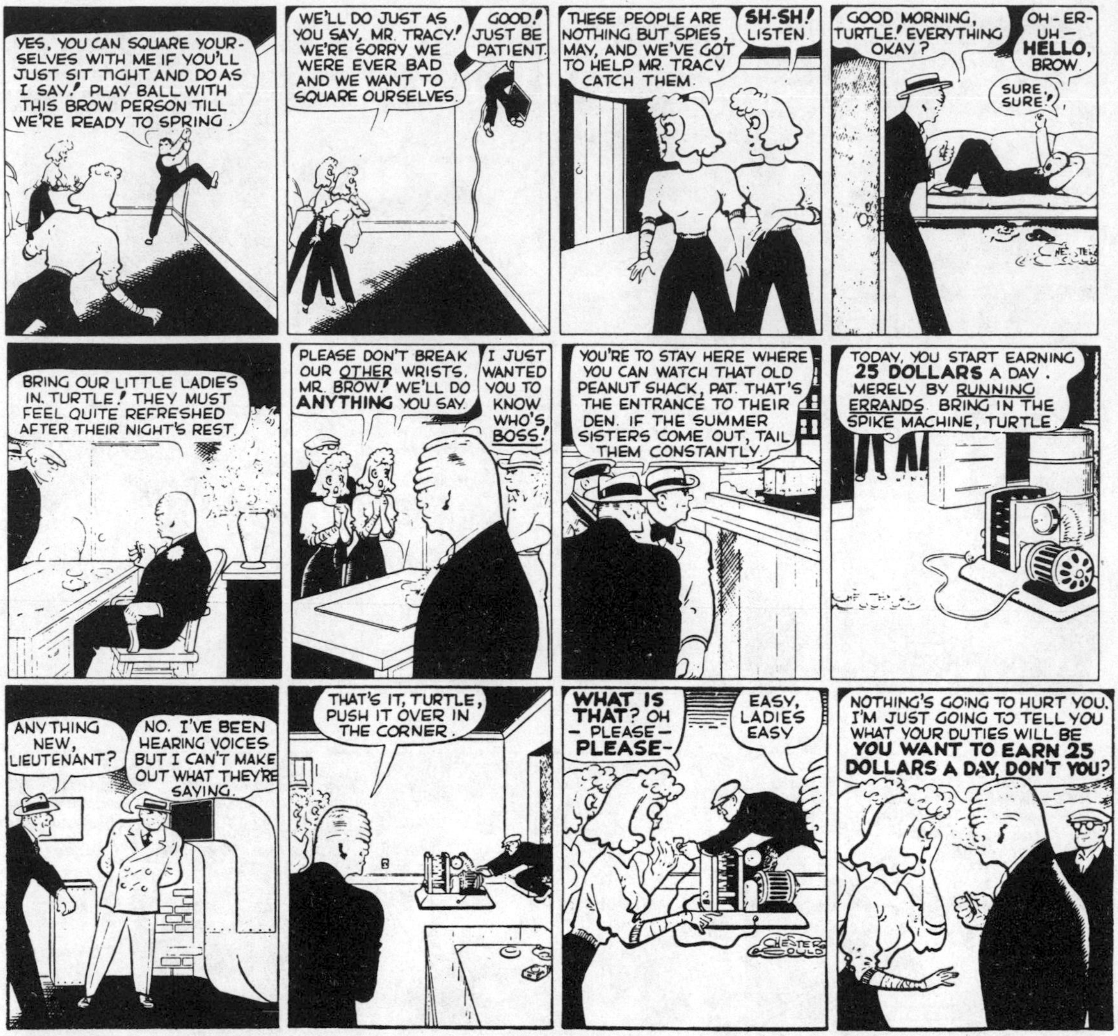

YES, YOU CAN SQUARE YOURSELVES WITH ME IF YOU'LL JUST SIT TIGHT AND DO AS I SAY! PLAY BALL WITH THIS BROW PERSON TILL WE'RE READY TO SPRING.

WE'LL DO JUST AS YOU SAY, MR. TRACY! WE'RE SORRY WE WERE EVER BAD AND WE WANT TO SQUARE OURSELVES.

GOOD! JUST BE PATIENT.

THESE PEOPLE ARE NOTHING BUT SPIES, MAY, AND WE'VE GOT TO HELP MR. TRACY CATCH THEM.

SH-SH! LISTEN.

GOOD MORNING, TURTLE! EVERYTHING OKAY?

OH-ER-UH-**HELLO,** BROW.

SURE, SURE!

BRING OUR LITTLE LADIES IN, TURTLE! THEY MUST FEEL QUITE REFRESHED AFTER THEIR NIGHT'S REST.

PLEASE DON'T BREAK OUR OTHER WRISTS, MR. BROW! WE'LL DO **ANYTHING** YOU SAY.

I JUST WANTED YOU TO KNOW WHO'S BOSS!

YOU'RE TO STAY HERE WHERE YOU CAN WATCH THAT OLD PEANUT SHACK, PAT. THAT'S THE ENTRANCE TO THEIR DEN. IF THE SUMMER SISTERS COME OUT, TAIL THEM CONSTANTLY.

TODAY, YOU START EARNING **25 DOLLARS** A DAY. MERELY BY RUNNING ERRANDS. BRING IN THE SPIKE MACHINE, TURTLE.

ANYTHING NEW, LIEUTENANT?

NO. I'VE BEEN HEARING VOICES BUT I CAN'T MAKE OUT WHAT THEY'RE SAYING.

THAT'S IT, TURTLE, PUSH IT OVER IN THE CORNER.

WHAT IS THAT? OH -PLEASE- **PLEASE-**

EASY, LADIES EASY

NOTHING'S GOING TO HURT YOU. I'M JUST GOING TO TELL YOU WHAT YOUR DUTIES WILL BE **YOU WANT TO EARN 25 DOLLARS A DAY, DON'T YOU?**

YOU SEE, I'M GOING TO USE YOU GIRLS TO PICK UP CODE MESSAGES FOR ME FROM MY OPERATIVES.

JUNE, HERE, WILL GO OUT ONE DAY AND MAY WILL GO OUT THE NEXT.

PLEASE, BROW, CAN'T WE GO OUT **TOGETHER?**

OH, HA, HA! **TOGETHER,** SHE SAYS! -AND **NEVER COME BACK?**

IF I KEEP ONE SISTER HERE-I **KNOW** THE OTHER ONE **WILL COME BACK.** IN FACT, MY LITTLE **MACHINE** WILL GUARANTEE THE OTHER SISTER WILL COME BACK

WHAT DO YOU-MEAN?

HM!??

MAY, YOUR FIRST ERRAND WILL BE TO CALL ON DOCTOR ZEE AT ROOM 6020, MOILER BUILDING. YOU WILL PICK UP A REPORT AND RETURN HERE.

THE VENTILATOR

WAIT! YOU ARE NOT TO LEAVE **YET.** I SHALL TELL YOU WHEN

AND YOU, JUNE, ARE TO OCCUPY THIS SEAT OF HONOR-OR SHOULD I SAY HORROR-WHILE SHE'S GONE!

SET THE TIME CLOCK FOR SIXTEEN MINUTES, TURTLE, AND TURN ON THE SWITCH.

IT TAKES SIXTEEN MINUTES TO PERFORM THE ERRAND I AM ASSIGNING YOU. IT ALSO TAKES SIXTEEN MINUTES FOR THOSE SPIKES TO REACH YOUR SISTER'S FLESH. THE MACHINE WILL NOT BE TURNED OFF TILL YOU RETURN. GO!

TRACY, ONE OF THE SUMMER SISTERS JUST CAME OUT OF THE DEN ENTRANCE. SHE'S WALKING LIKE MAD DOWN THIRD AVENUE.

GOOD! GLAD YOU CAME UP FOR ME, PAT. WE'LL CLIMB IN THE CAR AND SEE WHERE THAT BABY GOES.

ARE YOU THE DOCTOR?
AHA! THE GIRL WITH THE BROKEN WRIST. COME IN, MY DEAR.
6020

THIS IS INFORMATION FOR THE BROW. IT'S IN CODE OF COURSE. YOU WILL CARRY IT UNDER YOUR BANDAGE.

GOSH, HIS OFFICE OVERLOOKS THE HARBOR, TOO! HE CAN WATCH THE SHIPS' MOVEMENTS.
THERE! NOW TO PLACE A LITTLE SEALING WAX ON THE BANDAGE.

OKAY, BEAT IT. YOU HAVE 8 MINUTES TO RETURN TO THE BROW.
OH, MY POOR SISTER!

AND IN THE BROW'S LAIR —
IT ISN'T THAT I DON'T TRUST YOU GIRLS, MY DEAR, BUT, BY KEEPING ONE OF YOU HERE — I AM ASSURED THE OTHER WILL RETURN.

YOU SEE, ALL OF YOUR ERRANDS WILL BE TIMED. IF MAY IS NOT BACK HERE IN THE REQUIRED TIME YOU WILL SUFFER UNTOLD AGONIES.
TICK TOCK TICK TOCK

WE FOLLOWED HER UP TO THE OFFICE BUILDING. NOW SHE'S RETURNING.
IT'S ODD THAT SHE'S ALONE! DRIVE SLOWLY— I'LL HAIL HER.

HEY, MAY— OR JUNE— WHOEVER YOU ARE— I WANT TO TALK TO YOU.

I CAN'T STOP! I DON'T DARE WASTE A SECOND TALKING TO HIM OR MY POOR SISTER WILL BE TORTURED.

YOU SEE TOMORROW YOU WILL BE SENT OUT, MY SWEET, AND YOUR SISTER WILL OCCUPY THE CHAIR.
SHE'S HERE, BROW!

I-I WALKED AS FAST AS I COULD--I-EVEN RAN! I-I THINK I'M GOING TO FAINT.
YOU WERE ONLY ONE MINUTE LATE! TURN OFF THE MACHINE, TURTLE.
OH-OH! OH

I CAN'T UNDERSTAND IT! THE SISTERS PROMISED THEY WOULD COOPERATE WITH ME— BUT SHE WOULDN'T EVEN STOP TO TALK.
BUT, DICK, WHY DIDN'T YOU NAB HER?

IT WAS ONE OF THE SUMMER SISTERS, ALL RIGHT. BUT WHEN I SPOKE TO HER FROM THE CAR SHE ACTED AS THOUGH SHE DIDN'T HEAR ME
SHE WAS WALKING LIKE A CRAZY PERSON

SHE WENT TO THE OFFICE BUILDING. THEN SHE RETURNED. WHY DIDN'T YOU **NAB** HER, TRACY?
BECAUSE I DON'T WANT TO SPILL THE BEANS. THOSE SUMMER SISTERS ARE TIED UP TO SOMETHING **BIG**, PAT

DID I GET BACK IN TIME? DID THE SPIKES PIERCE YOUR LEG, JUNE?
ONLY A LITTLE WAY, MAY.

YOU SEE, JUNE, TOMORROW **YOU** WILL RUN THE ERRAND AND **MAY** WILL SIT IN THE CHAIR. HERE IS YOUR PAY.
YES BROW.

GOOD NIGHT, GIRLS. YOU'LL FIND HOT FOOD ON THE TABLE.

OH, JUNE, DID THAT SPIKE MACHINE HURT YOU BADLY? I-I RAN THE ERRAND AS FAST AS I COULD.

MAY, WE'VE **GOT TO GET OUT OF HERE.** THEY—THEY'RE **BAD MEN.** THEY MIGHT EVEN **MURDER** US.
MAY! WHAT ARE YOU THINKING OF??

I JUST HAPPENED TO REMEMBER THE PISTOL WE TOOK FROM MR. PATTON AND **HID** IN THAT **ROOMING HOUSE LINEN CLOSET!**
I WONDER IF IT'S STILL THERE?

IT'S OUR ONLY HOPE, JUNE— THAT GUN IN THE ROOMING HOUSE CLOSET
SH-SH! THE BROW'S CALLING US.

GOOD MORNING, LADIES. ARE YOU ALL READY FOR ANOTHER BUSY DAY?

SIT DOWN, MAY, DARLING, IN THE COZY LITTLE CHAIR. AND YOU, TURTLE, GIVE JUNE INSTRUCTIONS ON THE ERRAND SHE'S TO RUN.

PAT, CALL NESTOR AND GOODROW AND ZOY FROM THE EXERCISE ROOM. WE'RE GOING TO VISIT THAT HANGOUT THE SUMMER SISTERS ARE OCCUPYING —**NOW!**

YOU HAVE 23 MINUTES, JUNE, TO GO TO THIS ADDRESS. A MAN IN A JANITOR'S UNIFORM WILL GIVE YOU A SEALED ENVELOPE

IF YOU FAIL TO RETURN IN THE GIVEN TIME YOU KNOW THE FATE THAT AWAITS YOUR SISTER
THE CLOCK'S ALL SET, BROW.

THAT ROOMING HOUSE! —THAT PISTOL HID IN THE LINEN CLOSET! I'VE GOT TO GET IT IN **23 MINUTES!**
POPCORN

YOU GIRLS HAVEN'T HAD YOUR BREAKFAST YET, BUT YOU SHALL HAVE IT AS SOON AS YOUR SISTER RETURNS — THAT IS, IF YOU HAVE AN APPETITE
TICK TOCK

YOUR SISTER IS 2 MINUTES LATE. ARE THE SPIKES STARTING TO HURT?
SHE'S HERE, BROW!

WELL— LET'S HAVE THE ENVELOPE, MY DEAR. YOUR SISTER'S SUFFERING!

I DIDN'T GET AN ENVELOPE BUT I DID **GET A .38** THAT MY SISTER AND I HAD HID IN A **ROOMING HOUSE LINEN CLOSET.**

OH, **NO YOU DON'T!** WE CAME FROM THE MOUNTAINS WHERE A GIRL LEARNS TO SHOOT! **TURN OFF THAT MACHINE, BROW!**

CAN'T ANY OF YOU UNDERSTAND ENGLISH? I SAID TO TURN OFF THAT MACHINE.

WHY, YOU DIRTY LITTLE DAME — YOU CAN'T —

TWO DOWN! ONE TO GO!
DON'T SHOOT! DON'T SHOOT! THE MACHINE'S OFF.

OKAY— EVERYBODY'S HERE, TRACY.
GOOD. HERE'S THE DOPE, BOYS. —WE'RE GOING CALLING ON A COUPLE OF GIRLS.
CHESTER GOULD

AFTER TAKING DETECTIVE PATTON'S GUN ON THE TRAIN THAT DAY, WE HID IT IN A BATHROOM CLOSET IN THE ROOMING HOUSE WHERE WE STAYED. WHEN YOU SENT ME OUT THIS MORNING I WENT THERE AND GOT IT.

NOW, RELEASE MY SISTER FROM THAT AWFUL MACHINE, BROW, BEFORE I GIVE YOU THE SAME AS THEY GOT.

YOU ARE PLAYING A DANGEROUS GAME, SUMMER SISTERS. YOU'RE SIGNING YOUR OWN DEATH WARRANT!

KEEP YOUR HAND OUT OF THAT BOUQUET!

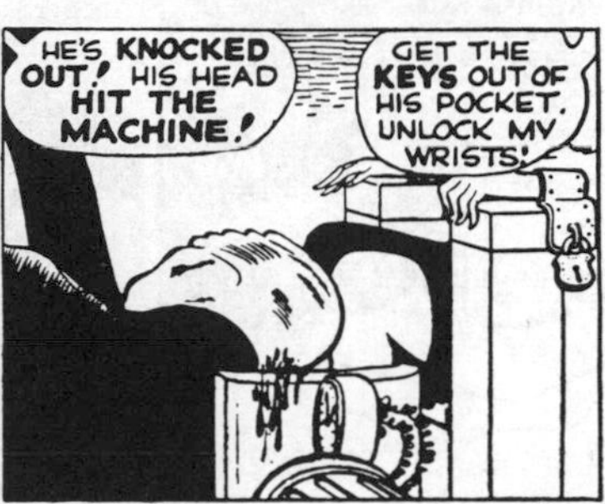
HE'S KNOCKED OUT! HIS HEAD HIT THE MACHINE!
GET THE KEYS OUT OF HIS POCKET. UNLOCK MY WRISTS!

I THOUGHT I COULD TRUST THOSE SUMMER SISTERS BUT I'VE CHANGED MY MIND. WE'RE GOING TO DROP DOWN ON THAT GANG AND TAKE THE WHOLE OUTFIT.

THOSE GIRLS MAY BE JUST AS VICIOUS AS THE REST— SO HAVE YOUR TRIGGER FINGERS READY, MEN.
I NEVER LIKED THOSE LITTLE WITCHES FROM THE FIRST.

WHAT WILL WE DO WITH HIM TO KEEP HIM PRISONER?
LEAVE HIM RIGHT WHERE HE IS! I'LL TURN THE MACHINE ON AGAIN.

THE BROW'S SHOULDER IS IN IT —— WE'LL SHOVE IT FURTHER IN!

AS THOSE TEETH CLOSE, THEY'LL KEEP HIM PRISONER TILL WE GET MR. TRACY AND THE POLICE.

SO! THE RUTHLESS, FIENDISH BROW LIES UNCONSCIOUS IN THE JAWS OF HIS OWN DIABOLICAL MACHINE! ARE THE SUMMER SISTERS TO BE HIS DOWNFALL??

TICK TOCK

LET US LOOK IN ON THE SCENE OF HAVOC IN THE BROW'S LAIR.
TICK TOCK

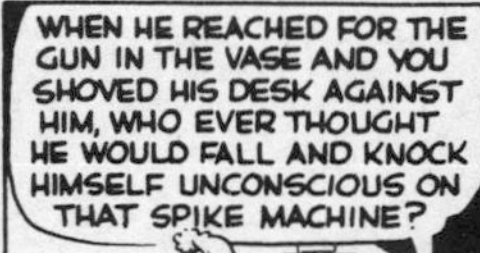
WHEN HE REACHED FOR THE GUN IN THE VASE AND YOU SHOVED HIS DESK AGAINST HIM, WHO EVER THOUGHT HE WOULD FALL AND KNOCK HIMSELF UNCONSCIOUS ON THAT SPIKE MACHINE?

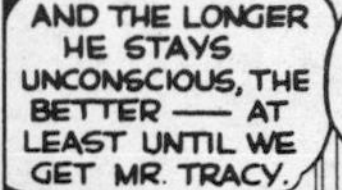
AND THE LONGER HE STAYS UNCONSCIOUS, THE BETTER — AT LEAST UNTIL WE GET MR. TRACY.
JUNE, WE'VE GOT TO GIVE OURSELVES UP.

TICK TOCK

AND AS THE UNCONSCIOUS BROW LIES IN THE JAWS OF HIS SPIKE MACHINE, THE TEETH MOVE CLOSER TOGETHER. THE COAT IS PIERCED. THEN THE POINTS PRESS INTO HIS FLESH.
TICK TOCK

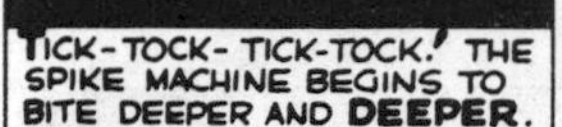
TICK-TOCK- TICK-TOCK! THE SPIKE MACHINE BEGINS TO BITE DEEPER AND DEEPER.

TICK TOCK TICK TICK TOCK

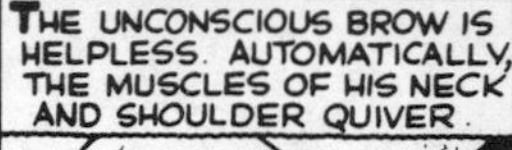
THE UNCONSCIOUS BROW IS HELPLESS. AUTOMATICALLY, THE MUSCLES OF HIS NECK AND SHOULDER QUIVER.

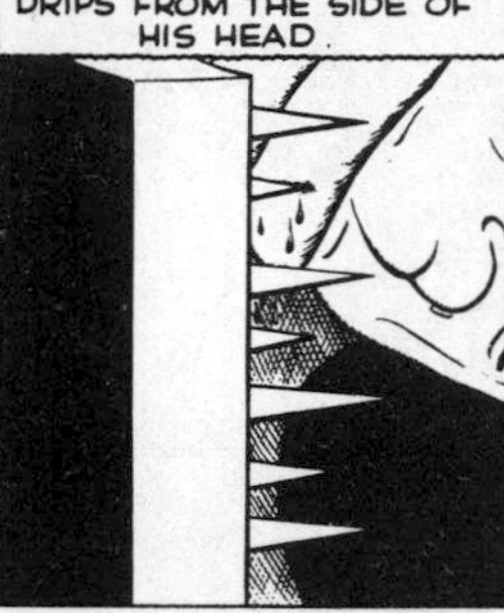
BLOOD BUBBLES OUT AND DRIPS FROM THE SIDE OF HIS HEAD.

MAY, I WANT YOU TO GO TO THE NEAREST DRUG STORE AND CALL MR. TRACY, WHILE I KEEP WATCH AT THIS TRAP DOOR.
OKAY, JUNE.

WITH THE INCREASING STING OF THE SHARP SPIKES, THE BROW'S SENSES SUDDENLY REVIVE.
BUZZ-ZZ-Z

OW! MY HEAD! MY HEAD! STOP THE SPIKE MACHINE SOMEBODY!
TICK TOCK TICK TOCK

AS THE BROW REPEATS HIS FRENZIED BUT VAIN CALLS FOR HELP, HIS HAND TOUCHES SOME THING. IT IS THE ELECTRIC CORD.
SNAP!

THERE! I CALLED THE POLICE. I ONLY HOPE THEY HURRY. HUH? WHA-??

HUH?

PULLING THE ELECTRIC CORD TO THE SPIKE MACHINE STOPS IT FROM FURTHUR CLOSING– BUT IT DOES NOT FREE THE BROW.

HE GRAPPLES WITH THE JAWS OF THE DIABOLICAL MACHINE. THEY WILL NOT BUDGE.
CRUNCH CRACK
TICK TOCK TOCK

EVERY MOMENT BRINGS EXCRUCIATING PAIN.
IF I TRY TO PULL MYSELF FREE I'LL TEAR THE FLESH RIGHT OFF.

SO! THERE SHE IS! COME HERE, SISTER, WE WANT YOU, TOO.
BUT I TELL YOU, WE WERENT TRYING TO MAKE A GETAWAY. WE WERE WAITING FOR YOU!

I'VE GOT TO DO IT. I'LL GRIT MY TEETH AND YANK!

THE SHOULDER OF HIS COAT RIPS AND TEARS AS BLOOD GUSHES FROM HIS HEAD.

THE BROW STRUGGLES TO HIS FEET AND LEANS HEAVILY ON THE WATER COOLER AS THE SOUND OF FOOTSTEPS REACHES HIS EARS.

I TELL YOU HE'S IN HERE! — AND TWO OF HIS MEN — DEAD! RIGHT DOWN THIS CORRIDOR.

YE GODS! SHE WAS TELLING THE TRUTH!

BUT THE BROW! HE — HE'S GONE!

LOOK OUT! — THERE ARE FRESH BLOOD SPOTS! THEY STOP AT THE WATER COOLER.

THERE ARE ONLY 2 ROOMS AND THAT ROOM HAS NO EXIT.
WHERE COULD HE HAVE GONE?
CHESTER GOULD

WE SHOT IN SELF, DEFENSE, MR. TRACY. IT WAS OUR ONLY HOPE.
WE HAD THE BROW IN HIS OWN MACHINE. HE WAS KNOCKED OUT!

WHAT A HORRIBLE CONTRAPTION! UGH!
IT'S OBVIOUS WHAT HAPPENED. HE REGAINED CONSCIOUSNESS AND WAS ABLE TO PULL THE ELECTRIC PLUG BEFORE THE SPIKES HAD CLOSED ENTIRELY ON HIM.

THERE ARE FRAGMENTS OF HIS COAT STILL ON THE SPIKES.
HE DIDN'T GO OUT THE FRONT WAY WHERE DID HE GO?

THIS OLD REAR DOOR HAS BEEN PLASTERED UP.
AND HE COULDN'T HAVE USED THAT OLD VENTILATOR SHAFT. THERE'S NO WAY TO GET UP TO IT.

MEANWHILE, THE BROW, HAVING MADE HIS WAY THROUGH A SECRET EXIT, STANDS AT THE REAR OF HIS QUARTERS
I HEARD THEM SAY COPS WERE COMING DOWN THE ALLEY. WHAT CAN I DO?

THAT LOOKS LIKE — A — A CASKET.
SCIENTIFIC TESTING LABORATORY

THERE'S NO TIME TO SPARE!

WAIT, BOYS! WHAT'S THIS? THAT WATER FOUNTAIN STANDS ON A RAISED PLATFORM.

AHA! LOOK! IT MOVES!! THERE'S A DOOR!

BILL, WHAT'S THAT CASKET DOING OUT ON THE PLATFORM?
IT'S A NEW PLASTIC TYPE THE STAR COMPANY HAS BROUGHT OUT.

THEY WANT US TO SUBMERGE IT IN THIS WATER VAT FOR TEN DAYS TO SEE HOW IT STANDS MOISTURE.

CAN YOU IMAGINE THAT! THIS WATER COOLER MOVES, REVEALING AN **EXIT** TO THE REAR.

WELL, BOYS, WE FOUND OUT HOW THE BROW GOT OUT. BUT WHERE DID HE GO?

WELL, BILL, THIS IS THE FIRST TIME OUR LABORATORY HAS BEEN ASKED TO TEST A PLASTIC CASKET, EH?

CHESTER GOULD

YEAH – WE'RE SUPPOSED TO SUBMERGE IT IN WATER FOR 10 DAYS. PUT THE CHAINS AROUND IT WHILE I GET THE RECORD BOOK TO MAKE OUT THE TIME SHEET.

A **PLASTIC** COFFIN! H'M? SO THE MANUFACTURER WANTS US TO GIVE IT THE MOISTURE TEST, EH? SUPPOSED TO SUBMERGE IT IN WATER FOR 10 DAYS, EH?

DID YOU FELLOWS SEE ANYONE? THE **BROW** CAME OUT THAT REAR DOOR!

SCIENTIFIC TESTING LABORATORY

POLICE

I WILL SAY ONE THING. THAT PLASTIC STUFF IS SURE HEAVY. I CAN HARDLY LIFT ONE END OF THE THING.

CHESTER GOULD

THINK I'LL TAKE A LOOK INSIDE—BEFORE WE SUBMERGE IT IN THE VAT OF WATER.

YEAH. I'D BETTER INSPECT THE INSIDE OF THIS COFFIN BEFORE WE SUBMERGE IT.

WH–? **UH**??

YI–YI–––

WH– **YE GODS!** ED'S HAD ANOTHER HEART ATTACK!

SLAM

PLOP

CHESTER GOULD

THAT LIFTING WAS TOO MUCH FOR HIM. I'D BETTER GET A DOC. **HELP – HEY– POLICE! HELP!**

GENTLEMEN! WILL ONE OF YOU GO FOR A **DOCTOR**? MY PARTNER HAS HAD A **HEART ATTACK!**

SCIENTIFIC TESTING LABORATORY

WHEN HE OPENED THE CASKET AND SAW ME HE **FAINTED**. JUST **PASSED OUT COLD!**

SO THEY WERE GOING TO SUBMERGE THIS CASKET IN WATER FOR A **10 DAY TEST**, EH? I'LL BE GETTING OUT.

WHY DON'T YOU USE YOUR **TELEPHONE**? THAT'S THE QUICKEST WAY TO GET A DOCTOR.

LET'S TAKE A LOOK PAT.

SCIENTIFIC TESTING LABORATORY

I CAN'T GO OUT THE FRONT WAY. THE BLOCK MUST BE SURROUNDED BY COPS.

HURRY, GENTLEMEN, PERHAPS WE CAN DRIVE HIM TO THE HOSPITAL

I'VE GOT TO DO SOMETHING QUICK! **AH!** HERE'S A LENGTH OF HOSE

AND THIS IRON WHEEL WILL GIVE ME WEIGHT. IT'S GOT TO WORK.

CHESTER GOULD

MY PARTNER HAD A HEART ATTACK BEFORE — BUT THIS LOOKS LIKE A BAD ONE.

LAY HIM THERE ON THE BENCH.

WE'RE AFTER A DESPERATE CRIMINAL, MISTER. AS SOON AS YOU CALL THE DOCTOR WE'LL BE ON OUR WAY.
YES, MR TRACY

HE'S COMING TO
IN THE CASKET! I-I SAW HIM — HE WAS ALIVE!

BUT I TELL YOU I DIDN'T HAVE A HEART ATTACK. I SAW A MAN IN THAT COFFIN.

MY PARTNER WENT INTO THE NEXT ROOM TO GET A PENCIL AND A RECORD SHEET. I OPENED THE LID TO LOOK IN AND THERE HE WAS — I FAINTED.

HE'S RIGHT! THE BROW WAS BLEEDING FROM SHOULDER WOUNDS CAUSED BY HIS SPIKE MACHINE. THERE ARE BLOODSTAINS IN THE CASKET.
WHEN I CAME BACK IN THE LAB, CHARLIE WAS LYING THERE AND I CALLED YOU GUYS TO GET A DOC.

THEN HE'S IN THIS BUILDING. HE COULDN'T HAVE ESCAPED. WE HAVE MEN SURROUNDING THE WHOLE BLOCK

REMEMBER, TRACY, WE'VE NEVER SEEN THE BROW.
WHAT'S THIS ROOM? WHO IS THAT MAN?

THAT'S OUR COLD-TESTING ROOM. IT'S FORTY BELOW ZERO IN THERE. THE MAN IS MURPHY.

IN THAT COSTUME HE COULD BE ANYBODY. GET HIM OUT!
MURPHY, COME OUT, WILL YOU?

YOU'RE RIGHT, PAT, WE'VE NEVER SEEN THE BROW. BUT GET THE SUMMER SISTERS IN HERE. THEY CAN IDENTIFY HIM.
HM?

THIS WAY, GIRLS.
OH!
LOOK OUT FOR THAT HOSE.

INCIDENTALLY, LET US EXAMINE THAT HOSE. ONE END HANGS OVER THE EDGE OF THE VAT AND DOWN INTO THE WATER.

AND STRANGELY ENOUGH, IN THAT WATER HIDES THE BROW, ANCHORED TO THE BOTTOM WITH AN IRON WHEEL. HE LIES FLAT ON THE BOTTOM OF THE VAT.

I DIDN'T HAVE A HEART ATTACK! I SAW A MAN **IN THAT CASKET!** I **FAINTED**.
BLOOD SPOTS VERIFY THAT.

BUT I TELL YOU I RUN THE COLD TEST ROOM. MY NAME'S O'BRIEN
NO, MR. TRACY, THAT **ISNT** THE BROW.

THAT ROOM IS FORTY BELOW ZERO, AND IT'S SOUND PROOF IN THERE. I DIDN'T HEAR ANYONE OR SEE ANYONE.

THAT'S IT, MAY. DRAW US A PICTURE OF THE BROW. YOU GIRLS ARE THE ONLY ONES WHO'VE SEEN HIM SO FAR.

YOU GIRLS WILL BE HELD IN POLICE CUSTODY FOR THE TIME BEING. IT'S OBVIOUS THAT THE SHOOTING OF THE BROW'S CONFEDERATES WAS SELF DEFENSE.

WE'VE SEARCHED THIS PLACE FROM FRONT TO BACK, TRACY. THE BROW JUST ISN'T HERE.

TAKE THE SPIKE MACHINE TO HEADQUARTERS AND CONFISCATE HIS SHORT WAVE OUTFIT.

IT'S FIVE O'CLOCK, CHARLIE. SHALL I LOCK UP FOR THE NIGHT?
NO, THE POLICE ARE COMING BACK FOR A FINAL SEARCH.

DON'T YOU SEE, GIRLS, YOU'RE OUR **KEY WITNESSES**? YOU'RE THE ONLY ONES WHO HAVE SEEN THE BROW. WE'VE GOT TO SEE THAT NO HARM BEFALLS YOU.

DOES THAT MEAN WE ALL ARE UNDER ARREST?
WELL, IT'S SOMETHING LIKE THAT, LADIES.

I COULDN'T STAY DOWN THERE ANY LONGER— MY HEAD'S BURSTING! MY SKIN'S LIKE ICE.

WHAT? NO ONE AROUND? THE PLACE MUST BE LOCKED UP FOR THE NIGHT! HA! THIS IS MY CHANCE!—OR IS IT?

DOC! IT'S ME. — THE BROW! LET ME IN.
BROW!

DOC. YOU AND I ARE THE ONLY ONES LEFT! TURTLE AND JOE ARE DEAD, AND 26 IS IN NAVAL CUSTODY.

WE WENT OVER THAT LABORATORY WITH A FINE-TOOTH COMB, TRACY. FINALLY, WE LOCKED THE PLACE UP— AND BEAT IT.

WHAT IS OUR NEXT MOVE, BROW?
OUR NEXT MOVE, DOC, IS TO **ERASE** TWO WOMEN— TWO LYING, DOUBLE-CROSSING WOMEN.

WHAT DID YOU FIND OUT, DOC?
THE SUMMER SISTERS ARE IN POLICE CUSTODY. BUT BENNY THE BONDSMAN SAID THE POLICE ARE GOING TO PLACE 'EM IN A HOTEL ROOM THIS AFTERNOON.

WHAT ARE YOU GETTING DRESSED FOR, BROW?
YOU AND I, DOC, ARE GOING TO GET IN THE CAR AND DO A LITTLE TOURING.

I WANT TO SURVEY THE BOULEVARDS AND PICK OUT ALL THE HIGH BRIDGES AND VIADUCTS.
HIGH BRIDGES, EH?

BUT, CHIEF, I DON'T THINK WE OUGHT TO LET THEM OUT OF OUR SIGHT.
MURPHY, CALL THE HOPP HOTEL AND GET A ROOM FOR THESE SUMMER SISTERS. THEY CAN'T STAY HERE.

BUT I TELL YOU, CHIEF, THE SUMMER SISTERS' LIVES AREN'T WORTH A NICKEL AS LONG AS THE BROW IS AT LARGE. WHY SEND THEM TO A HOTEL?

WHY NOT KEEP THEM RIGHT HERE IN THE WOMEN'S QUARTERS BEHIND BARS?
BUT WE DON'T WANT TO STAY BEHIND BARS, MR. TRACY.
HM?

BUT, BROW, YOU'VE GOT A LOT OF NERVE PARKING THIS CLOSE TO POLICE HEADQUARTERS.
STAY HERE, I TELL YOU.
CHESTER GOULD

AND KEEP YOUR EYES ON THAT POLICE BUILDING ENTRANCE. IF THOSE TWO DAMES COME OUT—— THEY'LL NEVER GO BACK!

I'VE RESERVED A ROOM FOR THEM IN THE HOPP HOTEL. I'M SENDING MURPHY ALONG FOR PROTECTION.

I STILL THINK, CHIEF, YOU'RE MAKING A MISTAKE IN LETTING THEM OUT OF OUR SIGHT. THEY COULD HAVE STAYED RIGHT HERE AT HEADQUARTERS.
LISTEN! THOSE TWO DAMES WOULD DRIVE THE MATRON NUTS.

YOU SEE, SUMMER SISTERS, THE DEPARTMENT WILL PAY YOUR EXPENSES TILL THE BROW IS CAUGHT. AND YOU'LL BE UNDER POLICE GUARD, TOO. YOU WON'T GET HURT.

OH, SIR, I WISH YOU COULD HAVE TAKEN US IN A SQUAD CAR. I'VE ALWAYS WANTED TO HEAR THOSE POLICE RADIOS.
DO THEY GET MUSIC, TOO?
SQUADS WERE ALL BUSY. WE'RE LUCKY TO GET A CAB.

DOC, YOUR TAILING WAS PERFECT. THEY'RE GOING OVER TO THE BOULEVARD. KEEP CLOSE TO THEIR CAB.

YOU NEVER DID FINISH TELLING ME HOW YOU GOT OUT OF THAT VAT OF WATER, BROW.
I WAITED TILL THEY CLOSED THE DUMP. THEN I CLIMBED OUT, YOU SAP! EASY—— WE'RE NEARING THE BRIDGE.

POLICE WORK FASCINATES ME SO, MAY!
ME TOO, JUNE
YEAH? YOU DAMES MUST BE PRETTY EASILY FASCINATED.

SUDDENLY, A GUN IS THRUST THROUGH THE CAB WINDOW.
KEEP DOWN THERE, COPPER, IF YOU DON'T WANT THE SAME.
IT'S THE BROW!

HOLDING THE STEERING WHEEL FOR A MOMENT, THE BROW DIRECTS THE CAB STRAIGHT THROUGH THE BRIDGE RAILING.

PLUNGING INTO THE MUDDY WATERS OF THE LAGOON, THE VEHICLE TURNS ON ITS SIDE AND SETTLES TO THE BOTTOM.

THE GIRLS FIGHT DESPERATELY TO FREE THEMSELVES FROM THEIR WATER CRYPT. ONLY OFFICER MURPHY IS THROWN CLEAR.

LET'S GO SOMEWHERE AND GET A STEAK.

WELL, THAT'S THAT

THAT FINISHES THE SUMMER SISTERS

FORCING THE GIRLS' CAB THROUGH THE BRIDGE RAILING BROW AND THE DOC SPEED ON

OFFICER MURPHY

IT'S THE **SUMMER SISTERS!** I WAS ABLE TO JUMP OUT, BUT THEY'RE **DOWN THERE!**

CHESTER GOULD

(GULP) OPEN THE **DOOR,** MAY. (ULP)

I CAN'T **I CAN'T** (ULP)

WHAT'LL WE DO?

THE **DOOR WON'T OPEN!**

HOLD ON TO ME, MAY—OH—MAY! (GLUB)

DOOR WON'T OPEN (GLUG)

THERE ARE **TWO GIRLS AND A CAB DRIVER DOWN THERE!** I'LL NEVER KNOW HOW I GOT OUT

THIS LAGOON OPENS INTO THE **RIVER!** CALL A COASTAL PATROL BOAT WE'LL NEED A **DIVER** TO GET INTO THAT CAB.

CHESTER GOULD

I **SAW** THE CAR THAT FORCED THEM THROUGH THE BRIDGE RAILING. I BELIEVE I COULD IDENTIFY IT.

LET'S GO!

THERE'S LIABLE TO BE A SWARM OF SQUAD CARS AFTER US, **DOC!** CUT UP TO THE PARK BEACH!

WEARING SWIMMING TRUNKS UNDER HIS CLOTHES, THE BROW DISROBES IN THE CAR, TOSSES A TOWEL OVER HIS HEAD AND PREPARES TO STEP OUT!

BEACH

MEANWHILE, IN THE CAB BELOW THE PARK BRIDGE, ALL IS QUIET.

CHESTER GOULD

KEEP GOING, DOC! I'LL MEET YOU AT YOUR PLACE LATE TONIGHT.

BEACH

JUST LIKE ANY OTHER CASUAL SWIMMER, THE BROW SAUNTERS ONTO THE BEACH.

LET THE COPS CHASE DOC'S CAR. I'LL BE SAFE ON THE BEACH

NONCHALANTLY, HE STRETCHES OUT ON THE SAND, HIS FACE HIDDEN BY THE TOWEL.

THE POOR SUMMER SISTERS! I TOLD THE CHIEF THEY SHOULD NEVER HAVE LEFT HEADQUARTERS.

THIS IS THE SPOT RIGHT HERE.

CHESTER GOULD

WELL, TESS, YOUR WAC UNIFORM CERTAINLY IS BECOMING

THANK YOU, JEAN, BUT IT WILL BE NICE TO SHED IT FOR A SWIMMING SUIT.

BEACH HOUSE

IT HARDLY SEEMS POSSIBLE THAT YOU'VE BELONGED SINCE LAST APRIL.

YES, THE TIME REALLY FLIES.

SHALL WE SIT DOWN HERE FOR A SUN BATH?

OKAY.

THE BROW

TRACY, ALL 3 OF THEM ARE DOWN THERE! —**DROWNED.**

BETTER SEND A CABLE DOWN—WE'LL PULL UP CAB AND ALL.

CHESTER GOULD

THE POOR SUMMER SISTERS! WHAT A PITY.

YOU CAN PUT AWAY YOUR INHALATOR, BOYS.
BRING THEM OUT ON DECK.

WELL, WAC TRUEHEART, HOW DO YOU LIKE THIS?
HOW PEACEFUL AND RELAXING IT IS TO BE A CIVILIAN! BOY, OH, BOY! PEACE AND QUIET!
THE BROW

THE SUMMER SISTERS AND THE CAB DRIVER ARE DEAD.
THAT FIEND!

YES, THE DASTARDLY BROW THOUGHT HE WAS ELIMINATING THE ONLY TWO PEOPLE WHO COULD IDENTIFY HIM — BUT HE DIDN'T GET MURPHY.
HOW I MANAGED TO GET OUT OF THAT CAB I'LL NEVER KNOW! AND I'LL NEVER FORGET THAT FACE.

I WAS OUT OF THE CAB BEFORE IT HIT THE WATER— BUT WATER PRESSURE MUST HAVE KEPT THE DOOR SHUT— THEY NEVER CAME UP.

A PASSING MOTORIST GOT THE BROW'S LICENSE NUMBER AND ATTEMPTED TO FOLLOW BUT LOST THE CAR IN TRAFFIC.
HIS LICENSE NUMBER WAS UNDOUBTEDLY STOLEN ANYWAY.

MEANWHILE—SOME DISTANCE AWAY ON THE PUBLIC BEACH.
WELL, TESS, IT MUST SEEM PRETTY NICE TO BE ON FURLOUGH AFTER HAVING BEEN A WAC FOR THREE MONTHS.
RIGHT YOU ARE, JEAN.

IT'S WONDERFUL TO BE ABLE TO SLEEP TILL YOU'RE GOOD AND READY TO GET UP— BOY, OH, BOY!

PAT, TESS IS UP AT OAK STREET BEACH WITH HER MOTHER AND A FRIEND. GO UP AND TELL HER I WON'T BE ABLE TO KEEP THAT DINNER DATE TONIGHT.

AS TESS OPENS HER HANDBAG TO GET HER COMPACT SHE FAILS TO NOTICE THE PIECE OF PAPER WHICH BLOWS OUT AND COMES TO REST NEAR THE HEAD OF A FIGURE FURTHUR DOWN THE BEACH
FLUTTER
FLUTTER

SLIPPING OUT OF DOC'S CAR AND SAUNTERING DOWN TO THE BEACH WITH A TOWEL OVER MY HEAD WAS A SWELL IDEA. LET THE COPS LOOK! H'M! WHAT'S THIS?

GAS COUPONS! "B" COUPONS. TWELVE OF THEM.

TEN MINUTES LATER IN A NEARBY DRUG STORE.
IT'S OUR CHANCE TO GET OUT OF TOWN, DOC! THE LICENSE NUMBER IS, 27A60. THE CAR IS PROBABLY PARKED SOMEWHERE NEAR THE BEACH. LIFT THE PLATES—THEN PICK ME UP IN FRONT OF THE DRUG STORE.
SODA

H'M? TESS TRUEHEART?? I WONDER WHO SHE IS?
SODA

MY **GAS COUPONS!** THEY— I'VE LOST THEM. I HAD THEM RIGHT HERE IN MY BAG.

AND IN THE APARTMENT OF BROW'S CONFEDERATE, DOC.

IT WAS THE BROW. HE SAID HE HAD GAS COUPONS. ENOUGH FOR US TO GET OUT OF TOWN. I WONDER WHERE HE GOT 'EM

IT'S QUITE WINDY, TESS. THEY MAY HAVE BLOWN OUT OF YOUR BAG.

TWELVE OF 'EM!— THEY BLEW RIGHT INTO MY HANDS. H'M. I'LL WAIT HERE TILL DOC COMES ALONG!

TESS, DON'T WORRY SO ABOUT THE GAS COUPONS. YOU PROBABLY LEFT THEM AT HOME ON THE DRESSER.

BUT, GEE, MOTHER, I DON'T REMEMBER TAKING THEM OUT OF MY BAG.

WE HAVE TO HAVE THE LICENSE PLATES THAT THOSE GAS COUPONS WERE ISSUED TO— H'M, LET'S SEE. THE BROW SAID 27A60.

THERE'S A COOL BREEZE BLOWING IN. I THINK I'LL WALK UP TO THE CAR AND GET MY SWEATER.

BRING MY JACKET, TOO, WILL YOU, TESS?

HERE, WE ARE— 27A60. WITH THIS BOLT CUTTER, THEY'LL BE OFF TOOT SWEET.

27A60

27A60

WELL, THAT'S NUMBER ONE. NOW FOR THIS FRONT PLATE.

BEACH

HEY! YOU! **WHAT ARE YOU DOING** TO MY LICENSE PLATES?

QUIET, SISTER, BEFORE I GET RECKLESS WITH THIS BOLT CUTTER.

WHY YOU—! **HELP!**

DRUGS

THOSE ARE MY LICENSE PLATES. **POLICE!**

BEACH

DRUGS

NOW, TO PICK UP THE BROW.

IT'S DOC, AT **LAST!**

I HAD TO SLUG THE DAME, BUT I GOT THE PLATES.

A BREEZE TAKES THE TOWEL

AS THE BROW RUNS TO THE CAR, THE TOWEL IS BLOWN FROM HIS HEAD.

WHAT'S UP, ED?

YE GODS! THAT GUY WITH THE TOWEL OVER HIS HEAD! WHY, HE HAS NO EARS! LOOK!

FIFTEEN MINUTES LATER.

I WONDER WHAT'S KEEPING TESS, JEAN?

GOSH, MRS TRUEHEART, SHE SHOULD BE BACK BY NOW.

TESS— —OH, TESS!
OH-H

-MY HEAD!

AS THE DOC'S CAR GLIDES ALONG THE BOULEVARD, THE BROW DRESSES.
ARE YOU ALL SET FOR A LONG TRIP, DOC?
YEAH, BROW, BUT I WANT TO STOP AT THE FIRST SECLUDED SPOT AND PUT ON THOSE OTHER PLATES.

I BROUGHT ALL OF OUR CLOTHES AND BELONGINGS. THEY'RE IN THE BACK SEAT.
SIXTY GALLONS. THAT OUGHT TO TAKE US AT LEAST 7 OR 8 HUNDRED MILES.

I LEFT THE BEACH TO GET A SWEATER THAT WAS IN MY CAR. I NOTICED A MAN REMOVING MY LICENSE PLATES.

I WAS EXCITED AND ANGRY! WHEN I SPOKE HE HIT ME WITH SOMETHING —A WRENCH, I GUESS
WHEN TESS DIDN'T COME BACK TO THE BEACH WE CAME UP TO LOOK FOR HER

PARDON ME — I'M THE DRUGGIST ACROSS THE PARK. I HAPPENED TO BE LOOKING THIS WAY WHEN THE LICENSE THIEF JUMPED IN HIS CAR AND SWUNG AROUND TO THE FRONT OF MY STORE!

HE PICKED UP A MAN IN BATHING TRUNKS WHO HAD BEEN USING A PHONE IN MY PLACE.

AS THE FELLOW RAN TO GET INTO THE CAR, A TOWEL HE WAS WEARING OVER HIS HEAD BLEW OFF. HE WAS HIDEOUS! HE HAD NO EARS —AND BIG WRINKLES IN HIS BROW.
WHAT?

TEN MINUTES LATER— RADIO ROOM OF STATE POLICE.
IT WAS A CALL FROM DICK TRACY— HE WANTS A FLASH SENT OUT TO ALL CARS ON THIS STOLEN LICENSE.

STILL LATER
WITH THAT DAME'S "B" COUPONS AND HER LICENSE PLATES, BUYING GAS IS A CINCH. WE'RE ALL SET.
HEY LOOK! WHAT'S THIS?

IT'S A STATE POLICE CAR! KEEP ROLLING— BUT NOT TOO FAST.
POLICE

HEY, BROW! THEY'VE STOPPED! THEY'RE TURNING AROUND.
WHAT?

THERE'S A DIP IN THE ROAD HERE. SLOW DOWN! I'M GETTING OUT. YOU KEEP GOING! ALL THEY'LL HAVE ON YOU IS A STOLEN LICENSE PLATE CHARGE! BUT ME—I'M HOT!

LOOKS LIKE THE RAIN'S OVER, ED. BETTER GET THE TARPAULIN OFF THE SEEDER AND GET THE REST OF THOSE SOY BEANS IN THE GROUND.

AS DOC AND THE BROW SPEED DOWN THE HIGHWAY, THE STOLEN LICENSE NUMBERS ARE ALREADY BEING BROADCAST TO ALL SQUAD CARS

I'M SURE THOSE WERE THE STOLEN NUMBERS, JOE. **STEP ON IT!**

POLICE

I'M INCLINED TO AGREE WITH YOU, GRANT, BECAUSE AS THEY SAW US TURN, THAT DRIVER **STEPPED** ON IT.

YEP, HERE THEY COME! THE BROW'S SAFE UNDER THAT FARM IMPLEMENT TARPAULIN. BUT ME— I'VE GOT TO TAKE IT ON THE CHIN.

YE GODS! I DIDN'T THINK ANYBODY SAW ME HIDE HERE.

THE HIGHWAY

CHUG CHUG

CHESTER GOULD

YEP, IF THE RAIN STAYS AWAY I OUGHT TO HAVE THE REST OF THOSE SOY-BEANS PLANTED BY DARK.

ULP!?? ?

?

MEANWHILE, DOC IS DOING HIS BEST TO GET AWAY FROM THE HIGHWAY OFFICERS

HE'S DOING ALMOST 85. THOSE OLD CIVILIAN TIRES WON'T STAND MUCH OF THAT.

CHESTER GOULD

AT 85 MILES AN HOUR, TRAGEDY STRIKES THE BROW'S FLEEING ACCOMPLICE, DOC!

SSS POP!

POLICE

HE'S **BLOWN** A **TIRE!**

BE ON YOUR WAY, MISTER. WE DON'T ALLOW BUMS SLEEPING AROUND OUR PROPERTY

YEAH? WELL, THIS BUM IS GOING TO TAKE YOUR TRACTOR

AND BACK DOWN THE ROAD

AND TAKE YOUR HAND OFF THAT TRACTOR THROTTLE

BANG BANG

WHAT? NOW, LOOK HERE. THAT'S GOING TOO FAR! I'VE A GOOD MIND TO—

I'M TAKING THE TRACTOR.

BANG

CHESTER GOULD

YE GODS! HE HIT THAT CULVERT WITH **TERRIFIC IMPACT**.

LOOKS LIKE THERE'S ONLY ONE OF 'EM. THE HEADQUARTER'S FLASH SAID THERE WERE **TWO!**

YEAH, ROUTE 62 AT GOLF ROAD! WE'VE FOUND YOUR STOLEN LICENSE PLATES ALL RIGHT.

AND ON A GRAVEL SIDE ROAD

CHESTER GOULD

IT'S GETTING DUSK. H'M? LOOKS LIKE A BIG BARN. BUT WHY ALL THOSE LIGHTS?

THERE ARE NO LIGHTS ON THIS TRACTOR—I'VE GOT TO GO ON AFOOT.

SUMMER THEATER

LOVE IN HASTE Starring the HICKORY BEAM PLAYERS

I'M IN LUCK! IT'S A **BARN THEATRE!** PEOPLE! CROWDS! IT'S A **BREAK!**

AND ACROSS THE FIELDS ON THE MAIN HIGHWAY

BUT I TELL YOU THERE'S JUST ONE OF 'EM, TRACY.

YEAH? THEN THE OTHER ISN'T FAR AWAY

CHESTER GOULD

LADIES AND GENTLEMEN, THE HICKORY BEAM PLAYERS PRESENT, "LOVE IN HASTE," A COMEDY IN 3 ACTS. THANK YOU.

AT LEAST, I'M THIS FAR WITHOUT THE COPS ON MY HEELS. H'M? WELL, I CAN'T STAND HERE.

BACKSTAGE! THE PLAY IS ON —— NOW, WHAT?

WHEN DOC SAW YOU BOYS WERE AFTER HIM HE MUST HAVE DONE NINETY MILES AN HOUR. THE OLD TIRES TODAY WON'T STAND IT.
THESE ARE TESS' STOLEN LICENSE PLATES ALL RIGHT, TRACY.

ALL EVIDENCE POINTS TO THE FACT THAT THE BROW WAS WITH HIM. BUT WHERE IS THE BROW, NOW?

HELP! POLICE! HEY! COME OVER HERE!!

IT'S MY HIRED MAN! MUSTA BEEN LAYING THERE ALL AFTERNOON AND MY TRACTOR'S GONE!
GET SOME COLD WATER. HE'S ALIVE.

MEANWHILE, HAVING ABANDONED THE TRACTOR, THE BROW CAUTIOUSLY ENTERS THE REAR DOOR OF AN OLD BARN WHICH HAS BEEN CONVERTED INTO A SUMMER THEATRE.

THE SHOW'S GOING ON! WHAT SHOULD I DO?

A LADDER! IT MUST HAVE LED TO THE HAYMOW WHEN THIS WAS A DAIRY BARN.

THERE'S A ROUGH PLATFORM UP HERE. I CAN HIDE OUT HERE OVERNIGHT. I GOTTA DO SOME THINKING.

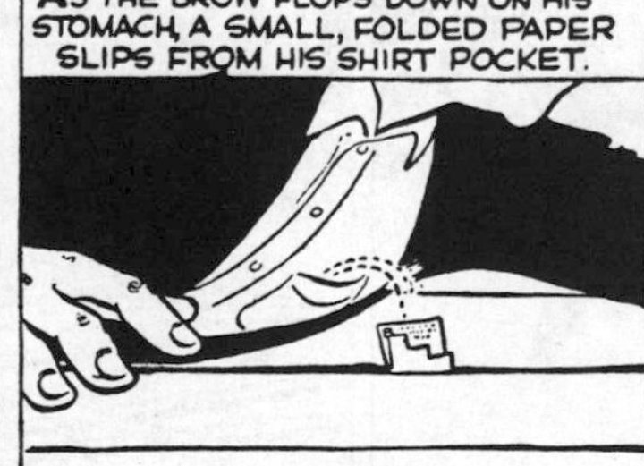
AS THE BROW FLOPS DOWN ON HIS STOMACH, A SMALL, FOLDED PAPER SLIPS FROM HIS SHIRT POCKET.

BUT, ALEXA, DARLING, OUR LOVE WILL NEVER DIE.
OH, JACK.

TEN MINUTES LATER, BETWEEN ACTS.
LOOK, GAS COUPONS
THEY MUST BELONG TO ONE OF THE SPONSORS. SOME LADIES WERE UP HERE BEFORE CURTAIN TIME.

WELL, WE'VE FOUND THE TRACTOR. H'M!? NOW WHERE? WHAT'S THAT OVER THERE?
THAT'S ONE OF THEM BARN THEATRES. STAGE ACTING THERE EVERY NIGHT
H'M? LET'S LOOK IN PAT.

IS MISS TESS TRUEHEART IN THE HOUSE? IF SO, KINDLY IDENTIFY YOURSELF AT THE BOX OFFICE. WE HAVE YOUR GAS COUPONS.
LOVE IN HASTE
Starring the HICKORY BEAM PLAYERS

FINDING THE WOUNDED FARMER, THE POSSE, HEADED BY DICK TRACY, TRAILS THE TRACTOR ON WHICH THE BROW ESCAPED.

TRACY SAID TO STAY HERE BY THE TRACTOR. HE AND PATTON HAVE GONE OVER TO THE BARN THEATRE.

WE JUST CAME UP IN TIME TO HEAR THE ANNOUNCEMENT THAT SOME GAS COUPONS HAD BEEN FOUND. MAY I SEE THEM?

SUMMER THEATRE

OH, YES, MR. TRACY.

NOW, I'M IN FOR IT. WHAT A BONER! THEY SLIPPED OUT OF MY SHIRT POCKET AND THROUGH THAT CRACK.

CHESTER GOULD

AT THE END OF THE SHOW

YES, MR. TRACY, WE FOUND THEM LYING RIGHT THERE ON THAT TABLE, AFTER THE FIRST ACT.

THEY'RE TESS' GAS COUPONS, ALL RIGHT.

THE BROW

MISS TRUEHEART MIGHT HAVE BEEN UP HERE ON STAGE BEFORE THE SHOW

NO. I HAPPEN TO KNOW SHE'S NOT ANYWHERE NEAR HERE.

THESE COUPONS WERE DROPPED OR LEFT HERE BY SOMEONE ELSE.

AS THE BROW LIES TENSE, HARDLY DARING TO BREATHE, HIS FOOT MOVES EVER SO SLIGHTLY! PARTICLES OF DRIED FIELD MUD LOOSEN FROM HIS SHOE.

CHESTER GOULD

CLICK CLICK

WHAT DID YOU SAY TRACY?

PIECES OF DIRT AND DUST CAME DOWN FROM THAT LOFT.

IF YOU'RE UP THERE, BROW, **COME DOWN NOW!**

CHESTER GOULD

I **HEARD SOMETHING** TRACY.

COME DOWN, BROW, OR **I'M COMING UP!**

THERE'S THE LADDER THAT GOES UPSTAIRS

LET ME GET HIM, TRACY.

I'M UP AGAINST IT! GUN'S OUT OF AMMUNITION. I USED MY LAST BULLET ON THAT FARMER.

THIS WINDOW'S TOO HIGH TO JUMP. WHAT ARE **THOSE**?

HUH??

METAL RODS — UH, **LIGHTNING** RODS—YEAH—OLD LIGHTNING RODS!

CHESTER GOULD

THEY MUST HAVE DISMANTLED THESE LIGHTNING RODS WHEN THEY REMODELED THIS OLD BARN INTO A THEATRE

THE BROW PICKS UP ONE OF THE POINTED TIPS AND WEIGHS IT NERVOUSLY IN HIS HAND.

AS TRACY'S HEAD EMERGES FROM THE LADDER SHAFT, THE BROW CROUCHES LIKE A JUNGLE HUNTSMAN IN THE SEMI-DARKNESS.

DO YOU SEE HIM, TRACY? HUH?

YEAH, I SEE HIM-

TRACY! GRAB HIM, SOMEBODY!
WHAT'S THAT IN HIS SHOULDER ???

EASY! DON'T PULL IT OUT TILL WE GET A DOCTOR.

IT'S PART OF A LIGHTNING ROD. WHEN WE REMODELED THIS BARN INTO A THEATRE WE LEFT THOSE RODS LYING IN THE HAY LOFT.
HE THREW IT LIKE A JAVELIN. EASY, BOYS!

COME ON, JOE, WE'RE GOING UPSTAIRS!!
LET'S GO, PATTON.

MEANWHILE, THE BROW MAKES HIS NEXT DESPERATE MOVE.
THESE OLD LIGHTNING RODS ARE EASY TO BEND — IF ONLY THEY DON'T BREAK!

HANGING THE HOOKED END OF THE ROD OVER THE WINDOW, THE BROW TAKES A CHANCE.

HEY, MEN! HE'S OUT HERE!

HE CLIMBED INTO MRS. McJACKEN'S STATION WAGON!
OH, DEAR, I WAS GIVING A FEED FOR THE ACTORS AFTER THE SHOW. ALL OF OUR SANDWICHES AND REFRESHMENTS ARE IN THERE.

GET THIS THING OUT OF HERE, BOYS. LET ME UP! I'VE GOT WORK TO DO.
TAKE IT EASY, TRACY. THE DOC WILL BE HERE IN TEN MINUTES.

WHY, THAT DIRTY ★¢!!☆ HE HOOKED THIS LIGHTNING ROD SECTION OVER THE WINDOW SILL AND SLID TO THE GROUND.
THE BROW

HOW BADLY IS TRACY HURT?
H'M. CAN'T TELL FOR SURE, PAT. WE'RE WAITING FOR THE DOCTOR

HE TOOK MY STATION WAGON! MY NEW STATION WAGON!
WE KNOW, LADY.

I'VE BEEN HIT. BULLET CUT MY FOREHEAD. I— I CAN'T SEE.
CHESTER GOULD

THE BLOOD'S GETTING IN MY EYES! I CAN'T SEE —BUT I'VE GOT TO KEEP GOING.

MURPHY SAID HE HEADED DOWN THE GRAVEL SHORT CUT TOWARD CRYSTAL LAKE.

IN HIS HELPLESS CONDITION, THE BROW LOSES CONTROL OF THE STATION WAGON. IT LEAPS ACROSS A GRASSY STRIP BESIDE THE ROAD AND INTO A PASTURE.
I CAN'T SEE—

STILL KEEPING ITS UPRIGHT POSITION, IT DROPS COMPLETELY OUT OF SIGHT INTO AN OLD ABANDONED GRAVEL PIT.
CHESTER GOULD

UNABLE TO SEE BECAUSE OF BLOOD, THE BROW MERELY TURNS OFF THE IGNITION AS THE STATION WAGON LEAPS INTO THE GRAVEL PIT!

TOO WEAK TO CARE WHAT HAPPENS NEXT, THE BROW LIES VERY STILL AND QUIET AS THE LAST OF THE POLICE CARS SPEEDS BY
POLICE CAR
THE BROW

BY THE WAY, LET US TAKE A LOOK AT THIS OLD GRAVEL PIT. IT'S LENGTH IS ABOUT A MILE. AND AT THE FURTHER END STANDS A SMALL SHACK.

STARING FROM A WINDOW OF THIS SHACK JUST NOW IS A PAIR OF EYES, THE OWNER OF WHICH IS THE ONLY WITNESS TO THE ACCIDENT.

SCENE: HOSPITAL ROOM IN A SMALL TOWN NEAR THE BARN THEATRE.
THEY'VE WITHDRAWN THE LIGHTNING ROD FROM HIS SHOULDER AND GIVEN HIM SHOTS.

WELL, PAT, OLD BOY, WHAT ABOUT THE BROW?
THE BROW AND THE STATION WAGON JUST DISAPPEARED.

YES, SIR. TRESPASSING! THAT'S WHAT IT IS! TRESPASSING!

DRIVING INTO MY PROPERTY WITHOUT PERMISSION. EVEN THE OWNER OF A GRAVEL PIT HAS GOT RIGHTS! I'LL SHOW 'EM.
THE BROW
CHESTER GOULD

I SAY, IN THERE— DO YOU KNOW YOU'RE TRESPASSING?

HEY, IN THERE— HEY! THIS CAR'S ON MY PROPERTY.

PLEASE— HELP ME— I—I NEED HELP!

AH! A MAN!

BUT TRACY, IT'S TRUE. THE BROW AND THE STATION WAGON JUST DISAPPEARED!

HONESTLY, I NEVER BELIEVED IN THE SUPERNATURAL BEFORE — BUT THIS BROW-
YOU SEE, TRACY, RIGHT AFTER WE LEFT THE THEATRE BARN—

EASY! I'M GETTING YOU OUT.
CHESTER GOULD

COMPANIONSHIP HAS COME TO GRAVEL GERTIE.

BUT IT'S TRUE, TRACY! WE HAD PATROLS BARRICADING ALL ROADS WITHIN 5 MINUTES AFTER THE BROW LEFT THAT BARN! HE AND THE STATION WAGON JUST DISAPPEARED!

THAT'S ODD! GRANTING THE BROW MAY HAVE FRIENDS LIVING IN THIS VICINITY, YOU WOULD STILL BE ABLE TO SPOT THE STATION WAGON.
WE SEARCHED EVERY FARM YARD AND GARAGE WITHIN 15 MILES.

THERE ARE NO SIGNS OF AN ACCIDENT! NO VISIBLE TRACKS LEAVING THE ROAD— HE JUST DISAPPEARED!

BUT LET US SEE HOW THE BROW DISAPPEARED. BADLY WOUNDED, HE LOSES CONTROL OF THE STATION WAGON, WHICH LEAPS INTO A GRASSY ROADSIDE SECTION AND PLUNGES STRAIGHT FORWARD INTO AN ABANDONED GRAVEL PIT.

IN THIS HOUR OF TRAGEDY, THE BROW'S ONLY WITNESS HAS BEEN A WITCH-LIKE CHARACTER WHOSE ABODE IS A SHACK OVERLOOKING THE SCENE.

NOBODY SAW YOU BUT ME. IF YOU HAD STAYED THERE YOU WOULD HAVE DIED — DIED JUST AS MY HUSBAND DIED YEARS AGO!

THIS USED TO BE OUR FARM TILL HE SOLD THE GRAVEL RIGHTS. THEY DUG UP OUR FARM — THEY LEFT A HOLE. THEN ONE DAY HE BACKED HIS CAR TOO NEAR THE EDGE.

YOUR HEAD IS CUT FROM THE GLASS, OR HAS IT BEEN GRAZED BY BULLETS? I SAW HOLES IN THE WINDSHIELD.

I SHALL TREAT YOUR WOUNDS! SOOT FROM A STOVE LID — THEN TO THE BASEMENT FOR SPIDER WEBS.

OLD FASHIONED, AM I? HA! THE CELLULOSE-LIKE SUBSTANCE IN THE SPIDER WEB CONGEALS THE BLOOD.

FIRST, THE WEBS — THEN THE SOOT. THE TWO BIND THE WOUND AGAINST INFECTION AND FURTHER BLEEDING.

YOUR NAME? WHO CARES?? AT LAST, GRAVEL GERTIE'S LONELY DAYS ARE OVER.
CAN THE BROW SURVIVE THE ANCIENT MEDICATION AT THE HANDS OF HIS WEIRD BENEFACTOR??—AND HOW LONG CAN HE ELUDE THE POLICE??

CARRYING THE BROW TO HER SHACK, THE FEMALE FIGURE ADMINISTERS FIRST AID
YES, GRAVEL GERTIE'S LONELY DAYS ARE OVER AT LAST, SHE HAS A **MAN**.

THAT COBWEB AND SOOT POULTICE WILL STOP THE BLEEDING OF YOUR WOUNDS AND ALSO HEAL THEM.

AN OLD MAMMY THAT WORKED FOR MY MOTHER YEARS AGO SHOWED ME THAT REMEDY AND IT WORKED ON MY ARM WHEN I CUT IT IN THE SAWMILL.

THERE'S ONLY ONE THING, MY DARLING — THAT SOOT WILL DISCOLOR THE SCARS! THE SCARS WILL BE BLACK — VERY BLACK.

WHEN MY HUSBAND SOLD THE GRAVEL RIGHTS TO OUR FARM YEARS AGO, LITTLE DID I DREAM HE WOULD BACK HIS CAR INTO THE GRAVEL PIT AND **DIE**.

ALL THESE 30 **YEARS** I HAVE WAITED — BUT NOW — ONCE AGAIN — I **HAVE** A MAN.

I SHALL WASH THESE BLOODSTAINS FROM MY COUCH AND FLOOR. I SHALL MAKE MY ENTIRE ABODE OVER — FOR YOU AND ME, WHO ARE STARTING LIFE ANEW — TOGETHER.
W-WH-WHERE AM I?

LISTEN, I MAY BE LAID UP — BUT I GIVE YOU GUYS **JUST 24 HOURS** TO FIND THAT **STATION WAGON AND THE BROW. NOW GET BUSY.**
YES, SIR, TRACY.
YES, SIR.

WHERE AM I?—I CAN'T **SEE!** WHAT HAPPENED?
PATIENCE, MY DARLING, YOU ARE IN GOOD HANDS!—VERY GOOD HANDS, MY SWEET.

LET US ONCE AGAIN LOOK AT THE STATION WAGON THE BROW SO RECENTLY DROVE INTO THE GRAVEL PIT. IS THAT A TINY WISP OF **SMOKE** WE SEE RISING FROM IT?

YES, WHILE THE CAR DID REMAIN UPRIGHT, THE IMPACT OF THE DROP HAS DISLODGED THE BATTERY FROM ITS MOUNTING UNDER THE HOOD. IT SHORT-CIRCUITS, AND THE CABLE INSULATION CATCHES FIRE.

GOSH, TRACY'S SORE ABOUT THE BROW'S ESCAPE! I'M AFRAID WE'RE IN FOR IT, PATTON.
YEAH—WE'RE GOING BACK TO THAT THEATRE BARN AND FIGURE THIS THING OUT FROM THE BEGINNING.

JUST A SONG AT TWILIGHT— WHEN THE LIGHTS ARE LOW.

WHAT DID YOU SAY YOUR NAME IS?
GRAVEL GERTIE, MY SWEET, BUT —JUST CALL ME GERTIE.

YOUR VOICE IS SOFT AND LOW. ARE YOU YOUNG?
WHAT DO YOU THINK, MY DARLING? HERE, HOLD MY SOFT HAIR IN YOUR HAND.

AND AT THE OTHER END OF THE GRAVEL PIT
PATTON, YOU'RE RIGHT. IT **IS THE STATION WAGON**.
YE GODS! **THE BROW'S BEING BURNED ALIVE**.

BUT—I'M ALL RIGHT, DOCTOR. I SEE NO REASON FOR STAYING IN BED.
YOU'RE RIGHT, TRACY, YOUR WOUND IS HEALING NICELY AND EXERCISE WON'T HURT.

WATCH OUT, PATTON. **DON'T GET BURNED**
YOU'RE RIGHT, DAVE, THERE'S NOBODY IN THERE.

THE BROW MUST HAVE JUMPED OUT BEFORE THE CAR WENT **OVER THE EDGE**, PATTON.
YEAH? H'M! STAY HERE, DAVE, AND KEEP WATCH. I'M GOING BACK AND REPORT TO TRACY.

THAT'S IT— SLEEP, MY DARLING! SLEEP AND RELAX WHILE GRAVEL GERTIE WATCHES OVER YOU. JUST DREAM AND REST.
Z Z Z Z Z

THANK GOODNESS, YOU'RE ABLE TO BE UP, TRACY. I HARDLY EXPECTED THIS.
WELL, I CAN'T GET INTO ANY FIST FIGHTS, PAT, BUT MY SHOULDER IS A LOT BETTER.

SUPPOSE I TOLD YOU THE BROW DROVE THE STATION WAGON OVER THE EDGE OF A GRAVEL PIT, SET IT AFIRE AND THEN DISAPPEARED?
I SHOULD GIVE YOU A BY-LINE ON PAGE ONE FOR BEING OUR STAR REPORTER —IF I WAS RUNNING A NEWSPAPER

WELL—THERE'S THE BLOOD-SPATTERED SEAT CUSHION. TRACY MAY BE INTERESTED IN THAT.
CHESTER GOULD

DRINK TO ME ONLY WITH THINE EYES
AND I WILL PLEDGE WITH MINE

IT'S THE RIGHT STATION WAGON, ALL RIGHT— BUT THERE IS NO SIGN OF THE BROW IN THE RUINS.
H'M?

MAYBE THE BROW STEPPED OUT AND THEN DELIBERATELY HEADED THE CAR OVER THE EDGE.
H'M? THE CAR DID NOT TURN OVER, BUT THE JAR TORE THE BATTERY LOOSE FROM ITS BRACKET. THAT COULD HAVE CAUSED A SHORT CIRCUIT.

OF COURSE, FOOTPRINTS DON'T SHOW ON THE GRAVEL, SO THERE'S NO WAY OF TELLING IF THE BROW WALKED AWAY FROM THE WRECK.
WHAT DO YOU SEE, TRACY?

H'M, LOOKS LIKE A COUPLE OF LONG WHITE HAIRS—THEY WERE CAUGHT ON THAT THISTLE. H'M?

MEANWHILE, IN THE SHACK OF GRAVEL GERTIE, AT THE OPPOSITE END OF THE PIT.
BUT THE COPS ARE AFTER ME —I'M—I'M THE BROW.
I'LL PROTECT YOU FROM THE COPS —I'LL PROTECT YOU FROM EVERYTHING.

I'LL NURSE YOU AND CARE FOR YOU FROM NOW ON, MY SWEET.
YOU DO HAVE A NICE VOICE —SOFT AND LOW.

AND YOUR HAIR! IT FEELS LIKE SILK.
THEN YOU DO LIKE ME, MY DEAREST? H'M? SMOKE! I SMELL SMOKE.

WHAT ABOUT THAT SHACK UP THERE? WHOSE IS IT?
HA! THAT'S THE HOME OF GRAVEL GERTIE. BUT THE BROW COULDN'T GO THERE, TRACY. THAT OLD DAME WON'T ALLOW ANY BODY WITHIN 500 YARDS OF HER PLACE.

QUICK, INTO THIS BOX! DO AS I SAY, BUT BE CAREFUL NOT TO DISTURB YOUR SOOT AND COBWEB POULTICE.

BUT I TELL YOU, TRACY, THIS OLD GIRL, GRAVEL GERTIE, IS A RECLUSE. SHE WOULDN'T HARBOR THE BROW.

NEVERTHELESS, THESE TWO GRAY HAIRS THAT WERE HANGING ON A THISTLE NEAR THE BURNING STATION WAGON BELONGED TO SOMEBODY.

SHALL I KICK THE DOOR IN?

NO. WAIT A MINUTE.

I HAVE MY SKELETON KEY!

EXCUSE US FOR INTRUDING, BUT—

—BUT **WHAT**?

OH MY NECK

CHESTER GOULD

BEG YOUR PARDON, LADY, BUT WE'RE LOOKING FOR SOMEONE — **A MAN**

BROW IN BOX

WELL, YOU'VE COME TO THE WRONG PLACE. I DON'T ALLOW STRANGERS ON MY PROPERTY — AND **THAT GOES FOR YOU, TOO**

SEARCH THE ENTIRE HOUSE, MEN. — BOTTOM TO TOP.

THAT'S A NICE HEAD OF HAIR YOU HAVE THERE, GERTIE — NICE LOOKING BRUSH, TOO.

CHESTER GOULD

I'LL THANK YOU TO GET OUT OF HERE AND LEAVE MY PROPERTY ALONE! NOW, **GIT OUT!**

WHILE GERTIE TALKS, TRACY PULLS SEVERAL OF THE LONG GRAY HAIRS FROM HER HAIRBRUSH.

THERE'S NOBODY IN THE BASEMENT, TRACY, AND WE LOOKED UP IN THE ATTIC, TOO.

HM?

EXCUSE US, GERTIE, I'M SORRY WE BUTTED IN. WE'LL BE GOING NOW.

YOU SEE, PAT, I SNEAKED A COUPLE OF HAIRS FROM HER HAIRBRUSH. I WANT YOU TO HURRY INTO THE LABORATORY AND COMPARE THEM WITH THESE I TOOK OFF THAT THISTLE WEED NEAR THE STATION WAGON. IF THEY MATCH, WE'LL TAKE GERTIE'S PLACE APART.

COME OUT, MY DARLING, — THEY'VE GONE.

OH-H- MY NECK!

CHESTER GOULD

DON'T YOU SEE, MY DARLING, I PROTECTED YOU? I SAT ON THE BOX AND LET MY HAIR HANG DOWN TO HIDE YOU FROM THE COPS.

OH-H- MY NECK!

IF **ONLY** I COULD **SEE YOU!** YOUR VOICE IS SOFT AND LOW. AND YOUR HAIR IS LONG AND SILKY — I KNOW YOU MUST BE BEAUTIFUL.

DON'T MY DEEDS SPEAK FOR THEMSELVES? DON'T YOU SEE **I LOVE YOU**??

YES — MY DEAREST! AND I'VE **GOT TO** SEE YOU. **OFF WITH THIS CURSED BANDAGE!**

CHESTER GOULD

RIPPING THE BANDAGE FROM HIS FACE IN A WAVE OF AFFECTION AND EMOTION FOR HIS BENEFACTOR, THE BROW GETS HIS FIRST GLIMPSE OF GRAVEL GERTIE.

NO-**NO** — **IT CAN'T BE!**

MY SWEET! MY DARLING!

THE SILKY HAIR! THE SOFT VOICE! **THEY BELONG TO YOU**??

LET ME OUT OF HERE! THE PLACE IS HAUNTED! YIE-EE-EEE-!!

CHESTER GOULD

PAT OUGHT TO BE BACK ANY MINUTE WITH THE COMPARISON TEST REPORT ON THOSE HAIRS. I FEEL POSITIVE GRAVEL GERTIE IS HIDING THE BROW IN HER HOUSE.

ONCE WE KNOW SHE'S INVOLVED, WE'LL TEAR THAT SHACK APART. AH! I SEE CAR LIGHTS COMING DOWN THAT SIDE ROAD, NOW.

BUT I WON'T LET YOU GO! I LOVE YOU, BROW. I LOVE YOU.

UNHAND ME, WITCH!
WATCH OUT—THE LAMP!

GRAVEL GERTIE ORDERED US OUT OF HER SHACK, BUT NOT BEFORE I HAD PALMED SOME HAIR FROM HER HAIR BRUSH.

IF THOSE HAIRS MATCH THE TWO HAIRS I FOUND ON A THISTLE NEAR THE BURNED STATION WAGON——OH, OH! HERE'S PAT NOW.

YOU WERE RIGHT, TRACY. THE LABORATORY FOUND THE HAIRS WERE FROM THE SAME HEAD! GRAVEL GERTIE HAD BEEN DOWN TO THAT STATION WAGON.
GOOD! NOW, WE CAN GET TOUGH! THE BROW IS IN THERE.

WHAT'S THAT?
PUFF

THE SHACK'S AFIRE! GERTIE'S PLACE IS IN FLAMES!

AN EERIE FORM, FIRE STREAMING FROM ITS HEAD, DASHES TOWARD THE GRAVEL PIT.

DOWN THE RICKETY STEPS AND INTO THE SPRING BELOW, IT FLIES-

HE WIPED THE POULTICE FROM HIS EYES AND SAW ME — HE STARTED TO LEAVE — WE ARGUED! —THE LAMP WAS KNOCKED OVER
AH! THEN THE BROW IS IN THERE?

OH, TRACY! HEY, TRACY!

HAS HE GONE INSIDE THE BURNING SHACK TO LOOK FOR THE BROW?

TRACY! DON'T SACRIFICE YOURSELF FOR THAT CROOK! WHERE ARE YOU, TRACY? WHERE ARE YOU??
CRASH

AND ACROSS THE VALLEY, STARTLED HIGHWAY POLICE, AWAITING FURTHUR ORDERS, SPY A SILHOUETTE IN THE FLARE OF THE BURNING SHACK!
THAT RUNNING FIGURE—WHO IS IT?
YEAH. WHO IS IT?

WHAT HAPPENED? **THE OLD DAME'S SHACK'S AFIRE**.
—AND I SEE SOMEONE RUNNING. **IT MUST BE THE BROW**.
POLICE
POLICE

MY HAIR! **MY BEAUTIFUL HAIR!** IT'S ALL **BURNED OFF!**
TRACY! WHERE **ARE YOU, TRACY?**

WHAT PAT DOESN'T KNOW IS THAT IN THE EXCITEMENT, TRACY SPOTTED THE BROW ESCAPING THROUGH THE UNDERBRUSH AND TOOK AFTER HIM.
CHESTER GOULD

IF ONLY I HADN'T KNOCKED THAT LAMP OVER!! I COULD HAVE STEPPED OUT OF THERE WITHOUT THE COPS SEEING ME—**OW-OW**.

I WENT INTO **BOTH ROOMS** —TRACY **ISN'T** IN THERE! **THANK HEAVEN!**

BUT **WHERE** IS HE? —SO YOU WERE HIDING THE BROW, EH?
HE-HE WAS SO HANDSOME

GRANNY, YOU'RE GOING TO **STICK** WITH ME. WE'LL BE WANTING YOU
WHO, ME?
CHESTER GOULD

I'M SURE HE CAME OUT IN THIS CLEARING —BUT WHERE **IS** HE? H'M? WHAT'S THIS?
CLICK CLICK

AH—I SEE WHAT THIS IS—IT'S AN **ELECTRIC CATTLE FENCE!** THAT'S THE CONTROL BOX.
CLICK CLICK

THAT MECHANISM BREAKS THE CIRCUIT EVERY SECOND OR SO TO SAVE THE BATTERY.
CLICK CLICK
HOT SHOT

BUT—I'M FORGETTING THE BROW—HUH?? WHAT'S **THIS?**
CLICK CLICK

THAT WIRE MOVED! AND I THOUGHT I HEARD A GRUNT! CAN IT BE OUR FRIEND THE BROW ISN'T ACQUAINTED WITH ELECTRIC FENCES?
CLICK CLICK
CHESTER GOULD

SO YOU GOT A **TASTE** OF THAT ELECTRIC FENCE, EH, BROW? **COME OUT OF THERE!**
BANG BANG

DON'T SHOOT ME—DON'T KILL ME—PLEASE—**DON'T KILL ME!**

I WAS ONLY DOING THAT TO FLUSH YOU OUT OF THERE. NOW YOU AND I ARE GOING TO HAVE A **PRIVATE CHAT**.
BUT-BUT
CHESTER GOULD

I-I THOUGHT I RAN A LIGHTNING ROD THROUGH YOUR SHOULDER. **HOW** CAN YOU FIGHT?
I'LL SHOW YOU, BROW

BROTHER, YOU'D BETTER START WORRYING 'CAUSE I'M GOING TO PUT ANOTHER WRINKLE IN THAT BROW!

STAND UP! I'M **NOT THROUGH** WITH YOU, YET—

WHEN THAT ELECTRIC FENCE GETS TOO HOT—GET UP—I'VE **GOT ANOTHER ONE** HERE—
CHESTER GOULD

THEY'RE COMING IN! THEY'VE GOT THE BROW! THE RADIO ROOM JUST HANDED ME A FLASH FROM PATTON.

WHAT DO YOU MEAN, THEY'RE COMING? THEY'RE HERE NOW.

GO EASY WITH HIM, BOYS, HE DOESN'T FEEL MUCH LIKE TALKING.

WHAT AN ASSIGNMENT, TRACY! WHO IS THE – ER –GIRL FRIEND?
WHAT? YOU MEAN TO TELL ME YOU DON'T KNOW GRAVEL GERTIE?

SCENE: THE EMERGENCY ROOM ON THE TOP FLOOR OF THE JAIL —
YOU SEE, WHEN GRAVEL GERTIE'S SHACK STARTED TO BURN, I SAW THE BROW DASH OUT THE REAR DOOR.

WHEN I CAUGHT UP WITH HIM IT TOOK A LITTLE KNUCKLE TREATMENT TO CONVINCE HIM.
I'LL SAY! YOU REALLY IRONED HIM OUT!

WHAT ABOUT GRAVEL GERTIE? WHAT ARE YOU GOING TO DO WITH HER, TRACY?

OH-H- MY HOME! IT'S BURNED TO THE GROUND! THE ONLY HOME I EVER HAD (SOB)
GRAB HER, CALLAHAN.

THE POOR OLD GIRL IS RATHER PATHETIC— WHAT IN?

USING THE FAINTING SPELL AS A RUSE, GRAVEL GERTIE GRABS THE OFFICER'S REVOLVER.
HERE, MY SWEET! KILL THEM! KILL THEM ALL!

HANDCUFFED THOUGH HE IS, THE BROW FUMBLES FOR THE SAFETY RELEASE ON THE GUN.

TRACY'S HAND TOUCHES AN INK WELL. THERE IS NO TIME TO LOSE.

THE IMPACT SENDS THE BROW BACKWARD! A CRASH! BROKEN GLASS! —AS THE BODY HURTLES DOWN.
CRASH

IN THE PARKWAY BELOW STANDS THE NEIGHBORHOOD HONOR ROLL — A PLAQUE WITH NAMES OF THE BOYS IN SERVICE — AND A FLAG POLE.

LIKE A MIGHTY SABER, THE FLAG POLE REACHES UP TO MEET THE EVIL FORM.

A THUD! AND ALL IS QUIET— VERY QUIET ON THIS BRIGHT SEPTEMBER DAY.
THUS, THE BROW, FOREIGN AGENT AND ESPIONAGE LEADER, LIES IMPALED BY A POLE BEARING THE FLAG OF THE COUNTRY HE TRIED TO HARM.

YOU THREW CALLAHAN'S PISTOL TO THE BROW. HE MIGHT HAVE SHOT US ALL!
YE GODS! WHEN I HURLED THAT INKWELL AT HIM, I NEVER DREAMED THE IMPACT WOULD KNOCK HIM THROUGH THE WINDOW
HE LANDED ON THE FLAGPOLE. FELL OUT OF THE DOCTOR'S OFFICE ON THE EIGHTH FLOOR.
CHESTER GOULD
OUR BOYS IN THE SERVICE
OUR BOYS IN THE SERVICE
HORRIBLE–HORRIBLE!
HE NEVER KNEW WHAT HIT HIM.
I'LL SAY!
OKAY, LET'S GET BUSY, MEN. GET HIM OUT OF THERE.
OUR BOYS IN THE SERVICE
WE WON'T GET HIM OUT OF THERE, CHIEF, TILL WE GET A COUPLE OF STEEL SETTERS AND A DERRICK TO REMOVE THE POLE.
YE GODS! I SEE!
CHESTER GOULD

THE 1950s

CREWY LOU

by Chester Gould

5/22/51–11/4/51

The 1950s are a special era to the editors of this book. *Tracy* artist Dick Locher began assisting Chester Gould on the strip as the fifties came to a close, a dream assignment for a young cartoonist; *Tracy* writer Max Allan Collins, as a young boy, discovered the strip in the early 1950s and has been fascinated with fictional detectives and crime ever since.

If the 1940s represent the pinnacle of *Tracy*'s commercial success, and the moment when Gould "put it together" creatively, the early 1950s represent Gould at his mature best.

This 1951 continuity, dubbed "The Case of the Fiendish Photographers" in the Harvey Comics serialization coeditor Collins followed circa 1954, may be Gould's masterpiece. A few months before the beginning of this continuity, Gould began drawing his originals smaller, reflecting the smaller size the strip was printed in in most newspapers (paper shortages during the war opened the door to editors shrinking the publication size of comics). Now somewhat limited visually, Gould poured on the steam where the stories themselves were concerned. Certainly this story—the first complete continuity of the shrunken-art period—demonstrates Gould flexing his every muscle as a writer.

The soap opera elements of the thirties are represented by the happy home life of the Tracys with their new daughter, Bonnie Braids, at the outset, and by the dramatic and moving disappearance of the child as the story progresses.

The depiction of crime—with small-time con-men/thieves Crewy Lou and Sphinx coming up against a Big Boy-like underworld kingpin—is at once reminiscent of Gould's thirties era outlaws and gangsters, yet more realistic, right out of W. R. Burnett or Dashiell Hammett, but updated. The "King" is definitely a post-war, executive-style organized crime figure we've not met before in *Dick Tracy*.

At the same time, we have the trademark violent action, with bullets flying, villains meeting grisly deaths; a villainess leading Tracy on an extended perilous chase; Tracy himself portrayed as an astute detective *and* a fast-shooting lawman *and* a tortured father.

And we have a charismatic adversary in Crewy Lou, a crafty three-dimensional human being who holds our attention and even, oddly, our sympathy.

PARDON ME, IS THAT THE DICK TRACY RESIDENCE?

IT IS.

BORN MAY 6TH! THE BABY'S THREE WEEKS OLD NOW.

I'LL JUST STAND HERE AND LOOK THINGS OVER! NOBODY WILL NOTICE.

CHESTER GOULD

BONNY BRAIDS! NOTHING MUST EVER HAPPEN TO YOU. YOU MUST GROW UP TO BE JUST AS SWEET AND GOOD-LOOKING AS YOUR MOTHER.

WHAT A PRETTY SPEECH! THANK YOU SO MUCH! AND NOW, IF—

WHAT WAS THAT?

POP

I WAS JUST TAKING A FLASH PHOTO OF YOU THREE WITH MY NEW CAMERA.

CHESTER GOULD

GOSH, TRACY, DID IT SCARE YOU **THAT MUCH**? YOU'RE SHAKING!

HONEY, ARE YOU JITTERY?

CHIEF PATTON CALLING TRACY! NOW, THAT YOU'VE HAD YOUR BABY, HOW ABOUT GETTING **BACK TO WORK**?

LISTEN, YOU IRISH BACHELOR, I'M ON MY WAY NOW.

2-WAY WRIST RADIO

I'D BETTER STOP AT THE SMOKE SHOP AND PICK UP A BOX OF CIGARS. THAT'S WHAT PATTON'S AFTER.

YES, THE MAIN SQUEEZE HIMSELF! NOW TO SEE WHAT TIME HE RETURNS.

CHESTER GOULD

TWO OR THREE SHOTS SHOULD DO IT—AT THE MOST, FOUR.

IT'S THE TRACY'S FIRST BABY, AND THEY'LL PAY PLENTY.

A LOT OF WINDOWS IN THE HOUSE, TOO. THAT'LL MAKE THE JOB EASIER.

CHESTER GOULD

YEAH—I NOTICED HER LOITERING THERE YES-TERDAY AND THE DAY BEFORE. I WONDER IF—

WHY NOT?

SPARKLE'S MOTHER SENT HER OVER TO SPEND THE DAY WITH BONNY BRAIDS.

SHE'S THE DOGGONEDEST PRETTY BABY I EVER SAW.
DO YOU REALLY THINK SO?

AND AT TRACY'S FRONT DOOR.
CHESTER GOULD

YES, WE WANT TO TALK TO YOU.
ME? WHAT HAVE I DONE?

BONNY BRAIDS IS NINETEEN DAYS OLD TODAY.
SHE'S STILL PRETTY DAD-BURNED LITTLE, THOUGH.

I LIKE THE NAME, BONNY BRAIDS. IT'S PURT NEAR AS PRETTY AS MINE.
THANK YOU, SPARKLE.

IT'S REAL NICE OF YOUR MOTHER TO LET YOU STAY WITH US TODAY. I THINK BONNY BRAIDS LIKES YOU VERY MUCH.

HEY! WHAT'S GOING ON DOWN THERE?
WHAT DO YOU SEE, JUNIOR?

SHE WAS STANDING ACROSS THE STREET AGAIN THIS MORNING, SO WE PICKED HER UP.

YOU'VE BEEN SEEN WATCHING MY HOUSE FOR SEVERAL DAYS NOW. WHAT'S THIS ALL ABOUT, MISS?

I'VE BEEN TRYING TO GET UP NERVE ENOUGH TO MEET YOU, MR. TRACY. I KNOW I'VE ACTED VERY STUPIDLY.

I'M A PHOTOGRAPHER—A BABY PHOTOGRAPHER. I THINK I'M THE BEST IN THE COUNTRY.

MY NAME'S LOUISE. YOU'VE SEEN MY PICTURES IN MANY NATIONAL MAGAZINE ADS.
WHY DIDN'T YOU TELEPHONE OR COME RIGHT OVER AND KNOCK ON THE DOOR?

MY BUSINESS IS HIGHLY COMPETITIVE. I WOULD LIKE TO BE THE FIRST TO TAKE BONNY BRAIDS' PICTURE. I THOUGHT IF I WROTE OR PHONED—
WHAT'S YOUR FULL NAME, LOUISE?

LOUISE BROWN. HOWEVER, MY FRIENDS CALL ME CREWY LOU.
CREWY LOU? I SEE. THE HAIRCUT, EH?

YEAH, I'M A CHARACTER, MR. TRACY! CREW-CUT ON TOP AND LONG HAIR BEHIND.
CREWY LOU, EH? OKAY. NOW WHAT ABOUT THOSE BABY PICTURES?

BABY PHOTOGRAPHER, EH? I'M SORRY TO SAY I NEVER HEARD OF YOU BEFORE, CREWY LOU.

AND ANOTHER THING, DON'T YOU THINK YOU NEED A FEW LESSONS IN SELLING?

I KNOW MY APPROACH WAS BAD, MR. TRACY.

BUT I **DO** WANT TO PHOTOGRAPH YOUR BABY—

—AND I KNEW IF I PHONED YOU, I'D BE TURNED DOWN.

WHERE IS YOUR STUDIO? WHERE'S YOUR CAMERA? WHY DID YOU PICK MY BABY?

EASY! ONE AT A TIME, PLEASE.

CHESTER GOULD

I TELL YOU, MR. TRACY, I'M AN EXPERT AT PHOTOGRAPHING BABIES. THESE ADS SPEAK FOR THEMSELVES.

CREWY LOU, THAT'S ALL VERY NICE BUT—IT'S NO SOAP!

MRS. TRACY AND ANOTHER WOMAN OWN A COMMERCIAL PHOTO STUDIO. WHEN BONNY BRAIDS IS PHOTOGRAPHED, THEY'LL DO IT.

CHESTER GOULD

WELL, THERE'S NOTHING MORE I CAN SAY, I GUESS. GOSH, I'M SORRY YOU WON'T LET ME.

SO LONG, CREWY LOU.

SPARKLE! WE'RE SO GLAD TO SEE YOU!

THANK YOU! **I'M FOUR YEARS OLD** TODAY!

HAPPY BIRTHDAY! THAT'S WHY BONNY BRAIDS AND I WANTED YOU TO COME OVER.

THEY'RE BIRTHDAY GIFTS FOR YOU, SPARKLE.

OH, GEE! THANKS AN AWFUL LOT, MRS. BRACY.

CHESTER GOULD

POOR BONNY BRAIDS! SHE WON'T HAVE A BIRTHDAY FOR A LONG TIME!

NO, SPARKLE, SHE'S ONLY 24 DAYS OLD TODAY.

I SAID I WANT THOSE PICTURES OF THE MAYOR'S GRANDSON PUT IN THE SAMPLE CASE.

I'LL PICK THEM UP IN 20 MINUTES. HAVE THEM READY.

MR. TRACY ISN'T RID OF ME YET. NO, SIR! HE'LL FIND OUT I'M A GIRL OF DETERMINATION.

CHESTER GOULD

TESS, DID YOU EVER HEAR OF A PHOTOGRAPHER BY THE NAME OF CREWY LOU?

CREWY LOU? NEVER.

I'M LOUISE BROWN, MRS. TRACY, BETTER KNOWN AS CREWY LOU.

MY HUSBAND TOLD ME ABOUT YOU. I THINK HE SAID WE WEREN'T INTERESTED IN HAVING BABY'S PICTURE MADE.

YES, HE DID.

BUT WON'T YOU LOOK AT THESE SAMPLES?

CHESTER GOULD

GOLLY! THESE ARE BEAUTIFUL PHOTOS! WON'T YOU COME IN, CREWY LOU?

THANK YOU.

I THOUGHT I TOLD YOU NO SOAP ON THIS BABY PICTURE BUSINESS.
BUT, MR. TRACY!

DICK, WAIT! THESE PORTRAITS ARE BEAUTIFUL!
BOO-HOO-SOB-
CHESTER GOULD

I KNEW SHE'D COME HERE. I PLANNED IT THAT WAY. I'M TRYING TO STALL HER WHILE SAM CHECKS ON HER.

I'M CO-OWNER OF A COMMERCIAL PHOTOGRAPHY STUDIO MYSELF, BUT WE CAN'T TAKE PICTURES LIKE THIS, MISS LOUISE—OR MISS BROWN.
JUST CALL ME CREWY LOU, MRS. TRACY.

ALL RIGHT, CREWY LOU! I THINK YOUR HAIRDO IS TERRIFIC.
THANK YOU.

REALLY, DICK, THESE PICTURES OF THE MAYOR'S GRANDSON AND GRAND-NEPHEW ARE WORKS OF ART. I THINK THEY'RE WONDERFUL.

SAY, WHAT IN—?? WHY ARE YOU SO SKEPTICAL? HONESTLY—!!
HEY, TRACY-PST!

SHE HAS A STUDIO, ALL RIGHT, WE JUST CHECKED. AND SHE PHOTOGRAPHED THE MAYOR'S GRANDSON. WE CHECKED THAT, TOO.
YOU KNOW I BROUGHT HER IN HERE JUST TO QUESTION HER.

BUT SHE LOOKS SCREWY TO ME!
DICK! DON'T YOU TRUST ANYBODY— ANYBODY AT ALL?

MIGHT I SEE LITTLE BONNY BRAIDS, MRS. TRACY?
CERTAINLY, YOU MAY.

YOU HAVE A TELEGUARD CAMERA IN BONNY BRAIDS' ROOM, TRACY?
SURE. IT'S SET IN A WALL CABINET—AND FOCUSED RIGHT ON HER CRIB.

IN ADDITION TO THE TELEVISION CAMERA, I'VE GOT THE ROOM WIRED WITH A COUPLE OF MIKES.
OH, BROTHER!

INCIDENTALLY, LETTERS ARE STILL COMING IN AND THEY ALL LIKE THAT NAME, BONNY BRAIDS.
I GUESS IT'S PERMANENT, JUNIOR.

OH, YOU BEAUTIFUL BABY! WHAT A GORGEOUS SUBJECT!
THE ROOM IS SO LIGHT, A COUPLE OF 1000-WATT FLOODS WOULD BE ALL I'D NEED.

"DO YOU HAVE A HELPER?" ASKS TESS. "YES, I HAVE A PARTNER WHO WORKS WITH THE DEVELOPING AND PRINTING. HE STAYS AT THE STUDIO," SAYS CREWY LOU.

SURE, I'VE HAD A TELEGUARD CAMERA SET UP IN BONNY BRAIDS' NURSERY FOR OVER A WEEK.

YOU SURE DON'T TRUST THIS DAME, CREWY LOU, DO YOU, TRACY?

WHAT DO YOU THINK?

I DON'T BLAME YOU, TRACY.

SHE'S THE MOST PHOTOGENIC BABY I EVER SAW IN MY LIFE, MRS. TRACY!

THEN, WE'LL LOOK FOR YOU TOMORROW.

I'LL BE BACK WITH CAMERA, LIGHTS AND EVERYTHING.

CHESTER GOULD

CREWY LOU WILL BE BACK TOMORROW TO TAKE BONNY BRAIDS' PICTURE. HER PRICE IS 50 DOLLARS FOR TWO.

WHAT?

I COULDN'T GET TO FIRST BASE WITH HIM, **BUT I SOLD HER!**

HAVE THE SMALL CAMERA AND A COUPLE OF 1000-WATT FLOODS READY FOR ME AT EIGHT.

DO YOU UNDERSTAND, SPHINX?

yes

CHESTER GOULD

THE PHONE-ANSWERING MACHINE IS ALL SET, SO YOU WON'T HAVE TO WORRY ABOUT THAT.

I EXPECT TO HAVE TRACY'S BABY PHOTOGRAPHED AND TO BE BACK HERE BY NOON.

I WANT THESE PRINTS TO BE YOUR **BEST!**

ARE YOU LISTENING TO ME, SPHINX?

yes

WE HAVE NO RECORDS OR FILES OF ANY KIND ON A "CREWY LOU".

MAYBE SHE'S OKAY AFTER ALL, TRACY.

CHESTER GOULD

GOOD! WE'RE **ALL** SET!

NOW, CREWY LOU WANTS UM BONNY BRAIDS TO LAUGH-UM AND LOOK REAL CUTE-UMS.

THAT'S IT—REAL BIG SMILE-COOCHY-COO! SEE BIRDY-BIRD. SEE UM BIG BIRDY BIRD.

CHESTER GOULD

WHAT A LINE! THE KID WILL BE SQUAWKING ANY MINUTE.

I WONDER WHAT THAT DAME'S AFTER.

OH— **HOW CUTE!**

NOW, BONNY BRAIDS, THIS WILL BE THE LAST ONE.

SHE SAYS HER STUDIO IS AT THIS ADDRESS. I JUST CALLED THERE AND GOT CREWY LOU'S OWN VOICE ON ONE OF THOSE PHONE-ANSWERING DEVICES.

AND SHE TOLD US SHE HAD AN ASSISTANT WHO STAYED IN THE STUDIO.

IS SHE KIDDIN'?

CHESTER GOULD

LOOK! SHE DOES HAVE A STUDIO, ALL RIGHT.
CREWY LOU BABY PHOTOS

KNOCK KNOCK

BUT SHE TOLD TRACY SHE HAS AN ASSISTANT WHO DOES THE DEVELOPING. THIS PLACE IS LOCKED UP!
HE MAY BE OUT TO LUNCH, SAM.

TRANSPARENT "ONE-WAY" MIRROR
CHESTER GOULD

SCENE: THE PHOTO STUDIO OF CREWY LOU
THEY WERE CRAZY ABOUT THE PICTURES. PAID ME ONE HUNDRED DOLLARS FOR THE SIX—JUST LIKE THAT!

AND THIS IS THE ONE WE'LL PUT IN OUR SAMPLE BOOK. MAKE TWO SEPIA PRINTS OF IT.

You got more than a hundred dollars. You're holding out on me

HA! HA! YOU HEARD ME FOLD SOME DOUGH AND PUT IT IN MY STOCKING, EH? HA, HA!

OKAY, THERE'S ANOTHER TWENTY-FIVE. I WAS JUST JOKING WITH YOU, SPHINX. ONLY KIDDING! HERE YOU ARE. HA, HA!
HE'S VOICELESS. BUT, OH, WHAT HEARING!

We've stalled long enough. Now let's get on with the big job

NOT YET, SPHINX! WE MUST BE PATIENT. THERE OUGHT TO BE A LITTLE TIME LAPSE. DON'T YOU SEE?

AND AT DICK TRACY'S HOUSE
AREN'T THEY GORGEOUS PICTURES, DICK? SAY—WHAT IS EATING YOU?

DO YOU STILL THINK CREWY LOU PLANNED TO HARM OUR BONNY BRAIDS?
NO—I DON'T THINK THAT! THIS THING HAS TAKEN ANOTHER ANGLE.

I BELIEVE THAT GIRL PHOTOG HAS SOME BIG PLAN OF SOME KIND AND TAKING OUR BABY'S PICTURE WAS JUST A COG IN IT.

DICK, DON'T YOU NEED A VACATION? REALLY, YOU'RE GETTING A WARPED MIND!
I AM?

TO OUR NEXT JOB—THE BIG JOB!

YES, SPHINX, THIS HAS ALL BEEN A BUILD-UP TO OUR **BIG** JOB.

WE HAVE A VERY IMPRESSIVE ALBUM NOW, INCLUDING THE MAYOR'S GRANDSON AND DICK TRACY'S DAUGHTER.

THAT BOOK GIVES US ENTRÉE TO **ANY** HOME IN AMERICA.

SAMPLES

CHESTER GOULD

IN SPITE OF THESE BEAUTIFUL PICTURES, YOU STILL THINK CREWY LOU'S A CROOK?

UH HUH!

DICK, TWO BABY SOAP MANUFACTURERS CALLED UP TODAY.

ABOUT **BONNY BRAIDS**?

YES. THEY WANT TO USE HER PICTURE IN AN AD.

TELL THEM WE'LL TAKE IT UP WITH HER AS SOON AS SHE CAN TALK.

THERE WON'T BE ANY PHOTO PRINTING TODAY, SO YOU CAN PRACTICE ON YOUR SAFE TUMBLERS TILL I GET BACK.

CLICK CLICK CLICK

HALF HOUR LATER.

FORTSON B. KNOX! TOUGH! HARD TO SEE! RICH! AND WITH A NEW BABY.

CHESTER GOULD

YOUR CAR IS READY, SIR.

JUST A MOMENT, JAMES.

I MUST SEE THE BABY ONCE MORE.

JUST LOOK AT HIM.

VIVIAN, I'M GOING TO WORK.

SHE'S DEAD TIRED, MR. KNOX. DIDN'T GET IN TILL 2 O'CLOCK.

SCRAM.

WHILE CREWY LOU WATCHES THE KNOX MANSION, ANOTHER PAIR OF EYES WATCHES HER—

SAME DEAL SHE WORKED AT OUR HOUSE.

CLICK CLICK

CHESTER GOULD

MR. KNOX IS DRIVEN TO HIS OFFICE EVERY DAY AT NINE. I GOT A GOOD LOOK AT HIS FACE TODAY. I'M SURE I CAN HANDLE HIM, SPHINX.

Why such roundabout methods? Make a date with him and lets go

DO YOU QUESTION CREWY LOU'S TECHNIQUE AFTER THE SUCCESS I'VE HAD?

REMEMBER THAT SAFE FULL OF DIAMONDS! **THIS** IS THE JOB WE'VE BEEN BUILDING UP TO. YOU MUST BE PATIENT!

CLICK CLICK CLICK

CHESTER GOULD

BUT, MA'M, THE BABY?

OH, LET THE BABY CRY! GET ME A DRINK!

WA WAA

THE BABY—THE BABY! ALL I HEAR IS THE BABY. I **HATE** HIM!

I QUIT.

AND IN THE STREET IN FRONT OF THE KNOX MANSION.

BUT YOU MIGHT HAVE BEEN KILLED—DIDN'T YOU SEE US?

NO HARM DONE. I'M OKAY.

CHESTER GOULD

YOU'RE MR. KNOX, AREN'T YOU? TO TELL THE TRUTH I'VE BEEN ANXIOUS TO MEET YOU.

MEET ME?

HELLO, MR. TRACY. I RECEIVED YOUR MESSAGE. WHAT IN THE WORLD DO YOU WANT TO SEE ME ABOUT?

I BELIEVE YOU HAVE A NEW BABY, A SON. RIGHT?
I AM HAPPY TO SAY -YES.
CHESTER GOULD

AND YOU WERE APPROACHED BY A GIRL CALLED CREWY LOU WHO WANTS TO PHOTOGRAPH YOUR CHILD.
WHY, YES, YES— A VERY CHARMING GIRL.

JUST BECAUSE YOU ONCE FIXED SOME POISON FOR A PAL OF YOURS AND THEN ACCIDENTALLY DRANK IT YOURSELF AND LOST YOUR VOICE—
KRACK!

IS THAT ANY REASON TO TAKE OUT YOUR FITS OF TEMPER ON ME?
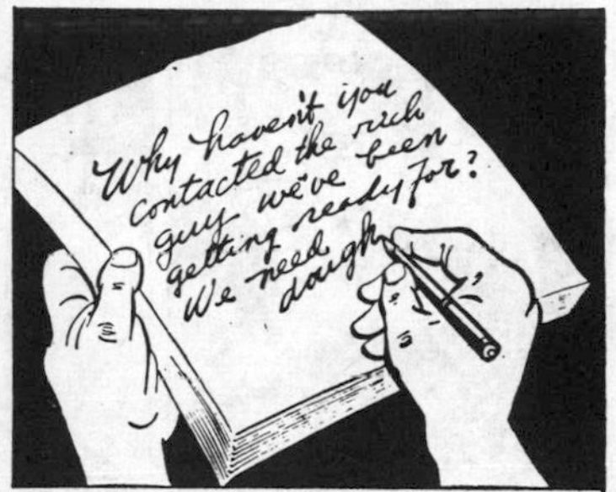
Why haven't you contacted the rich guy we've been getting ready for? We need dough

I TELL YOU, SPHINX, I'M GOING THERE TOMORROW. YOU HAVE TO BE PATIENT WITH THAT CLASS OF PERSON. YOU CAN'T FORCE THEM!

AND ANOTHER THING—DON'T LEAVE YOUR NOTES LYING AROUND! YOU KNOW IT'S DANGEROUS.

I BOUGHT THIS SPECIAL SYNTHETIC WRITING PAPER THAT DISAPPEARS IN ACID, JUST SO YOUR NOTES WOULD NEVER BE FOUND.

LOOK! THE PAPER DISAPPEARS WHEN IT HITS THE ACID!
PLEASE THROW THEM THERE!

OH, I KNOW YOUR FINGERS ARE ITCHING TO GET AT THIS JOB! YOU PRACTICE ALL THE TIME!
BUT YOU MUST BE PATIENT, SPHINX.

AND LET US TURN OUR ATTENTION NOW TO ANOTHER PART OF THE CITY.
YES, CREWY LOU IS HER NAME AND SHE TAKES EXCELLENT BABY PICTURES.

BUT—
BUT WHAT, MR. TRACY? SHE ACCOSTED ME AS I LEFT THE HOUSE YESTERDAY AND SHOWED ME HER PHOTO SAMPLES.

INCLUDING A PORTRAIT OF YOUR BABY. YES, THAT CONVINCED ME. I FIGURED IF DICK TRACY LET HER TAKE HIS CHILD—
MR. KNOX, THAT'S WHY I'M HERE TO WARN YOU.

AND UPSTAIRS IN THE SAME HOUSE—
BUT, MA'M, THE BABY!
OH, LET THE BABY CRY! COME, HAND ME MY JEWELS.
WAAA

THE POINT, MR. KNOX, IS THIS—I BELIEVE THIS GIRL PHOTOGRAPHER IS DANGEROUS.

I'M MERELY TRYING TO WARN YOU! YOU'RE VERY RICH AND YOU HAVE A NEW BABY—

MR. TRACY, I'M OVER TWENTY-ONE. I GUESS YOU KNOW THAT.

FURTHERMORE, I'VE ALWAYS MADE IT A POINT TO **MIND MY OWN BUSINESS**—WHY DON'T YOU TRY IT?

OKAY.

AND AT THIS MOMENT, WHO DO WE SEE ENTERING THE KNOX ESTATE, BUT CREWY LOU!

YOU GRANTED ME AN APPOINTMENT, MR. KNOX, AND HERE I AM.

THESE ARE BEAUTIFUL PICTURES. I'M SURE MRS. KNOX WOULD LOVE TO HAVE YOU PHOTOGRAPH OUR BABY.

MAY I SEE THE CHILD?

AND UPSTAIRS.

I'VE CHANGED MY MIND. I WON'T WEAR MY DIAMONDS TODAY. PUT THEM ALL IN THE SAFE.

TRACY JUST RADIOED THAT HE'S GOT A JOB FOR YOU, JUNIOR, USING THIS RING CAMERA.

THE RING CAMERA?

CLOSE-UP

WE'VE GOT TO GET SOME DOPE ON THIS MYSTERIOUS ASSISTANT OF CREWY LOU'S, AND YOU CAN DO IT FOR US, JUNIOR.

YOU'RE AN AMATEUR PHOTOGRAPHER. TAKE A ROLL OF YOUR UNDEVELOPED FILM AND GO TO HER STUDIO.

WAIT TILL SHE SHOWS UP, THEN GO INSIDE ON THE PRETENSE OF HAVING HER DEVELOP YOUR FILM.

WHILE YOU'RE IN THERE, TAKE A PICTURE OF **HER ASSISTANT** WITH THIS RING CAMERA.

IT'S A CINCH, TRACY.

THEN YOU'LL BE BACK SUNDAY TO TAKE THE BABY'S PICTURE?

I SURE WILL, MR. KNOX.

THE BABY, THE **BABY!** HE THINKS MORE OF THE BABY THAN HE DOES OF ME!

THIRTY MINUTES LATER.

I'VE GOT TO GET TO THE DOOR BEFORE THE SPRING LOCK CLICKS.

HELLO, CREWY LOU, I'M JUNIOR. REMEMBER ME? I'VE GOT SOME FILMS FOR YOU TO DEVELOP.

I'M SORRY, BUT WE DON'T DO COMMERCIAL FILM DEVELOPING.

THE BOY RESTS HIS HAND CASUALLY ON THE TABLE, WITH THE RING CAMERA TRAINED ON SPHINX.

AND PRESSES THE BUTTON.

CLICK

THE TELEPHOTO MACHINE IS ALL SET, TRACY.

GOOD! AS SOON AS JUNIOR RETURNS, WE'LL SEND AN ENLARGEMENT OF THAT PICTURE TO THE FBI.

CONGRATS, JUNIOR. THE RING CAMERA PICTURE OF CREWY LOU'S ASSISTANT ISN'T BAD.
ENLARGED
DARK ROOM

AND PICKING A CIGARETTE PACKAGE OUT OF THE WASTE-BASKET SO WE COULD GET HIS FINGERPRINTS, CLINCHES IT.

WE'LL PUT BOTH ENLARGEMENTS ON THE TELEPHOTO MACHINE.
THE FBI WILL HAVE THEM WITHIN 15 MINUTES.

OKAY, SPHINX! AT LAST, WE'RE HEADED FOR THE KNOX MANSION AND THE BIG JOB!
CHESTER GOULD

SCENE: THE HOME OF WEALTHY MR. KNOX—
THE PHOTOGRAPHER WILL BE HERE ANY MINUTE TO TAKE OUR BABY'S PICTURE.
BABY, BABY! ALL I HEAR IS THE BABY!

YOU THINK MORE OF THE BABY THAN YOU DO OF ME!
WHERE WERE YOU LAST NIGHT?

WHAT DO YOU CARE? YOU'VE NEVER REALLY LOVED ME, MEL.
IF I THOUGHT FOR ONE MINUTE THAT YOU WERE—

AND LOOK AT YOUR JEWELS! HALF A MILLION DOLLARS' WORTH OF DIAMONDS LYING ABOUT LIKE PEANUTS. WHY DIDN'T YOU PUT THEM IN THE SAFE?
DO IT YOURSELF!

AND AT THE FRONT DOOR—
WE'RE THE PHOTOGRAPHERS.
COME RIGHT IN. MR. KNOX IS EXPECTING YOU.

WAIT THERE. I'LL CALL HIM.

THE SAFE IS IN HER BEDROOM, SPHINX. WE'LL SET UP OUR EQUIPMENT DOWN HERE.

AND AT HEADQUARTERS.
YES, HE ACCUSED ME OF BUTTING INTO HIS BUSINESS AND ORDERED ME OUT OF HIS HOUSE.
THE INFORMATION YOU WANTED, TRACY, IS COMING IN ON THE TELEPHOTO MACHINE NOW.

YES, JUNIOR, THE INDICATOR SHOWS THE PICTURE IS ALMOST COMPLETELY TRANSMITTED.
GOSH! TO THINK OF GETTING A PICTURE BY TELEPHONE LINE!

JUNIOR TOOK A SNAPSHOT OF CREWY LOU'S ASSISTANT WITH HIS RING CAMERA. I SENT IT TO THE FBI FOR COMPARISON.
THAT FILM SAM'S TAKING TO THE DARK ROOM IS THEIR ANSWER.

TEN MINUTES LATER.
RIGHT ON THE BUTTON, TRACY!
"JON REN, ALIAS BEAKER, ALIAS SPHINX. SERVED TIME IN LEAVENWORTH FOR SAFECRACKING."

BUT KNOX WON'T LET YOU IN HIS HOUSE.
NEVERTHELESS, IF YOU WANT ME, CHIEF, THAT'S WHERE I'LL BE.
THE PICTURE

"JON REN, ALIAS BEAKER, ALIAS SPHINX, SERVED TIME IN LEAVENWORTH FOR SAFECRACKING."

TO THE KNOX MANSION, MURPHY. I'M GOING TO MAKE A CALL.

BUT THE PHOTOGRAPHERS WANT TO TAKE THE BABY'S PICTURE. THEY'RE DOWN-STAIRS NOW! GET **UP!**

NO! I WON'T BUDGE!

THE SAFE IS IN HER BEDROOM, BUT WE'VE GOT TO GET EVERYBODY DOWN HERE FIRST.

CHESTER GOULD

DRESS AND COME DOWNSTAIRS. THE PHOTOGRAPHER WANTS A PICTURE OF YOU HOLDING THE BABY.

YOU THINK MORE OF THE BABY THAN YOU DO OF ME. **YOU** HOLD THE BABY!

HAVE YOUR CLOTHES ON BY THE TIME I GET BACK, OR I'LL BREAK YOUR NECK!

CHESTER GOULD

WHAT A **BEAUTIFUL** CHILD! IS MRS. KNOX COMING DOWN?

YOU **BET**. SHE'S COMING DOWN.

GET DOWNSTAIRS! THE PHOTOGRAPHERS ARE WAITING FOR YOU!

NOT ME!

I'M SICK AND TIRED OF BEING ORDERED AROUND BY YOU. I HATE YOU— **HATE YOU!**

ANYWAY, **I'M IN LOVE WITH EDDIE,** AND EDDIE LOVES ME.

CAROL!

!

THAT WAS A SHOT!

CHESTER GOULD

I HATE YOU!

WHAT A BREAK! THIS IS MADE TO ORDER.

STEP ON IT, SPHINX. I'LL KEEP WATCH.

CHESTER GOULD

MEANWHILE, IN THE KITCHEN DOWNSTAIRS, A FOOD MIXER DROWNS OUT THE NOISE OF THE GUN, SO CREWY LOU AND SPHINX WORK UNDISTURBED.

RRR RRR RRR

SCENE: THE ENTRANCE OF THE KNOX MANSION.

NO ANSWER.

THE BABY! AND THE CAMERAS—WHAT IS THIS?

HEY! ANYONE HERE?

OH!

CHESTER GOULD

SORRY I FRIGHTENED YOU. I'M LOOKING FOR MR. KNOX.

WHY, HE—THEY—WERE **ALL** HERE A FEW MINUTES AGO.

I DON'T LIKE THIS. I CAN'T UNDERSTAND—

MEANWHILE, MRS. KNOX IS REGAINING CONSCIOUSNESS FROM THE BLOW ON THE HEAD.
CHESTER GOULD

AFTER I SHOT HIM—WHAT HAPPENED?

WHILE BLOCKS AWAY, CREWY LOU AND SPHINX GLOAT.
WE DOOD IT!

WHAT HAPPENED AFTER I SHOT HIM? I DON'T REMEMBER, BUT—

I HEAR FOOTSTEPS! I-I MUST HIDE THIS!

THEY SHOT MY HUSBAND—ROBBED OUR SAFE—ALL MY DIAMONDS—
THE BABY AND ALL THEIR PHOTO EQUIPMENT WAS ABANDONED IN THE LIVINGROOM.

I WAS IN THE KITCHEN BAKING A CAKE. HAD THE ELECTRIC MIXER GOING—I DIDN'T HEAR THIS.
TRACY CALLING SAM CATCHEM! GET THE MEDICAL EXAMINER OVER HERE PRONTO!

CREWY LOU AND HER ASSISTANT HAVE MADE A CLEAN SWEEP. HALF A MILLION DOLLARS IN DIAMONDS MISSING, AND MR. KNOX SHOT TO DEATH.
2-WAY WRIST RADIO

HE WAS SO DEVOTED AND WE WERE SO COMPLETELY HAPPY, ESPECIALLY SINCE THE BABY CAME.

LATER—
THAT BULLET HOLE WAS MADE BY A .22.
THAT'S VERY STRANGE.

STRANGE? ARE YOU KIDDING?
CROOKS USUALLY CARRY A LARGER CALIBER GUN THAN A .22—USUALLY A .32 OR 45.

SOON AS YOU BOYS HAVE FINISHED THE PHOTOGRAPHING, WE'LL REMOVE THE BODY.

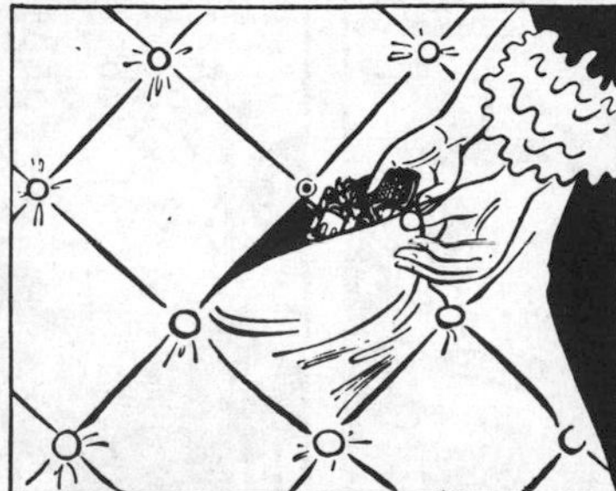

MRS. KNOX, WOULD YOU STEP OVER HERE AND LOOK AT A PHOTOGRAPH? WE HAVE TO SEE IF THIS MIGHT BE A PICTURE OF THE KILLER.
SNAP

KILLED BY A .22 SLUG! CROOKS USUALLY USE A BIGGER CALIBER GUN.

BUT IF YOU SAW HIM SHOOT YOUR HUSBAND, WOULDN'T YOU KNOW HIM?

HIS BACK WAS TOWARD ME, AND ANYWAY, THE GIRL GRABBED ME AND WAS BEATING ME.

KEEP MRS. KNOX HERE IN THE HALL TILL WE NEED HER, AND DON'T LET HER WASH HER HANDS.

WASH MY HANDS?

SOUNDS LIKE YOU'RE PLANNING TO MAKE A PARAFFIN TEST ON THE LADY. DO YOU DOUBT HER STORY?

WHAT DO **YOU** THINK!

CHESTER GOULD

WE'RE SENDING YOUR BABY TO YOUR SISTER'S HOUSE, MRS. KNOX.

WHY ARE YOU DOING **THAT**?

BECAUSE YOU WON'T BE ABLE TO TAKE CARE OF HER FOR AWHILE. WE'RE HOLDING YOU.

NO!

WE SEARCHED ABOUT AN HOUR—AND WE FOUND THE GUN. WE WANT YOU TO TELL US YOUR STORY ALL OVER AGAIN—AT HEADQUARTERS.

HOW DARE YOU INSINUATE I—

WE WANT TO RUN A PARAFFIN TEST ON THIS RIGHT HAND. DO YOU OBJECT?

CHESTER GOULD

SCENE: THE HANGOUT OF CREWY LOU AND SPHINX.

HERE ARE THE NECESSARY TOOLS. IT WILL TAKE GREAT CARE.

WE MUST REMOVE ALL THE STONES FROM THEIR MOUNTINGS. THEY WON'T BE MARKETABLE TILL THEY'RE RECUT.

AND AT HEADQUARTERS.

WHEN A PERSON FIRES A GUN, SMALL PARTICLES OF GUNPOWDER LODGE ON THE HAND.

COVERING THE HAND WITH WARM PARAFFIN PICKS UP THOSE PARTICLES, SO THAT THEY CAN BE MADE VISIBLE CHEMICALLY. ARE YOU WILLING, MRS. KNOX?

CHESTER GOULD

SCENE: AN APARTMENT IN ONE OF THE CITY'S MOST EXCLUSIVE SECTIONS.

FORTSON B. KNOX KILLED IN ROBBERY! $500,000 IN GEMS MISSING

HE WAS ONE OF OUR GANG, EDDIE! THIS WHOLE THING LOOKS FISHY TO ME.

WHAT DO YOU MEAN, KING?

HIS WIFE WAS CRAZY ABOUT YOU, BUT SHE **HATED** HER HUSBAND.

DON'T LOOK AT ME! I DIDN'T DO IT.

MEANWHILE, AT HEADQUARTERS.

THIS PARAFFIN IS WARM, BUT IT WON'T BURN, MRS. KNOX. EASY, NOW. DON'T MOVE YOUR FINGERS.

CHESTER GOULD

WE'VE REMOVED MOST OF THE DIAMONDS. WHAT A DAZZLING SIGHT!

HOW ABOUT MY GOING TO A DRUGSTORE AND CALLING THE FENCE? WE'LL HAVE TO MAKE A DATE WITH HIM.

TEN MINUTES LATER.

MY NAME'S CREWY LOU. SPHINX SAYS YOU KNOW HIM. WE'D LIKE TO COME OVER.

MEANWHILE—

ANOTHER COAT OF PARAFFIN, THEN WE'LL LET IT HARDEN AND REMOVE IT.

CHESTER GOULD

BUT I TELL YOU STICK-UPS KILLED KNOX. IT SAYS SO RIGHT HERE IN THE PAPER.

THEN WHY HAVE COPS GOT HIS WIFE?
AND HIS WIFE WAS IN LOVE WITH YOU, EDDIE!

IF HIS WIFE DOES A LITTLE TALKING AND SPILLS ABOUT OUR SYNDICATE— I'LL—
HEY, LISTEN! EASY!
CHESTER GOULD

MIX THE REAGENT, SAM. THIS PARAFFIN WILL BE READY IN 10 MINUTES.

CREWY LOU AND HER ASSISTANT HAVE ABSOLUTELY DISAPPEARED.
DON'T WORRY, WE'LL GET THEM IN GOOD TIME, INCLUDING THE HALF A MILLION IN DIAMONDS.
WANTED

RIGHT NOW, WE'VE GOT A MURDER ON OUR HANDS THAT WASN'T COMMITTED BY EITHER ONE OF THEM.

HOW IS IT, SAM?
WE'RE READY TO REMOVE THE PARAFFIN.

STRIP IT OFF CAREFULLY.
HOLD STILL, MRS. KNOX, PLEASE!

WE'LL ADD THE REAGENT AND LET IT SET A FEW MINUTES.

TRACY, LOOK! THE TELL-TALE BLUE SPECKS.

MRS. KNOX, IT'S UNMISTAKABLE! YOUR GUN—YOUR FINGERPRINTS—AND NOW, POWDER PARTICLES ON YOUR HAND.

THE PARAFFIN TEST ALONE SAYS YOU FIRED THE GUN. WON'T YOU TALK?

YES! I KNEW ALL ALONG I WOULD TALK. THAT'S WHY I FINALLY AGREED TO TAKE THE PARAFFIN TEST.

I DID IT BECAUSE HE WAS CRUEL. HE HATED ME.
AND HE WAS A CROOK, MR. TRACY. ONE OF A RING. THE BIGGEST IN THE COUNTRY.

YOU'VE HEARD OF THE CRIME SYNDICATE?
KEEP TALKING, MRS. KNOX.

AND ELSEWHERE—
SHE FELL IN LOVE WITH ME! WHAT COULD I DO?
IF SHE TALKS, YOU WON'T BE ABLE TO DO ANYTHING!
YOU'LL BE DEAD.

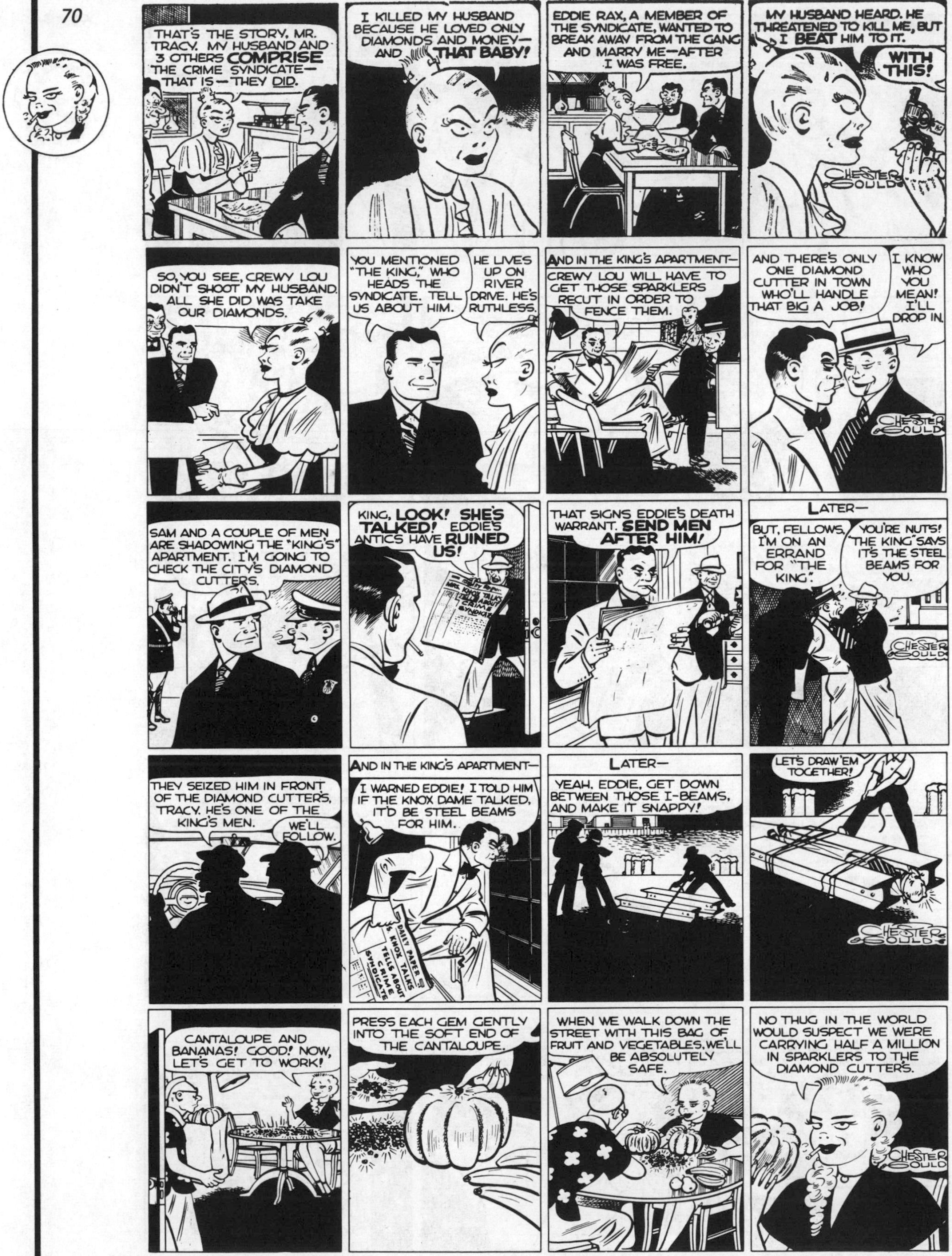

THAT'S THE STORY, MR. TRACY. MY HUSBAND AND 3 OTHERS **COMPRISE** THE CRIME SYNDICATE—THAT IS—THEY DID.

I KILLED MY HUSBAND BECAUSE HE LOVED ONLY DIAMONDS AND MONEY—AND **THAT BABY!**

EDDIE RAX, A MEMBER OF THE SYNDICATE, WANTED TO BREAK AWAY FROM THE GANG AND MARRY ME—AFTER I WAS FREE.

MY HUSBAND HEARD. HE THREATENED TO KILL ME, BUT I **BEAT** HIM TO IT.

WITH THIS!

CHESTER GOULD

SO, YOU SEE, CREWY LOU DIDN'T SHOOT MY HUSBAND. ALL SHE DID WAS TAKE OUR DIAMONDS.

YOU MENTIONED "THE KING," WHO HEADS THE SYNDICATE. TELL US ABOUT HIM.

HE LIVES UP ON RIVER DRIVE. HE'S RUTHLESS.

AND IN THE KING'S APARTMENT—

CREWY LOU WILL HAVE TO GET THOSE SPARKLERS RECUT IN ORDER TO FENCE THEM.

AND THERE'S ONLY ONE DIAMOND CUTTER IN TOWN WHO'LL HANDLE THAT BIG A JOB!

I KNOW WHO YOU MEAN! I'LL DROP IN.

CHESTER GOULD

SAM AND A COUPLE OF MEN ARE SHADOWING THE "KING'S" APARTMENT. I'M GOING TO CHECK THE CITY'S DIAMOND CUTTERS.

KING, **LOOK! SHE'S TALKED!** EDDIE'S ANTICS HAVE **RUINED US!**

MRS. KNOX TALKS TELLS ABOUT CRIME SYNDICATE

THAT SIGNS EDDIE'S DEATH WARRANT. **SEND MEN AFTER HIM!**

LATER—

BUT, FELLOWS, I'M ON AN ERRAND FOR "THE KING".

YOU'RE NUTS! "THE KING" SAYS IT'S THE STEEL BEAMS FOR YOU.

CHESTER GOULD

THEY SEIZED HIM IN FRONT OF THE DIAMOND CUTTER'S, TRACY. HE'S ONE OF THE KING'S MEN.

WE'LL FOLLOW.

AND IN THE KING'S APARTMENT—

I WARNED EDDIE! I TOLD HIM IF THE KNOX DAME TALKED, IT'D BE STEEL BEAMS FOR HIM.

DAILY PAPER MRS. KNOX TALKS TELLS ABOUT CRIME SYNDICATE

LATER—

YEAH, EDDIE, GET DOWN BETWEEN THOSE I-BEAMS, AND MAKE IT SNAPPY!

LET'S DRAW 'EM TOGETHER!

CHESTER GOULD

CANTALOUPE AND BANANAS! GOOD! NOW, LET'S GET TO WORK!

PRESS EACH GEM GENTLY INTO THE SOFT END OF THE CANTALOUPE.

WHEN WE WALK DOWN THE STREET WITH THIS BAG OF FRUIT AND VEGETABLES, WE'LL BE ABSOLUTELY SAFE.

NO THUG IN THE WORLD WOULD SUSPECT WE WERE CARRYING HALF A MILLION IN SPARKLERS TO THE DIAMOND CUTTER'S.

CHESTER GOULD

DID YOU GET THOSE CABLES TIGHT?

THEN, LET'S PUSH HIM OVER! WHAT ARE WE WAITING FOR?
NOT TILL NINE O'CLOCK, BOSS' ORDERS. 3 MINUTES TO GO.

THE LAMP'S IN FRONT OF THE WINDOW, KING.
OKAY, STAND BY.

WHAT KIND OF A CEREMONY IS THIS, TRACY?
I'M NOT SURE, SAM, BUT WE'RE GOING TO STOP IT.
CHESTER GOULD

OKAY— THE SECOND DOOR.
SMELTERS
DIAMOND CUTTERS

HALF A MILLION WORTH. WE'VE TAKEN THEM OUT OF THEIR MOUNTINGS.
LET'S SEE.

WE STUFFED THEM THROUGH A HOLE IN THE CANTALOUPE. GIVE ME A KNIFE.

WE WANT 'EM RE-CUT.
THESE ARE THE MOUNTINGS. WE'LL SELL THEM CHEAP.

AND IN AN UPTOWN APARTMENT—
MRS. KNOX CONFESSES! REVEAL SECRETS OF CRIME SYNDICATE

IT'S NINE O'CLOCK. THE BOYS WILL BE WAITING FOR OUR SIGNAL.
TURN ON THAT FLOOR LAMP.

THERE'S THE LIGHT.
LET'S GO!

WHEN ONE OF THE BOYS FALLS IN LOVE WITH ANOTHER MEMBER'S WIFE, AND SHE TALKS— THE KING DON'T LIKE IT.
OTHERWISE, EDDIE WAS A NICE GUY.

STICK 'EM UP!
RAISE 'EM!
SLAM

COPPERS! DIRTY COPPERS!

WELL! TWO DOWN AND ONE SAVED! IF HE'S THE CRIME SYNDICATE LAD WE THINK HE IS—THIS CASE IS JUST STARTING.

IT'S THE DIAMOND CUTTER. A GUY AND A DOLL HAVE JUST COME IN WITH THE KNOX ICE. WHAT'LL HE DO?
TELL 'IM TO HOLD 'EM. WE'LL BE RIGHT OVER.

THEY BROUGHT THE DIAMONDS IN A CANTALOUPE! THE DIAMOND CUTTER'S HOLDING 'EM TILL WE ARRIVE.

EXCUSE ME. I HAD TO MAKE A PHONE CALL.

COME ON! WHAT'LL YOU CHARGE TO RECUT 'EM? WE'RE IN A HURRY!

MEANWHILE, TRACY AND SAM HAVE BEEN BUSY—

WE HAD TO DO A LITTLE SHOOTING, BUT WE SAVED **HIM**!

CHESTER GOULD

SAVED HIM **TO DO A LITTLE TALKING!** MAYBE HE CAN TELL US **ALL ABOUT** "THE KING".

GLADLY!

THERE'S SOMETHING FUNNY HERE. WHY WON'T YOU GIVE ME A FIGURE ON RECUTTING THESE STONES?

SMELTERS DIAMOND CUTTERS

I MUST TAKE TIME. THIS IS THE BIGGEST JOB I HAVE EVER FIGURED. THIS WILL TAKE WEEKS!

LISTEN, YOU'RE **STALLING** ME! YOU GUYS KNOW YOUR BUSINESS! YOU DON'T HAVE TO FIGURE.

CHESTER GOULD

INCIDENTALLY, AREN'T THESE THE—ER—KNOX DIAMONDS?

LISTEN, I'M HERE TO GET THIS STUFF **RECUT!**

IT'S NONE OF YOUR BUSINESS WHERE IT—

HEL-LO!

AND AT HEADQUARTERS—

GIVE HIM SOME HOT COFFEE. THEN, HE AND I ARE GOING TO TALK.

POLIC

CHESTER GOULD

SO, YOU'RE EDDIE RAX, EH?

YEAH.

"THE KING" DOESN'T LIKE HIS BOYS FALLING IN LOVE WITH WOMEN WHO TALK, EH?

I GUESS THAT'S IT.

YOU WON'T HAVE TO PUMP ME, MR. TRACY. I'LL TELL YOU THE WHOLE STORY! "THE KING'S" STORY IS A BLOODY ONE. SIT DOWN.

CHESTER GOULD

AND AT THE DIAMOND CUTTER'S.

WHO IS THIS DOPE?

WHO **ARE** YOU?

WHAT DO **YOU** CARE?

THIS JOB'S TOO BIG FOR YOU, SIS. YOU CAN'T HANDLE THESE.

I'LL GIVE YOU FIVE GRAND FOR THE WHOLE SMEAR.

WILL SOMEBODY TELL ME WHO THIS CHISELER IS?

CHESTER GOULD

MEANWHILE.

STOLEN JEWELRY, GAMBLING, SMUGGLED ARTICLES, NARCOTICS! "THE KING" AND KNOX CONTROLLED 'EM ALL.

YOU'VE HEARD OF "THE KING", HAVEN'T YOU, SIS?
YEAH-- YOU'RE "THE KING", EH?

I'M CREWY LOU. NOW, WILL YOU STEP OUTSIDE WHILE I TRANSACT MY BUSINESS?
CUTE, ISN'T SHE?

AS CREWY LOU TALKS, HER HAND MOVES TOWARD ONE OF THE BANANAS SHE AND SPHINX BROUGHT IN THE PAPER BAG.
CHESTER GOULD

HOT ICE CAN GET YOU IN AN AWFUL LOT OF TROUBLE, CREW-CUT.
FOR INSTANCE?

THAT'S WHAT THEY CALL ME-YES.
"THE KING"! HEAD OF THE SYNDICATE! AND YOU WANT TO TAKE OUR DIAMONDS AND GIVE US PEANUTS, EH?

BY THE TIME YOU'D HAVE 'EM RECUT AND THEN PEDDLED, YOUR TAKE WOULD BE VERY SMALL.
SO, YOU'RE WILLING TO TAKE HALF A MILLION DOLLARS' WORTH OF ICE OFF OUR HANDS FOR 5 GRAND, EH?

WELL, MAYBE TEN GRAND. YOU'RE SMART, I'VE GOT TO ADMIT THAT! BRINGING THEM HERE IN A CANTALOUPE WAS CLEVER.

HERE'S SOMETHING ELSE THAT'S CLEVER!
A BANANA?

GET THE OTHER ONE, SPHINX, AND COVER THE LOOKOUT IN THE HALL, WHILE I COLLECT!

THERE'S ENOUGH DOUGH HERE TO START A U.S. MINT.

BESIDES TWENTY THOUSAND IN CASH IN THE KING'S POCKETS!

THE CRIME SYNDICATE, EH? WHAT A BUNCH OF SISSIES!

MEANWHILE—
THAT'S THE WHOLE STORY, MR. TRACY. "THE KING" RUNS THINGS.

THE GANG PAYS OFF ALMOST ENTIRELY IN RECUT DIAMONDS. THEY CAN'T BE TRACED LIKE MONEY AND THE FEDS CAN'T PIN YOU FOR TAXES.
THAT'S WHAT YOU THINK.

TRACY, AREN'T WE GETTING OFF ON A TANGENT? SHOULDN'T WE NAIL CREWY LOU FIRST?

LATER
WHAT DO YOU THINK OF ME NOW, SPHINX?

SHE HAD A **GUN** IN THAT **BANANA** SKIN! WHY, THAT ~★※~!!

IS SHE **GONE**?

HOW DO I KNOW? A SLUG CREASED MY SCALP! I WAS OUT.

CHESTER GOULD

THE KING MUST HAVE GOT IT BAD.

SUPPOSE THE COPS HEARD THEM SHOTS?

MY SAFE CLEANED OUT! DIAMONDS ALL OVER THE PLACE! BLOOD ON THE FLOOR! **GET HIM OUT OF HERE!**

OH, SHUT UP!

CREWY LOU'S BOUND TO SHOW UP AT THE DIAMOND CUTTER'S EVENTUALLY, TRACY, JUST LIKE EDDIE SAID.

RIGHT! WHAT'S HIS ADDRESS, SAM?

I'VE GOT IT WRITTEN ON A MEMO IN THE CAR.

MEANWHILE—

GET HIM **OUT OF HERE**—THAT'S ALL I ASK, JUST GET HIM **OUT**!

I THINK HE'S DEAD.

HE IS **NOT** DEAD—AND IF YOU ABANDON HIM AND HE LATER RECOVERS, YOU'LL WISH YOU WERE DEAD.

YOU'RE RIGHT. I'LL GET HIM OUT.

CHESTER GOULD

THIS IS THE PLACE.

SMELTER

HEY, MICK—HOLD IT!

EH?

SMELTERS DIAMOND CUTTERS

ON YOUR FEET! WOW! WHAT STRUCK HERE?

GET SOME SAMPLES OF THAT RED STUFF, SAM.

BLOOD AND DIAMONDS! LOOKS LIKE THE PARTY WAS A GOOD ONE.

CHESTER GOULD

—A STICK-UP —THAT'S ALL.

WHO GOT SHOT?

DUNNO!

THAT'S AS GOOD AN ANSWER AS ANY. PICK UP THOSE SPARKLERS AND PUT 'EM IN A BAG.

WE'LL HAVE THE LAB GET RIGHT TO WORK ON THESE BLOOD SCRAPINGS, AND WE'LL GET MRS. KNOX OUT OF HER CELL TO LOOK OVER THESE MOUNTINGS.

CHESTER GOULD

MEANWHILE, AT A PRIVATE HOSPITAL.

IT WAS A STICK-UP! MY FRIEND NEEDS ATTENTION!

SHOULD BE FINGERPRINTS ON THAT SAFE AND ON THE CHAIR BACKS. WE'VE GOT ABOUT AN HOUR'S WORK HERE, MURPHY.

AND AT HEADQUARTERS.

SIT DOWN, MICK.

DO YOU WANT MRS. KNOX NOW?

TRACY WANTS TO SEE YOU ABOUT IDENTIFYING SOME JEWELRY.

AND AT THE HOSPITAL.

THE BULLET LODGED NEAR THE SPINE.

CHESTER GOULD

THE REPORT JUST CAME THROUGH, SAM, FROM THE 4TH PRECINCT! INVESTIGATE IT AT ONCE!
2-WAY WRIST RADIO

TWENTY MINUTES LATER.
YES, WE REPORTED A GUNSHOT CASE. PATIENT'S IN ROOM 522.

WORRY? WHO'S WORRYING? OUR SKIRTS ARE CLEAN.

YOU'RE THE KING, AREN'T YOU?
CHESTER GOULD

A DIAMOND CUTTER TRYING TO MAKE A LIVING—THAT'S ME. I WAS STUCK UP AND MY SAFE WAS ROBBED.

THESE DIAMONDS AND PLATINUM SETTINGS HAVE BEEN IDENTIFIED BY MRS. KNOX AS HER STOLEN JEWELRY. WHAT WERE YOU DOING WITH THEM?

I DON'T KNOW NOTHING ABOUT IT.
LOOK! ISN'T IT TRUE THIS COUPLE BROUGHT THE GEMS TO YOU, AND A GUNFIGHT TOOK PLACE?

THERE WAS BLOOD ON YOUR FLOOR. WHOSE BLOOD WAS THAT?
ISN'T IT POSSIBLE "THE KING" WAS THERE AND YOU SHOT HIM?

ME? NOT ME! SHE DID IT! THAT VIXEN — THAT SHE-DEVIL, CREWY LOU!
AHA! NOW, WE'RE GETTING SOME PLACE!

MEANWHILE, SAM CATCHEM IS MAKING A CALL IN A PRIVATE HOSPITAL.
YEAH—THEY HAVE TO. REPORT ALL SHOOTINGS. THAT'S HOW WE FOUND OUT, KING.
ALL RIGHT, SO NOW YOU KNOW.

I TELL YOU IT WAS A STICKUP IN THE ALLEY BACK OF MY APARTMENT. THE GUY SHOT ME.
AND YOUR BLOOD SQUIRTED 3 MILES THROUGH A SECOND STORY WINDOW.

KING, WE GOT SOME BLOOD SCRAPINGS OFF THE FLOOR AT A 38TH STREET ADDRESS, AND IT'S VERY INTERESTING.
YEAH?

TESTS PROVE THAT BLOOD WAS YOUR BLOOD! YOU GOT PLUGGED IN A DIAMOND CUTTER'S SHOP. ISN'T THAT SMALL POTATOES FOR YOU?
OH, YOU LITTLE SCIENTIST, YOU! YOU BORE ME.

WHY DON'T YOU RUN OUT TO THE TRACK AND MAKE A COUPLE OF BETS FOR YOURSELF? HERE'S TWO GRAND.

KING, YOU'RE THROUGH BUYING YOUR WAY! THIS GAME TRACY AND I ARE PLAYING IS FOR KEEPS—THE HARD WAY. TA,TA, YOU'LL BE SEEING US!

THANKS FOR THE BRIBE, KING, BUT NO SOAP!

TRACY AND I ARE GOING TO CRACK YOUR CRIME SYNDICATE WIDE OPEN— AND BRIBERY WON'T HELP YOU!

CREWY LOU COULD HAVE SAVED US A LOT OF TROUBLE, IF HER AIM HAD BEEN MORE ACCURATE!

—BUT, THEN, THINK OF THE FUN WE'RE GOING TO HAVE WITH YOU BEFORE WE GET THROUGH! SO LONG, KING!
CHESTER GOULD

SO CREWY LOU SHOT THE KING! THAT MUST HAVE BEEN PRETTY HUMILIATING FOR HIM!

LISTEN. THAT WOMAN'S LIFE ISN'T WORTH A DIME NOW! THE KING WON'T REST TILL SHE'S—
SAM CATCHEM CALLING TRACY!
2-WAY WRIST RADIO

AS I WAS ABOUT TO LEAVE THE HOSPITAL, A NEW CHARACTER WENT INTO THE KING'S ROOM. I'M STICKING AROUND A BIT.

DO YOU KNOW WHERE SHE'S STAYING?
YEAH. I FOUND HER AND THE MUTE, BOTH.
CHESTER GOULD

CREWY LOU AND THE MUTE ARE BOTH ON THIS FLOOR. HER ROOM IS RIGHT ACROSS FROM HIS.

WE'LL TAKE A ROOM AT A TIME—

AHA! WE'RE IN LUCK! THE DUMMY IS HAVING HIS SIESTA!
CHESTER GOULD

IT WAS HER! SHE'S BEEN OUT SHOPPING.
TAKE THIS HOOK AND OPEN THE SHAFT DOOR. THAT'LL BREAK THE CIRCUIT AND STOP THE CAR.
SLAM

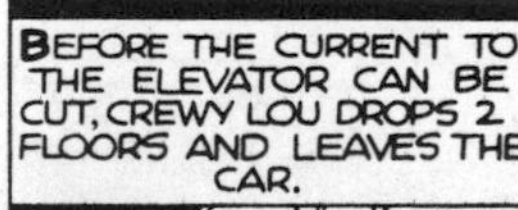
BEFORE THE CURRENT TO THE ELEVATOR CAN BE CUT, CREWY LOU DROPS 2 FLOORS AND LEAVES THE CAR.

SHE'S TRYING TO CROSS US.
DON'T LET HER GET AWAY!

A SERVICE MAID'S LAUNDRY WAGON IS STANDING IN THE HALL.
LAUNDRY

DID A GIRL GET OFF THAT ELEVATOR?
I NO SEE ANYBODY.
LAUNDRY
CHESTER GOULD

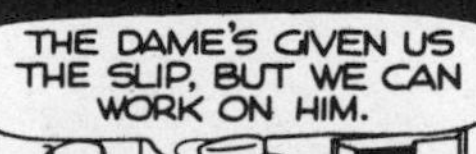
THE DAME'S GIVEN US THE SLIP, BUT WE CAN WORK ON HIM.

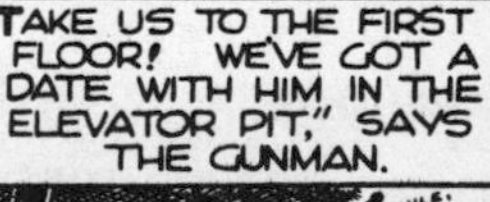
"TAKE US TO THE FIRST FLOOR! WE'VE GOT A DATE WITH HIM IN THE ELEVATOR PIT," SAYS THE GUNMAN.

WHILE, ON AN UPPER FLOOR.
LAUNDRY

JUMP! IT'S ONLY FIVE FEET.
CHESTER GOULD

WHEN THE CAR GOES TO THE TOP FLOOR, A 2-TON COUNTER-WEIGHT DROPS ON THAT BUMPER! CATCH ON?

THEY HAVE THE GUY, BUT THE GIRL GOT AWAY.
GOOD! TELL HIM TO WATCH MY WINDOW.

MEANWHILE, TRACY AND SAM HAVE BEEN COVERING THE KING'S OPERATIVE FROM RENTED AUTOS.
HE SEEMS TO BE GIVING OR RECEIVING SIGNALS.
2-WAY WRIST RADIO

WE'RE TO WAIT HERE TILL THE KING GIVES THE WORD.
WE'VE MADE PEOPLE THINK WE'RE ELEVATOR REPAIRMEN, BUT THEY'LL GET WISE TO US SOON.

YEAH—I WANT TO GET THIS JOB OVER WITH AND GET OUT OF HERE.
CHESTER GOULD

MILLING ABOUT THE CORNER IN RENTED CARS, TRACY AND SAM REPORT TO EACH OTHER BY 2-WAY WRIST RADIO.
HE'S USING A PAIR OF FIELD GLASSES!
2-WAY WRIST RADIO

AND HE'S GOT 'EM FOCUSED ON THE HOSPITAL—ABOUT THREE BLOCKS AWAY.

IT'S EXACTLY 8 O'CLOCK, KING!
PUT THE LIGHT IN THE WINDOW.

THE KING RAISES HIS HAND AND TILTS THE LAMP SHADE.

I GET IT!
OKAY! SO, THAT'S THE ORDER!

AS THE HOODLUM HAILS A CAB, TRACY AND SAM TRANSFER TO A SQUAD CAR.
DON'T LOSE THAT CAB.

FIFTEEN MINUTES LATER.
LET'S GO!
THE COPS ARE RIGHT BEHIND!

AN AUTOMATIC ELEVATOR—IT'S GOING UP NOW!
SOMEONE IN THAT SHAFT.
OHOO
WA

THIS IS THE TOP FLOOR! PROP THE DOORS OPEN SO THE CAR WON'T OPERATE.

GETTING THE BUILDING ENGINEER TO OPEN THE SHAFT DOOR, TRACY AND SAM GASP AT WHAT THEY SEE.

IT'S SPHINX! CRUSHED BY THIS COUNTER-WEIGHT!
WHEN THE ELEVATOR'S AT THE TOP FLOOR, THAT 2-TON WEIGHT RESTS ON THE BUFFER.

"THEY MUST STILL BE IN THE BUILDING," SAYS TRACY. "THERE'S THE STAIRWAY," SAYS SAM, "WE CAN SOON FIND OUT!"
AND INTO A PENTHOUSE GARDEN.

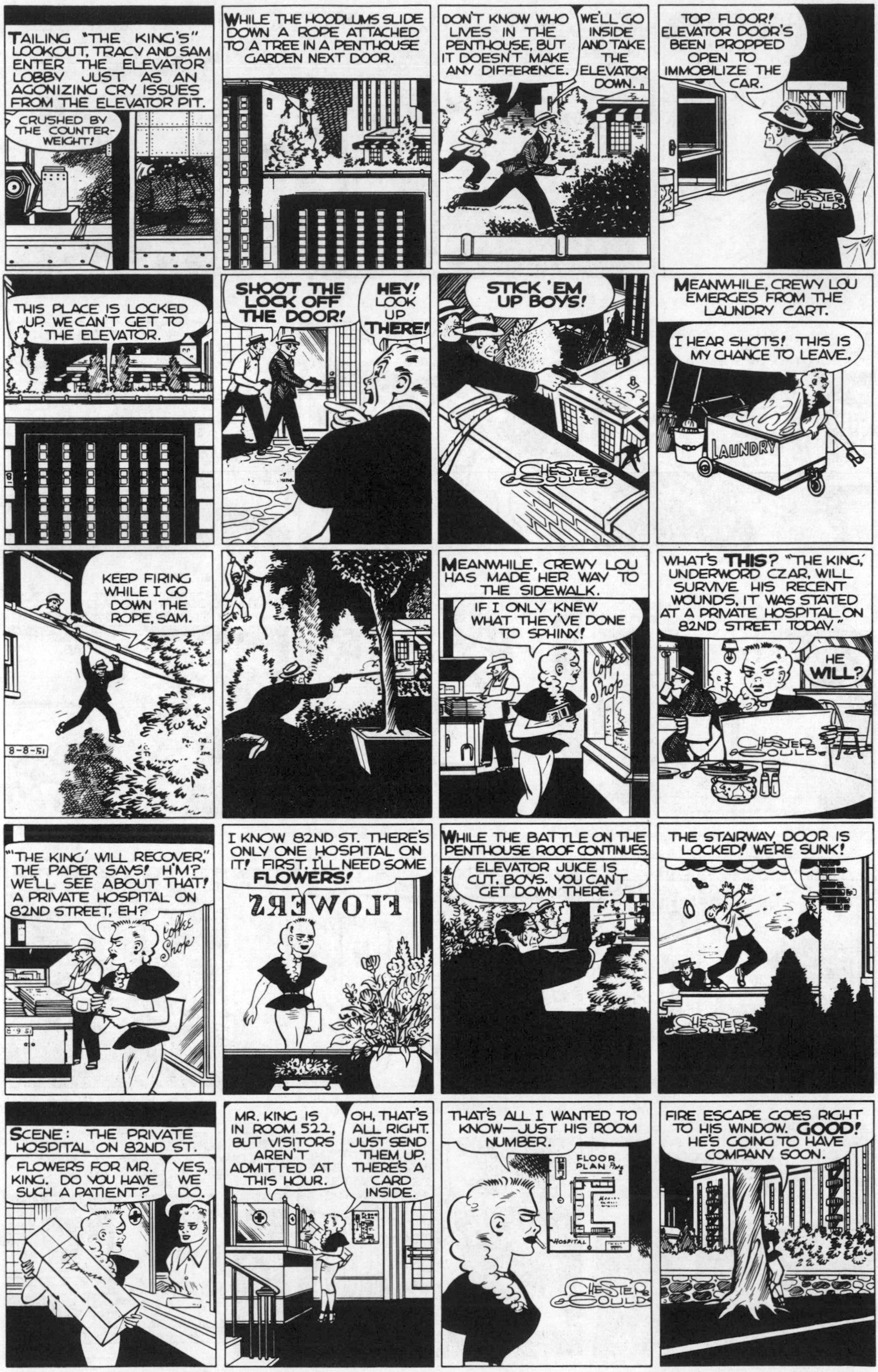

TAILING "THE KING'S" LOOKOUT, TRACY AND SAM ENTER THE ELEVATOR LOBBY JUST AS AN AGONIZING CRY ISSUES FROM THE ELEVATOR PIT.
CRUSHED BY THE COUNTER-WEIGHT!

WHILE THE HOODLUMS SLIDE DOWN A ROPE ATTACHED TO A TREE IN A PENTHOUSE GARDEN NEXT DOOR.

DON'T KNOW WHO LIVES IN THE PENTHOUSE, BUT IT DOESN'T MAKE ANY DIFFERENCE.
WE'LL GO INSIDE AND TAKE THE ELEVATOR DOWN.

TOP FLOOR! ELEVATOR DOOR'S BEEN PROPPED OPEN TO IMMOBILIZE THE CAR.

THIS PLACE IS LOCKED UP. WE CAN'T GET TO THE ELEVATOR.

SHOOT THE LOCK OFF THE DOOR!
HEY! LOOK UP **THERE!**

STICK 'EM UP BOYS!

MEANWHILE, CREWY LOU EMERGES FROM THE LAUNDRY CART.
I HEAR SHOTS! THIS IS MY CHANCE TO LEAVE.
LAUNDRY

KEEP FIRING WHILE I GO DOWN THE ROPE, SAM.
8-8-51

MEANWHILE, CREWY LOU HAS MADE HER WAY TO THE SIDEWALK.
IF I ONLY KNEW WHAT THEY'VE DONE TO SPHINX!
Coffee Shop

WHAT'S **THIS?** "THE KING,' UNDERWORD CZAR, WILL SURVIVE HIS RECENT WOUNDS, IT WAS STATED AT A PRIVATE HOSPITAL ON 82ND STREET TODAY."
HE **WILL?**

"THE KING' WILL RECOVER," THE PAPER SAYS! H'M? WE'LL SEE ABOUT THAT! A PRIVATE HOSPITAL ON 82ND STREET, EH?
Coffee Shop

I KNOW 82ND ST. THERE'S ONLY ONE HOSPITAL ON IT! FIRST, I'LL NEED SOME **FLOWERS!**
FLOWERS

WHILE THE BATTLE ON THE PENTHOUSE ROOF CONTINUES,
ELEVATOR JUICE IS CUT, BOYS. YOU CAN'T GET DOWN THERE.

THE STAIRWAY DOOR IS LOCKED! WE'RE SUNK!

SCENE: THE PRIVATE HOSPITAL ON 82ND ST.
FLOWERS FOR MR. KING. DO YOU HAVE SUCH A PATIENT?
YES, WE DO.
Flowers

MR. KING IS IN ROOM 522, BUT VISITORS AREN'T ADMITTED AT THIS HOUR.
OH, THAT'S ALL RIGHT. JUST SEND THEM UP. THERE'S A CARD INSIDE.

THAT'S ALL I WANTED TO KNOW—JUST HIS ROOM NUMBER.
FLOOR PLAN
HOSPITAL

FIRE ESCAPE GOES RIGHT TO HIS WINDOW. **GOOD!** HE'S GOING TO HAVE COMPANY SOON.

ALL RIGHT, COPPER, THAT'S IT! I'M OUT OF METAL.

THAT MAKES IT A CLEAN SWEEP, SAM. WE'VE GOT ALL THREE.

WHILE "THE KING" DOZES IN HIS HOSPITAL ROOM—
THE FLOWERS

A FIGURE AT THE WINDOW PEEKS INSIDE AND SOFTLY RAISES THE SASH.
CHESTER GOULD

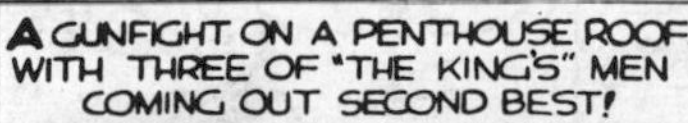

A GUNFIGHT ON A PENTHOUSE ROOF, WITH THREE OF "THE KING'S" MEN COMING OUT SECOND BEST!

SEND AN AMBULANCE AND SOME MEN TO 20 ARMS AVENUE, BUT ASK THE JANITOR TO TURN ON THE CURRENT TO THE PENTHOUSE ELEVATOR SO YOU CAN GET UP HERE.
2-WAY WRIST RADIO

THIS PLACE HAS BEEN VACANT FOR SOME TIME. THE SERVICES WERE CUT OFF. YOU GUYS MADE A BAD GUESS.

THEY'RE BRINGING THE MEDICAL EXAMINER, TOO, SO THE SPHINX'S BODY CAN BE REMOVED FROM NEXT DOOR.
BUT WHERE IS CREWY LOU, TRACY—WHERE?

LATER
THE SCENE: "THE KING'S" HOSPITAL ROOM. THE TIME: TWO A.M.

WHO IS IT?
KEEP YOUR MOUTH SHUT!

YOU! AGAIN?
YEAH—I SEE YOU HAVE MY FLOWERS—"FROM AN ADMIRER"! THAT'S HOW I FOUND OUT. YOUR ROOM NUMBER.

KEEP YOUR HANDS FROM UNDER THE PILLOW—

A GUNSHOT WOULD BE TOO NOISY—
WHAT'S THIS?

YOU GOT THE SPHINX, BUT YOU DIDN'T GET ME! AND YOU WON'T GET ANYBODY EVER AGAIN, "KING."

WHAT'S GOING ON HERE?
STERILIZER

TAKE YOUR HAND AWAY FROM THAT STEAM VALVE!
STERILIZER
TRY TO STOP ME.

BUT HE'LL BE **STEAMED ALIVE!** I BEG OF YOU, **DON'T TURN THAT VALVE!**
STERILIZER

YOU TAKE ONE STEP TOWARD ME, AND THERE'LL BE TWO OF YOU MISSING AROUND HERE.

NEVERTHELESS, I **CAN'T** STAND BY AND LET YOU **SCALD THAT MAN TO DEATH!**
CLICK

THE POWERS-THAT-BE ARE WITH ME—**IT MISSED FIRE!**
AND NOW, SISTER—
CHESTER GOULD

YOU'RE STRONG AS AN OX, BUT I'VE HAD TO HANDLE SOME TOUGHIES IN MY DAY!

THE NURSE PUSHES WITH ALL HER STRENGTH. BACK GOES CREWY LOU'S HEAD CRASHING AGAINST THE STERILIZER VALVE.

BRING ME A NEEDLE OF **SODIUM PENTOTHAL!**
CHESTER GOULD

THERE! SHE'LL BE QUIET!
NOW LET'S GET **HIM** OUT OF THE STERILIZER.

SCENE: HEADQUARTERS.
YES, CHIEF, WHILE "THE KING'S" IN THE HOSPITAL, WE'VE ARRANGED TO SEARCH HIS APARTMENT.

DO YOU EXPECT TO FIND RECORDS OF THE CRIME SYNDICATE THERE?
HARDLY. BUT WE MAY FIND CLEWS THAT WILL LEAD US TO THOSE RECORDS.
CHESTER GOULD

SHE'S OUT. GET THAT STERILIZER OPEN.

LUCKILY, SHE DIDN'T GET THE STEAM VALVE TURNED! HE'S **ALL RIGHT!**

SEARCHING "THE KING'S" APARTMENT, TRACY AND SAM FIND LITTLE OF VALUE.
NOTHING!

THE PLACE IS PRACTICALLY EMPTY. NOTHING MUCH BUT THESE COLORED SNAPSHOT SLIDES AND VIEWER.

HEY! THESE MUST BE PICTURES OF "THE KING'S" FARM! YEAH—THERE'S "THE KING" STANDING WITH SOME OF HIS COWS.

SHALL I ANSWER THAT PHONE?
RRRR
CHESTER GOULD

SCENE: THE KING'S APARTMENT.
SHE TRIED TO KILL HIM IN THE STERILIZER. THEY'RE BOTH AT THE HOSPITAL.
WE'LL TAKE THESE SLIDES WITH US. LET'S GO!

GET THE **COPS!** IF SHE COMES TO, **SHE'LL KILL ME!**
SHE WON'T COME TO.

THAT GAL WAS GIVEN ENOUGH SODIUM PENTOTHAL TO HOLD 6 WOMEN. ANWAY, THE POLICE ARE ON THEIR WAY.
CHESTER GOULD

I NEVER EXPECTED CREWY LOU'S CAPTURE TO BE AS EASY AS THIS. DID YOU, TRACY?
LET'S NOT COUNT THE CHICKEN-ER, BEFORE SHE'S HANDCUFFED, SAM.

WELL, WELL! I WOULDN'T HAVE BELIEVED IT, IF I HADN'T SEEN IT!

SHE TRIED TO COOK ME ALIVE! HANDCUFF HER!
MY, OH, MY! OUR FARMER FRIEND! AND HOW ARE YOUR CATTLE?
CHESTER GOULD

FARMER? CATTLE? WHAT TH—??
AH! AH! DON'T STRAIN YOURSELF, KING! WE'LL TALK LATER.

GOSH! WE FORGOT TO TELL YOU—IT WAS JUST 5 YEARS AGO TODAY THAT GRAVEL GERTIE AND B.O. PLENTY WERE MARRIED!
I SAID WOODEN ANNIVERSARY.
WOULDN'T ANNA WHAT?

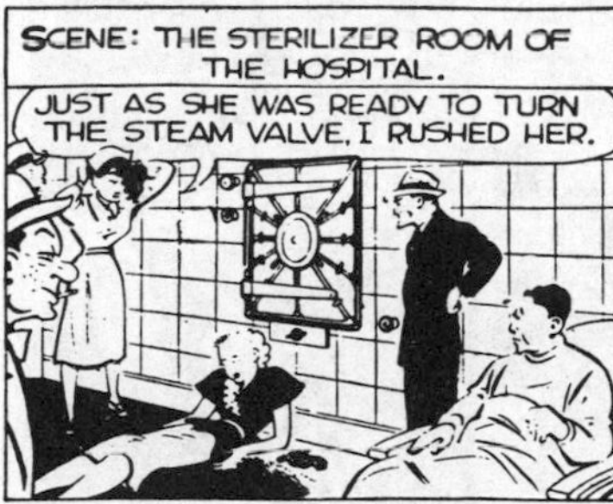
SCENE: THE STERILIZER ROOM OF THE HOSPITAL.
JUST AS SHE WAS READY TO TURN THE STEAM VALVE, I RUSHED HER.

HER GUN MISSED FIRE! THAT WAS THE KEY TO THE WHOLE THING! IT SAVED MY LIFE, AND IN THE SCUFFLE, I KNOCKED HER HEAD AGAINST THE STEEL DOOR OF THE STERILIZER.

THEN, NURSE JONES HANDED ME THE HYPO NEEDLE—THE REST WAS EASY!

YOU'VE DONE A HEROIC JOB!
FIVE MORE SECONDS AND THE KING WOULD HAVE LOOKED LIKE A PIECE OF STEAMED FISH.

I NEVER EXPECTED THAT CREWY LOU WOULD TAKE HER LAST TRIP WITH US SO PEACEFULLY.
YES. BUT WATCH HER, BOYS.

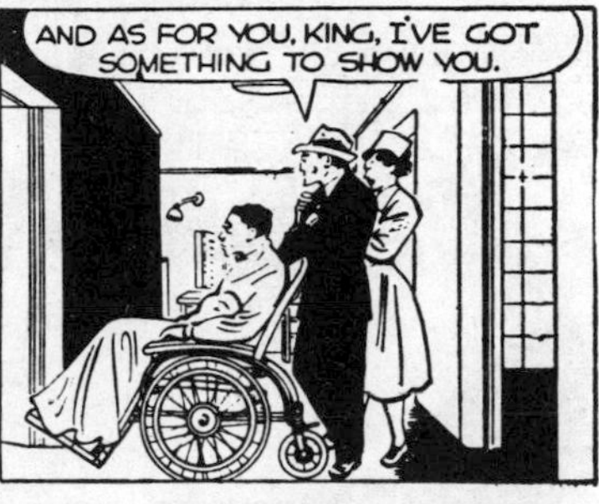
AND AS FOR YOU, KING, I'VE GOT SOMETHING TO SHOW YOU.

THESE ARE COLOR PICTURES WE FOUND IN YOUR APARTMENT.
MY APARTMENT? WHY, YOU—!!

OH, WE HAD A WARRANT.
WE ALSO FOUND THIS LITTLE VIEWER—FOR VIEWING SUCH COLOR SLIDES.

"YOUR MAN, EDDIE, SAYS YOU WENT OUT TO YOUR FARM ABOUT ONCE A MONTH—AND ALWAYS SHOWED A LOT OF INTEREST IN YOUR CATTLE."

STRANGELY ENOUGH, MOST OF THESE PICTURES WERE TAKEN AROUND YOUR CATTLE WATER TANK!
SO WHAT?

EVERYBODY KNOWS YOU RUN THIS CRIME SYNDICATE, BUT NOBODY'S BEEN ABLE TO PROVE IT. WELL, I THINK I CAN PROVE IT, IF WE GET OUT TO THAT FARM.

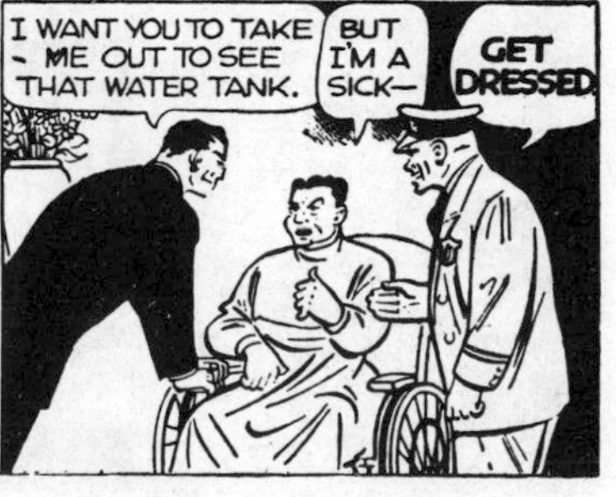
I WANT YOU TO TAKE ME OUT TO SEE THAT WATER TANK.
BUT I'M A SICK—
GET DRESSED.

YES, I WANT TO **SEE** THAT FARM OF YOURS. I WANT **YOU** TO SHOW ME THAT CATTLE WATER TANK.

I'M A PATIENT! I'M IN NO CONDITION TO—

THE DOCTOR SAID YOU COULD TRAVEL! NOW, **DRESS!**

IT'S A SWELL DAY! A TRIP TO YOUR FARM WOULD BE JUST DUCKY! NOW, MOVE!

WHY, YOU ✶★⁘!!

MEANWHILE, SAM IS GETTING THE KNOCKED-OUT CREWY LOU INTO A SQUAD CAR.

SISTER, YOUR NEXT STOP IS A CELL!

CHESTER GOULD

THE NURSE SAID SHE'D SLEEP FOR AN HOUR.

YEAH? BUT I DON'T TRUST THIS DAME.

SODIUM PENTOTHAL! I NEVER HEARD OF THE STUFF.

IT'S ONE OF THE FASTEST SEDATIVES KNOWN. IT CERTAINLY WORKED ON HER.

RIGHT HERE, LET US NOTE A TRANSACTION THAT IS BEING MADE IN ANOTHER PART OF TOWN.

I'M DOCTOR BROWN FROM THE UNIVERSITY. I WISH TO RENT AN AMBULANCE.

VEHICLES for HIRE

IT'S ALL READY FOR YOU, DOCTOR.

THANK YOU. I MAY NEED IT A COUPLE OF DAYS.

CHESTER GOULD

IT'S A BEAUTIFUL FARM, KING. I IMAGINE YOU SPEND A LOT OF TIME HERE?

WHAT'S THE IDEA? WHY, **BOSS!**

IT'S OKAY, JAKE. THEY'RE GOING IN.

SHOW US YOUR CATTLE WATER TANK, AND MAKE IT SNAPPY!

CATTLE TANK?

POLICE

NOW, GET ME A STILLSON WRENCH. WE'RE GOING TO DRAIN IT.

CHESTER GOULD

I PROTEST THIS SILLY PROCEDURE! **I'M A SICK MAN!**

I NOTICED IN YOUR COLOR PICTURES THE PLUG WAS ALWAYS OUT OF THE TANK AND IT WAS DRAINED.

THE KING HAS COLLAPSED.

GET HIM A CHAIR. HAVE HIM SIT DOWN. I WANT HIM TO SEE THIS OPERATION.

WE'RE **LOOKING FOR** EVIDENCE TO **BUST THE** CRIME SYNDICATE. **MY** HUNCH IS THERE'S **MORE** IN THIS WATER TANK THAN WATER.

CHESTER GOULD

LET US GO BACK TO SAM CATCHEM, FOR A MOMENT, AND HIS TRIP TO HEADQUARTERS WITH CREWY LOU.

SHE'S STARTING TO WAKE.

MAYBE WE'D BETTER PUT A PAIR OF **CUFFS** ON THE LITTLE DARLING.

HEY! **WATCH IT!** THAT **AMBULANCE!**

DRIVING AT TERRIFIC SPEED, THE AMBULANCE RAMS THE SQUAD CAR AMIDSHIPS! BOTH CARS SKID—

CRASH

CHESTER GOULD

THE WATER'S ALL OUT, TRACY. BUT THERE'S NOTHING IN THERE.

JUST MUCK!
GET ME A GARDEN HOSE—AND A BROOM.

WHEN WE WASH THE MUCK OUT OF THERE, I BELIEVE WE'LL FIND A TRAPDOOR!

A **TRAPDOOR!**
THIS GUY ISN'T A DETECTIVE! HE'S A MADMAN! RETURN ME TO TOWN!
CHESTER GOULD

SCENE: THE CATTLE YARD OF "THE KING'S" FARM.
SO WHAT DO YOU EXPECT TO FIND IN A CATTLE WATER TANK?
ANYTHING —MAYBE.

ALL I KNOW IS THAT THOSE COLOR PICTURES WE FOUND IN YOUR APARTMENT ALWAYS SHOWED THE WATER TANK! AND IN ONE OF THEM THE PLUG WAS OUT OF THE TANK.

TRACY, WHAT'S THAT THE HOSE HAS UNCOVERED?
LOOKS LIKE A **RING!**

IT **IS** A RING! THERE'S A **TRAP DOOR** HERE.

A WATER-TIGHT COMPARTMENT WITH A **BOX IN IT!**

HOLD 'IM, BOYS! DON'T LET HIM OUT OF YOUR GRIP!
WHY, YOU

JUST **WHAT** WILL BE IN THE BOX?
IF IT'S WHAT I THINK IT IS, THE CRIME SYNDICATE IS **DONE!**

MEANWHILE, IN THE CITY, THE SQUAD CAR TAKING CREWY LOU TO HEADQUARTERS HAS MET WITH TRAGEDY.
THE AMBULANCE HIT THE SQUAD CAR.

THE DRIVER'S OUT COLD—AND I CAN'T MOVE—CAN'T EVEN RAISE MY HANDS!
I'M SEPARATED FROM CREWY LOU BY THE CAR TOP.

IT'S ME. GET OUT OF THERE!
BRAINERD! **MY BROTHER, BRAINERD!**
POLICE

HEY, **STOP THAT WOMAN!** SHE'S A MURDERESS!
SAM'S VOICE
I RENTED THAT AMBULANCE AND DECIDED TO KILL YOU, EVEN IF I KILLED MYSELF! YOU'RE A DISGRACE TO THE FAMILY!

GET IN THAT CAR! I WANT TO METE OUT JUSTICE IN THIS CASE MYSELF!
WHAT? **TO YOUR OWN SISTER?**

IN THE BOTTOM OF THE STOCK TANK, A WATERPROOF DOOR!

BENEATH THE DOOR, A METAL BOX!
GIVE ME A SCREWDRIVER.

WHAT IS **THAT?**

CHESTER GOULD

MEANWHILE—
HE SAID HE WAS HER BROTHER! HE TOOK HER AWAY TO **KILL** HER.
HER **BROTHER?**

YOU ARE A DISGRACE TO THE FAMILY. I HAVE APPOINTED MYSELF A COMMITTEE OF ONE TO END YOUR CAREER!
MY OWN **BROTHER?**

BRAINERD, YOU'RE **INSANE!**
I, INSANE? I, PROFESSOR IN THE SCHOOL OF MEDICINE AT THE UNIVERSITY?

YOU'RE THE ONLY CRIMINAL IN OUR FAMILY IN FIVE GENERATIONS—AND I'M ENDING IT NOW!

ONE CLICK OF THIS, AND IT WILL BE ALL OVER. THEY'LL FIND YOUR BODY IN THE RIVER.
MY **OWN BROTHER!**

CHESTER GOULD

UNAWARE OF WHAT HAS HAPPENED TO CREWY LOU AND SAM CATCHEM, TRACY EXAMINES THE BOX.
NAMES! NAMES AND CITIES!

A LIST OF THE CRIME SYNDICATE HEADS IN EACH CITY—AND AMOUNTS COLLECTED IN JULY.

ANOTHER THING, KING! THESE ENTRIES ALL APPEAR TO BE IN YOUR HANDWRITING. THAT MAKES IT PERFECT.
COME ON—LET'S GO!

MEANWHILE—
BUT IF THEY CATCH YOU, BRAINERD, YOU WON'T HAVE A QUICK DEATH LIKE I. YOU'LL HAVE A TRIAL, WEEKS OF TORTURE IN A COURT ROOM—THEN, THE ELECTRIC CHAIR.

CHESTER GOULD

YOU'RE RIGHT! SHOOTING YOU IN THE CAR WOULD BE STUPID. FURTHERMORE, IF I WERE CAUGHT, IT WOULD JUST BRING MORE DISGRACE TO OUR FAMILY.

POISON! THAT'S THE ANSWER—CYANIDE OF POTASSIUM! I CAN GET IT AT THE MEDICAL SCHOOL, AND THEY CAN'T TRACE IT.

BUT, BROTHER OF MINE, YOU CAN'T **FORCE** ME TO SWALLOW! I **WON'T SWALLOW IT!**

MEANWHILE, SAM CHECKS THE OWNERSHIP OF THE AMBULANCE.
HE'S A PROFESSOR IN THE SCHOOL OF MEDICINE. HE RENTED IT.
BROWN? PROFESSOR BROWN? WHO IN—
VEHICLES HIRE

CHESTER GOULD

THIS IS A SUMMER COTTAGE I BUILT YEARS AGO. IT'S 300 MILES FROM THE CITY. **GO INSIDE!**

THE BASEMENT? BROTHER, WHAT ARE YOU GOING TO DO?
SOON AS I TIE YOUR HANDS, I'LL SHOW YOU.

THIS CEMENT FLOOR IS PAPER THIN! IT'LL BREAK EASY.
BRAINERD, REMEMBER I'M YOUR **SISTER!**

THERE'LL BE NO TRACE! I CAN CEMENT THE SPOT OVER! ONLY **I** WILL EVER KNOW WHAT HAPPENED TO YOU.

CHESTER GOULD

BRAINERD! I'M YOUR SISTER!

THE HOLE WON'T HAVE TO BE VERY DEEP FOR YOU— YOU'RE LITTLE.

BROTHER BRAINERD, HAVE YOU NO MERCY?
I'LL BUY A NEW BAG OF CEMENT IN TOWN. I CAN THROW THESE BROKEN CONCRETE PIECES IN THE LAKE.

COME OVER HERE.
CHESTER GOULD

SCENE: THE BASEMENT OF A RIVER COTTAGE.
YOU'RE THE ONLY BLACK SHEEP IN THE FAMILY! I'VE BEEN A TEACHER FOR 10 YEARS. FATHER WAS A LEADER IN THE BUSINESS WORLD.

OUR BROTHER DIED A HERO IN THE WORLD WAR—BUT YOU—A CRIMINAL BLACK SHEEP! A DISGRACE! GET DOWN IN THAT HOLE! YOU MUST DIE!
BRAINERD! I'M YOUR SISTER.

NO, BRAINERD! THEN YOU WILL BE A MURDERER! THAT'S WORSE THAN I! YOU WILL BE THE BIGGER CRIMINAL!

RIGHT! IF I KILL YOU—I'LL HAVE BLOOD ON MY HANDS! IF YOU LIVE, I'LL BE DISGRACED!

WE MUST BOTH DIE TOGETHER! BOTH OF US! GET UP!

MEANWHILE, DICK TRACY REVEALS TO CHIEF PATTON HOW THE KING AND HIS CRIME SYNDICATE HAVE BEEN SMASHED
COMPLETE RECORDS, CHIEF.
HID IN A METAL BOX IN THE BOTTOM OF A CATTLE WATER TANK.

NAMES OF FIXERS— AMOUNTS PAID— PEOPLE INVOLVED!
TRACY, HERE'S SAM!

THE CRASH SMASHED MY WRIST RADIO—CREWY LOU HAS ESCAPED! TAKEN FROM OUR SQUAD CAR!

A RENTED AMBULANCE DELIBERATELY CRASHED US! THE DRIVER—I CHECKED UP—CREWY LOU'S BROTHER!

HE'S BEEN A PROFESSOR AT THE UNIVERSITY SCHOOL OF MEDICINE SINCE 1941.

YES—WE WILL DIE TOGETHER! THAT'S THE PRICE I MUST PAY FOR YOUR SINS.

"THREE MILES DOWNSTREAM IS 'DEATH WHIRLPOOL'. ANIMALS AND OBJECTS THAT ENTER IT ARE NEVER SEEN AGAIN. THAT'S WHERE WE'RE GOING!"

YES, I HAVE CHANGED MY MIND. WE SHALL DIE IN THE WHIRLPOOL TOGETHER—BOTH OF US!

IT WILL BE A BROTHER GIVING HIS OWN LIFE TO RID THE WORLD OF A CRIMINAL SISTER.

"THE TRIP TO THE WHIRLPOOL WILL TAKE ABOUT AN HOUR. TIME ENOUGH FOR YOU TO REPENT YOUR SINS."

NO OARS! WE WILL BE AT THE MERCY OF THE CURRENT. CURRENT THAT WILL CARRY US BOTH TO **ETERNITY!**

CHESTER GOULD

YES, "THE KING" IS DETHRONED! AND THIS TIME, FOR KEEPS.

INCIDENTALLY, WHERE'S TRACY, CHIEF?

TRACY DROVE UP TO SHADOW LAKE LAST NIGHT TO PICK UP TESS AND BONNY BRAIDS, WHO HAVE BEEN ON VACATION.

WHY DO YOU ASK, SAM?

A VERY WEAK SIGNAL FROM AN UPSTATE PATROL CAR KEEPS COMING IN ON THE RADIO—CALLING FOR TRACY.

MEANTIME—

MUST BE A MADMAN—BOAT'S DRIFTING ABOUT 3 MILES AN HOUR, AND THE WOMAN LOOKS LIKE CREWY LOU.

CHESTER GOULD

SCENE: THE NORTH WOODS. TRACY AND JUNIOR ARE BRINGING TESS AND BONNY BRAIDS HOME FROM A MONTH'S VACATION.

DID YOU BOYS MISS US?

I'LL SAY! **HEY!** WHAT'S THIS—

CHESTER GOULD

THAT'S SAM'S VOICE.

TRACY, ARE YOU ANYWHERE NEAR "DEATH WHIRLPOOL" ON THE OTT RIVER?

2-WAY WRIST RADIO

YES, SISTER OF MINE, THE CURRENT'S GETTING STRONGER NOW. ANOTHER MILE—THEN, THE WHIRLPOOL!

WE FIGURE THE BOAT WILL PASS OLSON FORD IN 20 MINUTES. IT'S DRIFTING FASTER NOW!

I'LL CUT ACROSS ON THE FIRST GRAVEL ROAD. WE'RE NOT MORE THAN FIVE MILES FROM THERE!

2-WAY WRIST RADIO

CHESTER GOULD

MEANWHILE, THE BOAT ROUNDS A BEND IN THE RIVER AND HEADS INTO SOME RAPIDS.

IT LURCHES! BOTH SISTER AND BROTHER ARE NEARLY THROWN FROM THE BOAT! CREWY LOU DECIDES TO ACT.

WE'RE GETTING NEAR THE RIVER—OH!

HEY! LOOK! ON THAT TRUCK!

THERE'S A 20 IN IT IF YOU TAKE THAT ROLL OF CHICKEN WIRE TO OLSON FORD.

FOR THE POLICE, OF COURSE.

MEANWHILE—

HE FELL AND HIS HEAD STRUCK THAT **ANCHOR!** HE'S OUT!

CHESTER GOULD

EVEN IF I CAN'T GET THESE ROPES OFF MY WRIST, I'LL JUMP OVERBOARD ANYWAY! THE WATER'S QUIETER HERE AND I'M A GOOD SWIMMER.

WITH THE TRUCK CARRYING THE ROLL OF CHICKEN WIRE FOLLOWING, TRACY REACHES THE SPOT WHERE THE DRIFTING BOAT WILL PASS.

I'LL DRIVE OFF THE ROAD AND PARK. YOU TOSS THE ROLL OF WIRE DOWN THERE WHERE THE MEN ARE.

JUNIOR, YOU STAY WITH TESS AND BONNY BRAIDS. I'LL GO DOWN AND HELP.
CHESTER GOULD

"THE BOAT SHOULD PASS HERE IN 12 MINUTES," ONE OF THE OFFICERS TELLS TRACY.
EMPTY?

TRACY HAD GONE UP IN THAT NECK OF THE WOODS TO BRING HOME TESS AND BONNY BRAIDS, WHO HAVE BEEN ON A VACATION.
THEN, HE'S ON THE SCENE NOW?

"YES. THEY WERE ON THEIR WAY BACK WHEN I GOT THROUGH TO TRACY ON HIS 2-WAY WRIST RADIO," SAYS CHIEF PATTON.
JUNIOR, YOU STAY HERE WITH TESS AND BONNY BRAIDS. I'M GOING DOWN TO THE RIVER.

NEIGHBORS SAW THE PROFESSOR SHOVE OFF WITH THE GIRL AND NOTIFIED US. I RECOGNIZED CREWY LOU THROUGH MY FIELD GLASSES.

YOU'VE DONE A GREAT JOB, OFFICER.
AH! HERE COMES OUR CHICKEN WIRE.

I SAW A FARMER WITH THIS ROLL OF WIRE ON HIS TRUCK. I MADE A DEAL WITH HIM. IT'S OUR ONLY CHANCE.

"DEATH WHIRLPOOL" IS JUST 2 BLOCKS BELOW THESE RAPIDS. IF THIS DOESN'T WORK, THEY'RE GONERS!

PAY OUT THE ROPE AS I CROSS, THEN I'LL PULL THE CHICKEN WIRE AFTER ME.

ONE SLIP, AND WE MAY NEVER SEE HIM AGAIN.

HE'S ACROSS!
FEED OUT THAT FENCING!

HERE COMES THE BOAT!
WE WON'T MAKE IT!

OH, YES, WE WILL.
HEY, IT'S EMPTY!

GOSH! I SURE WOULD LIKE TO SEE THAT RESCUE AND CAPTURE!
JUNIOR, WHY DON'T YOU GO DOWN TO THE RIVER AND WATCH? BONNY BRAIDS AND I WILL BE ALL RIGHT HERE.

WHY, OF COURSE, JUNIOR. BONNY BRAIDS AND I WILL BE ALL RIGHT HERE. GO DOWN AND WATCH THEM.

I WOULD LIKE TO SEE CREWY LOU'S CAPTURE! I'LL BE RIGHT BACK.

YES, THE CHICKEN WIRE HOLDS THE BOAT, BUT—

IT ISN'T EMPTY. I SEE A PAIR OF FEET.

CHESTER GOULD

THIS GUY'S **DEAD!**

YES—DEAD!

LET'S GET THE BOAT ASHORE.

BACK OF HIS HEAD'S CUT.

IS **THIS** HER BROTHER? DID SHE—?

CHESTER GOULD

AND BACK ON THE RIVER BANK, WHERE TESS AND BONNY BRAIDS WAIT IN THE CAR.

SOUND ASLEEP. THE TRIP HAS COMPLETELY TIRED THE LITTLE DARLING.

ROCK

I DIDN'T FEED HER ON SCHEDULE, BECAUSE MY WATCH STOPPED. I'LL TURN ON THE RADIO AND GET THE TIME.

ROCK

50 60 70 80 90

CHESTER GOULD

THIS BROTHER AND SISTER ACT IS OVER, CHIEF, AND THE BROTHER LOST.

YEAH, A MORGUE CASE.

2-WAY WRIST RADIO

CRACK

ROCK

OUTSIDE, MRS. BIG SHOT! I'VE GOT PLACES TO GO!

I DON'T KNOW THE ROADS TOO WELL AROUND HERE— BUT THIS THING'LL DO A HUNDRED, AND IT'S FULL OF GAS.

WHOOSH

AND **UNNOTICED** BY CREWY LOU, BONNY BRAIDS LIES ON THE BACK SEAT— **SOUND ASLEEP!**

CHESTER GOULD

UNAWARE THAT BONNY BRAIDS LIES SLEEPING ON THE REAR SEAT, CREWY LOU FLEES IN DICK TRACY'S CAR.

IT'LL BE AT LEAST 30 MINUTES BEFORE THEY CAN GET ROAD BLOCKS ORGANIZED. MEANWHILE, I'LL STICK TO THE MAIN HIGHWAY.

AND DOWN AT THE RIVER.

I'LL WANT THE EXAMINER'S REPORT AS SOON AS POSSIBLE.

HEY! WE CAME UP AT THE WRONG SPOT. WHERE'S THE **CAR**?

HUH?

CHESTER GOULD

THE CAR'S GONE! -AND- TESS-

WHAT HAPPENED?
BLOOD! SHE'S BEEN STRUCK!
WHERE'S THE BABY?

THE CROSS ROADS THROUGH THESE MOUNTAINS DON'T LOOK TOO GOOD, BUT I'LL HAVE TO LEAVE THE CONCRETE SOON.
CHESTER GOULD

IF I CAN FIND ONE OF THOSE MOUNTAIN TRAILS, I'LL DRIVE BACK INTO THE TIMBER. THEY'D NEVER FIND ME.
AND BONNY BRAIDS SLEEPS ON! WHEN WILL CREWY LOU DISCOVER HER?

TESS!
STRUCK BY SOME HARD OBJECT- UNCONSCIOUS.

AFTER FINDING THE BODY OF CREWY LOU'S BROTHER IN THE BOAT, TRACY AND THE OTHERS RETURN TO THE SPOT WHERE TRACY'S CAR WAS PARKED— AND TO A SCENE OF HORROR.
THE BABY! WHERE IS THE BABY?

SHE MUST BE HOSPITALIZED!
THERE'S A GOOD ONE AT BEAVER FALLS.

I LEFT TESS AND THE BABY! I DISOBEYED YOUR ORDERS, TRACY.
IT'S ALL RIGHT, JUNIOR. TESS TOLD YOU YOU COULD GO.

ROAD BLOCKS, EVERYTHING! LEAVE NOTHING UNDONE. SHE HASN'T BEEN GONE MORE THAN TWENTY MINUTES.
2-WAY WRIST RADIO

MEANWHILE, SEVERAL MILES AWAY—
THIS JOB DOES A HUNDRED ON GOOD ROADS, BUT I CAN'T STAY ON GOOD ROADS! I'VE GOT TO HIT THE SIDE ROADS.
SIDE ROAD

OFF THE CONCRETE AND ONTO GRAVEL— THE CAR BUMPS A FEW TIMES—AND FROM THE BACK SEAT—
WA-WAA

WHAT?

A KID! THEIR KID! MUST HAVE BEEN ASLEEP BACK THERE WHEN I TOOK OVER.
I DIDN'T SEE HER!

OF ALL THE ✱!✱! LUCK! I DON'T WANT A KID ALONG! THIS IS BAD!

WHAT CAN I DO WITH THE BRAT? WHAT---??

OH, WELL! I DIDN'T WANT IT THIS WAY—BUT THAT'S THE WAY IT IS, SO—THAT'S THE WAY IT'LL STAY.
MAYBE THIS IS BETTER.

DISCOVERING BONNY BRAIDS, CREWY LOU AT FIRST DECIDES TO ABANDON THE CHILD, THEN CHANGES HER MIND

I DIDN'T PLAN IT THIS WAY, BUT NOW, THAT YOU'RE ALONG, IT MAY KEEP COPS FROM SHOOTING AT US.

AND DON'T GO BAWLING FOR FOOD! **YOU MAY NOT EAT FOR A WEEK!**

BAW-WWA

THERE'S A HOSPITAL AT PHELPS.

MY BABY! MY BABY!

WHY DID I LEAVE THE CAR?

CHESTER GOULD

SCENE: THE SMALL HOSPITAL IN A NORTH WOODS TOWN.

SHE'LL BE ALL RIGHT.

MY BONNY BRAIDS! MY BABY!

SHE CAN BE TAKEN HOME THIS AFTERNOON.

HOW CAN I GO HOME WITHOUT BONNY BRAIDS?

HERE'S SOMETHING ODD, TRACY—ROAD BLOCKS REPORT CREWY LOU HASN'T BEEN ON ANY OF THE HIGHWAYS.

THEN, SHE'S STILL IN THIS VICINITY?

"SHE MUST BE," REPLIES THE OFFICER, "UNLESS SHE'S DRIVEN RIGHT UP THE SIDE OF A MOUNTAIN."

ROCKS, TREES, DITCHES! THEY'LL NEVER FIND ME!

BUMP!

CHESTER GOULD

THIS IS DIET SMITH. I'VE BEEN TRYING TO GET YOU EVER SINCE I HEARD THE TRAGIC NEWS.

I'LL BRING TESS HOME IN MY HELICOPTER AND THEN TURN THE MACHINE OVER TO YOU TO SEARCH FOR BONNY BRAIDS.

PARIS CALLING, SIR.

HE EXPECTS TO LAND HERE AT 10 O'CLOCK. YOU AND JUNIOR GO BACK HOME. I'LL STAY HERE TILL OUR BABY IS FOUND.

AND UP IN THE MOUNTAINS—

JUST LET ANY MOTORIZED STATE TROOPERS TRY TO CATCH US, EH, KID?

BUMP

CHESTER GOULD

THERE GOES ANOTHER FENDER! SO **WHAT**? AS LONG AS THIS CRATE WILL TRAVEL, WE'RE NOT STOPPING.

ANY DUMB THUG CAN SPEED DOWN THE HIGHWAY AND GET TRAPPED—BUT IT TAKES BRAINS TO MANEUVER A CAR UP A MOUNTAIN.

EVEN IF THE POLICE HAD US SPOTTED, THEY'D BE CAREFUL WITH THE LEAD AND TEAR GAS, WITH YOU AT MY SIDE.

BUT THIS MAY BE THE END OF THE TRAIL, KID! **HOLD ON!**

CHESTER GOULD

EASY, TESS! WE'LL FIND HER. COME, THEY'RE GOING TO FLY YOU HOME.

I WANT TO STAY WITH **YOU**. I WANT TO HELP FIND OUR **BABY!**

I'M GOING WITH YOU, TESS. THEN I'M COMING BACK.

MEANWHILE—

WELL, WE MADE IT, BUT THAT WAS QUITE A DROP.

YOU GOT KNOCKED OFF ON THE FLOOR, EH? OKAY, **STOP YELLING!** IT JARRED ME UP, TOO.

CHESTER GOULD

NO WORD ON THE BABY. SEARCHING PARTIES ARE BEING ORGANIZED.

AT HEADQUARTERS.
TRACY AND SAM ARE AT DIET SMITH'S AIRPORT NOW. THEY'RE REFUELING THE HELICOPTER.

AND AT DIET SMITH'S—
I'M TURNING IT OVER TO THE POLICE DEPARTMENT TO USE TILL THE CHILD IS FOUND. MY PILOT WILL FLY YOU.

AND CREWY LOU DRIVES ON—
I MUST BE 15 MILES BACK IN THE MOUNTAINS. NOBODY WOULD BELIEVE A CAR COULD MAKE IT. THEY'LL NEVER FIND ME!
CHESTER GOULD

NO WORD—
NO WORD?

NO WORD—

NO WORD—
NO WORD! OH, BONNY BRAIDS, MY BABY! WHAT HAVE THEY DONE WITH YOU?

MRS. TRACY—PLEASE! TRY TO CONTROL YOURSELF.
THE TELEPHONE.
RRR

I'M AT DIET SMITH'S FACTORY. HE'S LENDING THE POLICE DEPARTMENT HIS HELICOPTER. WE'RE TAKING OFF IN TEN MINUTES.

THERE'S NO TRACE OF THE CAR! OUR ROAD BLOCKS HAVE BEEN PERFECT, BUT THE CAR HAS VANISHED!
GET THE MAPS, SAM.

VANISHED? WELL, ALMOST! THE PANICKY, FEAR-CRAZED CREWY LOU, BEHIND THE WHEEL OF TRACY'S CAR, IS TRAVELING A MOUNTAIN PATH.

ROCKS, NARROW PASSES, FALLEN TREES! NO AUTOMOBILE EVER TOOK SUCH PUNISHMENT.

RACING MOTOR! BURNING RUBBER! BENT FENDERS!
THEY'LL BE DAYS FINDING ME! MEANWHILE, I'LL THINK OF SOMETHING!

AS FOR YOU—YOUR BEING ALONG WAS AN ACCIDENT. I'M NOT RESPONSIBLE!

"WHEN I ABANDON THIS CRATE, YOU'LL BE EXCESS BAGGAGE—YOU'LL BE LEFT RIGHT HERE."

IT'S HER FEEDING TIME AGAIN! SHE'S MISSED THREE OF HER FEEDINGS—OH, MY BABY!
NOW, MRS. TRACY.

BUT SHE'S MISSED SIX FEEDINGS! OH, MY POOR BABY!

I'M SURE THEY'LL FIND BONNY BRAIDS, MRS. TRACY, WITH THE HELICOPTER.

NO WORD—

AND AT DIET SMITH'S AIRPORT.

WE HAVEN'T TOO MUCH TIME. IT WILL SOON BE DARK.

CHESTER GOULD

STAY HIGH TILL WE'VE CHECKED THE MOUNTAIN ROADS. THEN, GO DOWN TO TREETOP LEVEL TO SEARCH THE HILLSIDES!

WHAT'S THAT **ROAR**? IS THIS CRATE ABOUT TO EXPLODE?

THAT WAS A PLANE!

EH? A HELICOPTER!

CHESTER GOULD

I GET IT! WE'VE GOT TO STAY UNDER THE TREES!

THEY'RE **AFTER ME!**

IS THAT A **CAVE?**

A HELICOPTER! I HEARD IT—I SAW IT! THEY'RE AFTER US!

THIS YELLOW CAR WILL SHINE LIKE A TORCH! I'VE GOT TO KEEP IT **HID!**

BUT I CAN'T HIDE IN HERE! CAVE ISN'T BIG ENOUGH.

ANYWAY— NOT ENOUGH FOLIAGE AROUND THIS SPOT.

WAAA WAA

CHESTER GOULD

GOT TO STICK TO THE BRUSH AND UNDERGROWTH TILL DARK, ANYWAY.

SHUT UP, KID!

WAAA

RADIATOR'S BOILING DRY! THIS MAY BE THE END OF THE LINE, KID.

GO AHEAD AND BLOW UP! THIS CAR'S A **WRECK**, ANYWAY.

I CAN STRIKE OUT **AFOOT.**

WHAT DO YOU SEE, SAM?

CHESTER GOULD

THOUGHT I SAW A WISP OF SMOKE OR SOMETHING OVER THERE.

WHERE?

ROAD BLOCKS HAVE ELIMINATED ANY POSSIBILITY OF HER TRAVELING THE HIGHWAYS. SHE'S GOT TO BE DOWN THERE.

I KNOW THAT— BUT I JUST CAN'T IMAGINE ANY CAR TRAVELING THE SIDES OF THIS MOUNTAIN.

CHESTER GOULD

"ANYWAY, THAT SMOKE YOU SAW, SAM, MUST HAVE BEEN FOG. THERE'S NOTHING DOWN THERE."

GONE! THOSE BRANCHES HELPED! AND WITH THIS CANVAS BUCKET FROM THE TRUNK, I PUT WATER IN THE RADIATOR! SO, WE'RE READY TO GO AGAIN.

SLUP SLUP

IT'LL BE DARK IN ANOTHER 15 MINUTES. THAT'S A BREAK FOR ME.

SHUT UP! HAVEN'T I GOT ENOUGH ON MY MIND WITHOUT YOUR YOWLING?
SMACK

HEY! THEY'RE FLYING LOW AGAIN.
I WONDER, IN SPITE OF BRANCHES, IF THEY—

WELL?
YEAH—TOO DARK!
CHESTER GOULD

I STILL HEAR THAT HELICOPTER! THEY THINK THEY CAN SPOT THIS CAR, DO THEY?

WELL, THEY'VE GOT ANOTHER THINK COMING. THIS CAR IS SO CAMOUFLAGED RADAR COULDN'T FIND IT!

AND YOU, YOU NOISY LITTLE WORM, SHUT UP!

IT'S GETTING DARK, TRACY! SEARCHING FURTHER IS SENSELESS.

BESIDES, NO CAR COULD PENETRATE SMOKY RIDGE MOUNTAINS, I CAN'T BELIEVE IT.

ROAD CHECKS PROVE THAT THE CAR NEVER GOT FURTHER THAN A 5-MILE RADIUS FROM THE SPOT WHERE CREWY LOU SEIZED IT.
SHE'S GOT TO BE IN THAT REGION.

MEANWHILE, DIET SMITH CALLS TRACY BY RADIO.
IT'S A SPECIAL HIGH-POWERED BINOCULAR WE'VE BEEN WORKING ON FOR 3 YEARS. THE BOYS JUST BROUGHT IT IN.
PARIS CALLING

IT'S A PRODUCT OF OUR LABORATORY MADE FOR NIGHT USE. I WANT TO GO UP WITH YOU AS SOON AS YOU GET BACK HERE, TRACY.

OKAY! I'LL PUT DOWN THERE IN 20 MINUTES. MEANWHILE, I WANT TO CHECK WITH CHIEF PATTON AND SEE HOW TESS IS.
2-WAY WRIST RADIO

BONNY BRAIDS! BONNY BRAIDS!
SHE'S QUIETER NOW, CHIEF—YES—SEVERAL SEDATIVES.

THIS WAGON ISN'T BIG ENOUGH FOR BOTH OF US, BABY. ANYWAY, IT'S DARK NOW.
WAA
WAAA

IT'S ALL YOURS, KID! SO LONG!
BAWAA

I'M STRIKING OUT FOR MYSELF!

IT'S DARK NOW, AND THE HELICOPTER BOYS CAN'T SEE ME.

"I'M RID OF THE CAR AND RID OF THE BABY. LET 'EM FIND THE BUS IF THEY WANT TO. THEY WON'T FIND **ME**!"

WAA WAAA

CHESTER GOULD

AND AT DIET SMITH'S AIRPORT.

THEY'RE ELECTRONIC! JUST OUT OF OUR LABORATORY FOR USE AT NIGHT. YOU AND I ARE GOING UP AGAIN.

WITH BONNY BRAIDS STILL MISSING—THE SEARCH GOES ON!

IT'LL TAKE A WHILE TO ADJUST THEM TO YOUR EYES, TRACY.

AH, YES! THERE! EVERYTHING'S AS CLEAR AS **DAYTIME**!

"IF CREWY LOU WAS STILL DRIVING WE COULD SEE THE HEADLIGHTS OF THE CAR," SAYS TRACY. "SHE MUST BE PARKED."

WAA WAA WAAA

IN THIS DARKNESS, THE ROCKS AND UNDERBRUSH ARE MURDER! I'LL HAVE TO SIT THINGS OUT TILL IT'S DAYLIGHT.

BUMP!

CHESTER GOULD

IT'S THAT SILLY HELICOPTER AGAIN! DON'T THEY EVER GIVE UP?

WHAT DO THEY THINK THEY CAN SEE AT **NIGHT**?

UH!

WHAT IS IT, TRACY?

I THOUGHT I SAW SOMETHING MOVE, BUT IT'S GONE NOW.

AND BENEATH THE BOUGHS, A LITTLE VOICE, EXHAUSTED AND WEAK, TURNS INTO A WHIMPER AS THE CHILL NIGHT AIR FILLS THE CAR.

CHESTER GOULD

I FELL OFF THAT LEDGE! I'VE GOT TO STAY PUT TILL DAYLIGHT! IT'S DANGEROUS MOVING ABOUT.

MUST BE ABOUT MIDNIGHT—COLD, TOO! **HEY, I SMELL WOOD SMOKE!**

"MUST BE A SHACK OR A CABIN SOMEWHERE AROUND HERE—ONE OF THOSE MOUNTAIN FAMILIES."

CHESTER GOULD

"MOUNTAIN PEOPLE ARE UNUSUALLY FRIENDLY—AND NOT TOO WELL POSTED," SAYS CREWY LOU. "MIGHT GIVE ME FOOD."

FOREST FIRE PREVENTION SERVICE

STILL IN THE ABANDONED AUTO, THE BABY'S CRIES GROW FAINTER AND FAINTER.

THE CRISP NIGHT MOUNTAIN AIR PERMEATES THE CAR AS THE LITTLE HANDS TURN BLUE.

AND UP IN THE HELICOPTER.

SEE IT, TRACY? IT'S SOMETHING SHINY!

CHESTER GOULD

I SAW IT, TOO, BUT IT'S TOO SMALL FOR A CAR. PROBABLY A PUDDLE OF WATER.

LET'S TAKE ANOTHER LOOK.

AND SEVERAL MILES IN THE OPPOSITE DIRECTION, TRACY'S CAR STILL SITS BENEATH THE TREE BOUGHS WHERE CREWY LOU LEFT IT! BUT FROM WITHIN, COMES **NO** BABY'S CRY. ALL IS QUIET NOW!

THE "SHINY" OBJECT SIGHTED FROM THE HELICOPTER PROVES TO BE PART OF TRACY'S CAR, AND IS THE FIRST TANGIBLE EVIDENCE

BROKEN BRANCHES, PAINT MARKS ON ROCKS! THE CAR'S ROUTE IS OBVIOUS.

MEANWHILE, SEVERAL MILES AWAY.

BACON, COFFEE! THE RANGER'S LEAVING THE TOWER. THIS IS MY CHANCE!

CHESTER GOULD

FOOTSTEPS ON THE STAIRS! A **WOMAN?**

THE SIGHT OF A WOMAN MOUNTING THE TOWER STEPS MAKES THE FOREST RANGER RETRACE HIS STEPS.

THAT CREW CUT! THE PIGTAIL OF HAIR! IT FITS THE RADIO DESCRIPTION! IT'S **HER!**

HALT!

NOT TILL I'VE **HAD SOME GRUB!**

CHESTER GOULD

SEIZING ANOTHER OF THE RANGER'S RIFLES, CREWY LOU GOES TO WORK AT THE STOVE.

IF NOTHING ELSE— I'LL **EAT!**

NOW, THAT YOU'RE UP THERE, YOU'D BETTER STAY WHERE YOU ARE.

I SAID STAY **WHERE YOU ARE!**

ZING

I SEE A **HELICOPTER!** THE RADIO MENTIONED IT. IF ONLY I CAN GET THEIR ATTENTION.

WHEENG

TRACY, WE'RE 5 MILES TO YOUR NORTH NEAR A FIRE TOWER. THERE'S A GUY SIGNALING US WITH HIS SHIRT.

GO DOWN AND REPORT BACK.

2-WAY WRIST RADIO

CHESTER GOULD

TRACY, WE JUST TALKED TO A FOREST RANGER! **CREWY LOU IS UP IN THE LOOKOUT TOWER!**

UNDOUBTEDLY, THE BABY'S WITH HER, TOO!

I'LL DROP THE SEARCH FOR THE CAR AND JOIN YOU. COME BACK AND PICK ME UP.

2-WAY WRIST RADIO

I SHOULD HAVE DRILLED THAT 'COPTER, BUT THEY WENT OUT OF RANGE OF THIS .22 WHEN THEY TALKED.

AHA! SO SHE'S COMING DOWN— AGAIN.

I'M WARNING YOU, SISTER, HALT!

CHESTER GOULD

WHILE TRACY'S CAR STILL SITS BENEATH THE BOUGHS IN TRAGIC ABANDONMENT—

ACTIVITY SEETHES SEVERAL MILES AWAY, AS DIET SMITH PICKS UP TRACY.

HEAD FOR THE FIRE TOWER.

IF THE BABY'S **WITH** HER, CREWY LOU MAY THROW IT FROM THE LOOKOUT TOWER IF WE TRY TO CAPTURE HER.

I NEVER THOUGHT OF THAT.

CHESTER GOULD

EVERY TIME SHE STARTS DOWN I HAVE TO SHOOT, BUT I BROUGHT ONLY THE CARTRIDGES THAT WERE IN THIS CLIP. SHE HAS THE **WHOLE** BOX.

BEFORE WE APPROACH THE FIRE TOWER, BETTER HOOK ON THE LOUDSPEAKER.

THERE! TAKE OVER, TRACY.
HELLO, RANGER. WE'RE COMING IN.

IF CREWY LOU IS STILL IN THE TOWER, WAVE YOUR CAP TO US.

OKAY, NOW CIRCLE THE TOWER, PILOT. I WANT TO ASK HER A COUPLE OF QUESTIONS.
CHESTER GOULD

NO, CHIEF, WE HAVEN'T FOUND THE BABY NOR THE CAR, BUT WE **HAVE** LOCATED CREWY LOU.

THE FOREST RANGER HAD JUST GONE DOWN WITH HIS RIFLE TO SHOOT A RABBIT FOR HIS DINNER, WHEN HE SAW CREWY LOU MOUNT THE TOWER STEPS.

HE SIGNALED US WITH HIS SHIRT AND TOLD US SHE WAS IN THE TOWER.

SHE MUST HAVE BONNIE BRAIDS **WITH HER!**
PILOT, GO DOWN NEAR THE TOWER.

ARMED WITH ANOTHER RIFLE FOUND IN THE LOOKOUT TOWER, THE CRAZED CREWY LOU KEEPS VIGIL.
HAVE YOU GOT THE BABY WITH YOU?
LOUDSPEAKER

NO! BUT I'VE GOT A **SLUG!** TAKE THAT!
CRACK

WHERE IS BONNY BRAIDS?
TRACY, SHE'LL **KILL** YOU.

I SAW HER AS SHE WENT UP THE STAIRS. SHE WAS **EMPTY-HANDED.** I DIDN'T SEE THE BABY.

WHAT DID YOU DO WITH THE BABY?
HA. HA. HA! WHAT BABY?
ZING

WE'LL HOVER DIRECTLY OVER THE TOWER OUT OF GUNSHOT RANGE WHILE WE FIGURE.

IF SHE HASN'T GOT THE BABY, I'M JUST WASTING MY TIME HERE. **I MUST FIND THAT CAR!**
WE CAN GET HER OUT WITH THIS, TRACY.
TEAR GAS GUN

AND THE CAR STILL SITS BENEATH THE BOUGHS! ITS TOP, TORN BY BRANCHES DURING THE WILD RIDE, GIVES EASY ACCESS TO THE BEASTS OF THE MOUNTAINS.

GR-R-R-R

R-R-R-RR

OWOOO

WHETHER SHE'S GOT THE BABY OR NOT, WE'VE GOT TO GET HER **OUT** NOW.

THIS IS YOUR LAST CHANCE TO WALK DOWN THOSE STEPS AND SURRENDER, CREWY LOU!

WHOSE LAST CHANCE?

OKAY! HERE COMES THE **TEAR GAS!**

TEAR GAS, EH?

I'LL SMASH ALL THE WINDOWS! IT'S WINDY UP HERE. THE GAS WILL SOON CLEAR OUT.

CAN'T DO IT—CAN'T **SEE!** OW—MY EYES! OH—!

I'LL LIE DOWN ON THE WALKWAY OUTSIDE! THE AIR'S BETTER HERE AND THEY WON'T SEE ME.

I'LL **DRILL 'EM!** NO—I CAN'T SEE! EYES ARE WATERING TOO MUCH FROM THE TEAR GAS!

I HEAR THE 'COPTER, BUT I CAN'T SEE IT.

THE GUN—I **DROPPED** THE GUN!

I'LL PUT THIS ONE RIGHT AT HER FEET.

FLOODED WITH **TEAR GAS** — THE WALKWAY AROUND THE FIRE TOWER BECOMES UNTENABLE.

CREWY LOU GROPES FOR THE STAIRWAY TO GO DOWN! SHE **CAN'T SEE,** AND MISTAKENLY ENTERS THE TOWER AGAIN.

MY EYES! MY LUNGS! **I CAN'T STAND THE PAIN! I CAN'T STAND—**

SIXTY-FIVE FEET TO THE ROCKS!

SHE DROPPED! SHE FELL THROUGH THE WINDOW.

THERE'S PLENTY OF ROOM. WE CAN SIT DOWN WITH NO DANGER NOW.

IS SHE DEAD?

SHOOTING A TEAR GAS BOMB INTO THE LOOKOUT TOWER FROM THE HELICOPTER, DICK TRACY FINALLY DISLODGES CREWY LOU.
IN HER PANIC, SHE FELL THROUGH THE WINDOW.

THAT 65-FOOT FALL WAS TOO MUCH FOR HER. SHE'S DYING.
WE DARE NOT MOVE HER.

ONCE MORE—WHAT DID YOU DO WITH THE BABY?
HER EVELIDS MOVED, TRACY.

SHE'S TRYING TO TALK.
SH!
I LEFT THE BABY IN THE CAR—

SAM! SEND MEN UP TO THE TOWER TO PICK UP HER BODY. DIET SMITH AND I ARE GOING BACK TO THE PLACE WHERE I FOUND THE FENDER SKIRT.
2-WAY WRIST RADIO

THIRTY MINUTES LATER.
WE'LL GUIDE A SEARCHING PARTY TO YOU FROM THE AIR.

BROKEN LIMBS AND TWIGS, PAINT MARKS ON THE BOULDERS! THE CAR'S TRAIL SHOULDN'T BE TOO HARD TO FOLLOW.
THE FENDER SKIRT

SHE APPARENTLY LEAPED CRAGS AND CLIFFS! I DON'T SEE HOW THE CHILD COULD HAVE SURVIVED THE RIDE.

DAYS AND DAYS WITHOUT FOOD AND WITHOUT CARE IN THIS COLD MOUNTAIN AIR!

IT'S THE PARTY!
WE CUT ACROSS FROM THE PARK ROAD! WE SAW SOMETHING YELLOW UP THERE.

YES, I SEE IT, TOO! I SEE IT!

WILL BONNY BRAIDS BE ALIVE? TRACY CHOKES AND TREMBLES AS HE SLOWLY MOVES TOWARD THE CAR.

AT LAST! DICK TRACY AND A POSSE CONVERGE ON THE ABANDONED CAR.
BONNY BRAIDS! I'M AFRAID TO LOOK!

THE TENSION IS SICKENING–
WEEKS IN THE CAR! THE TOT WILL BE BONES.
A TORN BLANKET AND A BOTTLE! WHAT–?

TRACY CLUTCHES THE DOOR HANDLE!

HE YANKS! HIS BRAIN REELS! HIS VISION BLURS! HE BRACES HIMSELF–

CHESTER GOULD

THE BABY'S **NOT HERE**– SHE–SHE'S **GONE!**

NOT IN THE TRUNK– OR ANYWHERE!

UPHOLSTERY TORN– EVERYTHING A WRECK. THE BAG OF BABY'S THINGS RIPPED AND CHEWED.

THE WORK OF FOREST ANIMALS! UNMISTAKABLE SIGNS OF THEM.
HAVE THE COYOTES–? NO–NO! THEY **COULDN'T!**

CHESTER GOULD

LET'S KEEP BACK FROM THE CAR. WE MUST AVOID DESTROYING ANY TRACKS THAT MAY BE ON THE SURROUNDING GROUND.

EVERYTHING'S IN RUINS, AND BONNY BRAIDS IS **NOT HERE!** WHAT? NO, THANK HEAVEN–NO SIGNS OF BLOOD.
2-WAY WRIST RADIO

IT'S GETTING DUSK. BRING US SOME PORTABLE SPOT LIGHTS WITH EXTENSION CORDS.

WE'LL SEARCH THE GROUND FOR TRACKS, USING **OBLIQUE LIGHT!** THE BABY'S BEEN CARRIED AWAY!

CHESTER GOULD

THE CAR HAS BEEN FOUND– THAT'S ALL THE BULLETIN SAID! THERE WAS NO MENTION OF THE BABY.

MEANWHILE, DIET SMITH'S HELICOPTER IS LOWERING PORTABLE LIGHTS TO TRACY AND THE MEN.

TRACKS THAT ARE INVISIBLE, EVEN IN SUNLIGHT, OFTEN SHOW UP IN OBLIQUE LIGHT.

THIS MOUNTAIN IS ALMOST SOLID STONE, BUT WE'LL SEARCH THE DIRT PATCHES AROUND THE CAR.

CHESTER GOULD

LOOK–ISN'T THAT A MAN'S SHOE PRINT?
YES– YOURS. SEE THAT IMPRINT OF YOUR RUBBER HEEL?

BUT HERE'S ANOTHER ONE! IT DOESN'T BELONG TO ANY OF US. THE SOLE AND HEEL ARE ALMOST ONE.

HE STOOD AT THE CAR–THEN TURNED IN THIS DIRECTION.
WE'VE PICKED UP THE SAME TRACKS OVER HERE, TRACY.

CHESTER GOULD

WHAT WAS THAT NOISE? SEEMED TO COME FROM FAR AWAY.
SOUNDED LIKE THE BLEAT OF A **GOAT** TO ME.

IF ONLY THERE WAS SOME WORD WE COULD PASS ALONG TO TESS.

NOTHING SPECIFIC YET. PAT—BUT THERE'S HOPE! SOMEBODY APPROACHED THE CAR AND LEFT TRACKS. WE'RE FOLLOWING THEM—THAT IS, THE ONES WE CAN FIND.
HEAR THAT? A GOAT?
2-WAY WRIST RADIO

MEANWHILE, IN THE AIR ABOVE TRACY, DIET SMITH TALKS TO HIS PILOT.
LOOK THROUGH THESE GLASSES, DAN. SEE IF YOU SEE WHAT I SEE.

THE CORNER OF A ROOF? YEAH—THAT'S WHAT IT IS!
CHESTER GOULD

A SEARCH OF THE GROUND AROUND THE CAR IN OBLIQUE LIGHT REVEALED ANIMAL TRACKS AS WELL AS THOSE OF A **MAN**.

FOLLOWING THE TRACKS IS VERY DIFFICULT AS THE GROUND IS STONY, BUT WE'RE MAKING PROGRESS.

THE FACT THAT THE CHILD HAS NOT BEEN FOUND DEAD IS—AT LEAST—HOPEFUL.
2-WAY WRIST RADIO

THEY'VE PICKED UP THE TRACKS AGAIN, TRACY, OVER TO THE NORTH.

THE SHOES WOULD APPEAR TO HAVE BEEN HOMEMADE—AND RATHER LARGE.

TRACY, THIS IS DIET SMITH. WE'RE OVER A SPOT ABOUT HALF A MILE NORTH OF YOU. **WE THINK WE'VE SPOTTED A SHACK!**

WE'RE GOING DOWN TO GET A BETTER LOOK.
OKAY. WE HEAR YOUR MOTOR. WE'LL FOLLOW.

AND BACK IN THE CITY, TESS WAITS—AS HOPE FADES.
THE CAR WAS A WRECK—INSIDE AND OUTSIDE! THERE WERE NO SIGNS OF THE BABY.

A TORN BLANKET AND' NURSING BOTTLES, FOUND AS FAR AS 60 FEET FROM THE CAR, REVEALED ANIMALS HAD—
TURN IT OFF! TURN IT OFF!

TRACY, **LOOK!**
IT **IS** A SHACK!

BAAA

HERE! BETTER LET HER HAVE THIS WHILE IT'S WARM.

THE WARM GOAT'S MILK SAVED HER LIFE, MA.
THE COLOR'S BACK IN HER CHEEKS, MA, AND SHE SMILES.
THAT'S WHERE THE GOAT'S VOICE IS COMING FROM!
BAAA
CHESTER GOULD
I HEAR FOOTSTEPS— SOMEBODY'S COMING.
EXCUSE ME—BUT I WONDERED IF YOU—
CHESTER GOULD
A FINE WAY TO ENTER A BODY'S HOUSE! NONE OF YE EVEN KNOCKED.
WE'RE SORRY, MA'M. YOU SEE—
WHO IS HE?
OUTSIDE! OUTSIDE, ALL OF YE!
SHE SAID ALL OF YE!
CHESTER GOULD
BUT SHE'S HIS CHILD.
SHE WAS TAKEN AWAY BY AUTOMOBILE. THE NEWS HAS BEEN ON RADIO—IN THE NEWSPAPERS. HAVEN'T YOU HEARD?
WE DON'T BELIEVE IN RADIOS OR AUTOMOBILES, BUT WE DO BELIEVE IN SAVING A HUMAN LIFE. WE SAVED HERS.
AND NOW, SHE'S OURS! WE'RE KEEPING HER!
CHESTER GOULD
HERE'S A PICTURE OF HER—WITH HER MOTHER AND ME.
NOW, DO YOU BELIEVE SHE'S HIS?
LOWER THE GUN, PA.
PA WENT 'COON HUNTING ONE NIGHT. HE HEARD CRIES. HE FOUND HER. SHE WAS DYING. WE FED HER GOAT'S MILK.
HERE— TAKE 'ER.
MEANWHILE, OUTSIDE.
IT'S NEWSPAPER PHOTOGRAPHERS AND DIET SMITH.
OUR CONVERSATION HAS BEEN GOING OUT ON THE 2-WAY WRIST RADIO.
CHESTER GOULD

WE WANT A SHOT OF THE TWO OF YOU—WITH THE GOAT.

YOU'VE SAVED HER LIFE. I CAN NEVER REPAY YOU.

YOU MUST BOTH COME TO THE CITY WITH US. YOU'LL BE HEROES. I WANT TO REWARD YOU SOME WAY.

WE JUST DONE OUR DUTY, ME AND PA! WE'RE STAYING RIGHT HERE.
CHESTER GOULD

SEARCH STILL HOPEFUL!

2-WAY WRIST RADIO

ONE HOUR

MODEL

by Chester Gould

1/23/52–3/27/52

Because the 1950s are such a strong and under-reprinted period of Gould's work, and because these years have a special meaning to the editors of this volume, we have chosen to include a second fifties continuity.

The uncharacteristically brief "Model" story harks back slightly to the earlier soap-opera period of *Dick Tracy*'s formative thirties. Significantly, in those years, Tracy's adoptive son Junior, an urchin who wanted to be a detective like his father, was a major character. By the early fifties, this male Orphan Annie was outdated, and Gould decided to bring Junior "of age." Junior, with his wacky hacked-off haircut, is suddenly a teenager, and in meeting the sweet, lovely Model Jones at a skating rink, has his first romance.

This tender story reveals that the hard-boiled, right-wing Gould was not unaffected by certain social concerns of the times. Model's brother Larry is a j.d. who loots parking meters, and their parents are alcoholics. Gould places the responsibility for Larry's actions clearly at his parents' feet.

While this love story may seem a departure for Gould, he does not cut back on the violence or the action; a rooftop chase, near the end of the story, shows the detective in fine heroic form. Tracy's world is a precarious one, where anything can happen, and even the most sympathetic of creatures can fall prey to crime.

And if Gould, during this period, was putting his emphasis on the story, in response to the shrinking size his work (and the work of his fellow cartoonists) was suffering at the hands of newspaper editors, he does not shirk his artistic responsibilities. Note the moving sequence when Junior is rebuffed by his girl; the bleak, expressionistic winter landscape Junior slouch-shoulderedly moves through is hauntingly evocative of the boy's mental state. Some of the best writing in comics is done through silent panels, as witness the sequences in which a despondent Model slumps in her seat on the bus while in the adjacent panel Junior watches dejectedly as the bus recedes in the distance.

SCENE: ONE OF THOSE QUONSET HUT SKATING RINKS.
ROLLER RINK
ANDY'S
PARADISE
I WONDER IF SHE'LL BE BACK AGAIN.
SO DANCE ME LOOSE
MODEL! YOU KEPT YOUR WORD LIKE YOU SAID YOU WOULD!
SURE! LET'S SKATE.
DON'T HOLD THE ARM SO EXTRA OUT.
CHESTER GOULD
GEE, MODEL, YOU'RE SURE A SWELL GIRL. CAN I TAKE YOU HOME?
OH, IT'S NOT VERY FAR. I CAN WALK.
DA DA DA DA
SO DANCE ME LOOSE
CAN I WALK WITH YOU?
IF YOU WANT TO.
ROLLER RINK
ANDY'S
PARADISE
CHESTER GOULD
MEANWHILE, IN ANOTHER PART OF TOWN.
LISTEN, YOUR SISTER ALWAYS HAS DOUGH. GET SOME FROM HER. WHERE IS SHE?
SKATING.
BUMP IT AGAIN, THEN PULL BACK.
THAT MAKES TWO OF 'EM.
I THOUGHT YOU WERE GOING TO YOUR SISTER AND GET DOUGH FOR GAS BEFORE, WE START THE NIGHT'S WORK.
CHESTER GOULD
"I AM! BUT FIRST, I WANTED TO KNOCK OFF THESE TWO METERS BEFORE THE BEAT COP COMES AROUND AGAIN."
GEE, MODEL, YOU SKATE SWELL.
MEANWHILE—
I TELL YOU, TESS, HE'S GOT A GIRL.
ARE YOU JUST FINDING THAT OUT?

HERE'S WHAT I DIDN'T TELL YOU, TESS. I FOLLOWED HIM.

YOU MEAN YOU FOLLOWED JUNIOR?
I COULDN'T RESIST. I SAW HIM ENTER THE SKATING RINK.

MAKE YOUR SISTER LOAN YOU THE DOUGH, LARRY! WE'LL WAIT FOR YOU.
ANDY'S
PARADISE
CHESTER GOULD

GEE, MODEL, YOU'RE WONDERFUL!

YES, TESS, THE KID'S GOT A GIRL SOMEWHERE. JUNIOR HAS CHANGED.
I'VE NOTICED IT, TOO, DICK.

COMBING HIS HAIR, WASHING HIS NECK, AND SHINING HIS SHOES. ONLY A GIRL COULD MAKE HIM DO ALL THAT!
BUT WHY MUST HE MEET HER AT A SKATING RINK?

"I DIDN'T ASK ANY QUESTIONS," SAYS TRACY. "ALL I KNOW IS I FOLLOWED AND SAW HIM GO THERE. I SUPPOSE THAT'S WHERE THEY MEET."
ANDY'S
ROLLER RINK
PARADISE

SHALL WE SIT DOWN AWHILE, MODEL?
WHY NOT? OH, BOY!

HOW ABOUT A COKE?
OH, I'D LOVE ONE.
AHA! THERE YOU ARE!

WH-? OH, JUNIOR, THIS IS MY BROTHER LARRY—
LISTEN, LET ME HAVE A COUPLE OF DOLLARS, WILL YOU, SIS? I KNOW YOU'VE GOT 'EM— GIVE!

A COUPLE OF DOLLARS? I WILL NOT!
HUH? YOU GIVE ME 2 BUCKS, BEFORE I SMACK YOU.

HEY! BROTHER OR NOT— YOU CAN'T DO THAT TO HER!
WHY, YOU GOOFY-LOOKIN' LITTLE JERK—

HERE'S THE MONEY— NOW, STOP IT! STOP IT!

FOR GOSH SAKE, MODEL, WHAT KIND OF A BROTHER IS THAT?

OKAY, WE'VE GOT MONEY! NOW, WE CAN GET SOME GAS.
PARADISE

I'LL PULL IN AT THE FIRST FILLING STATION! KEEP YOUR WINDOWS ROLLED SHUT, BOYS!
THEY'RE FOGGED UP! AND THAT WAY, NOBODY CAN SEE INSIDE.

GOSH, MODEL, IF YOU HADN'T GIVEN HIM THE 2 DOLLARS, HE WOULD HAVE SMASHED YOU! WHAT A BROTHER!

THINK NOTHING OF IT, JUNIOR—HE'S REALLY A GOOD BROTHER. I—I'VE SPOILED HIM, I GUESS.

AND A SHORT DISTANCE AWAY!
THERE! NOW, WE'VE GOT GAS.
CHESTER GOULD

LET'S KNOCK OFF A COUPLE MORE METERS BEFORE WE HEAD OUT IN THE COUNTRY TO BUST 'EM OPEN.
YEAH, THAT'LL MAKE IT WORTH WHILE.

ALL I KNOW IS IT WAS A RED CAR. I FIRED OVER THEIR HEADS. THEN, I TRIED TO HIT A TIRE.

THAT'S TEN PARKING METERS IN THE LAST 3 NIGHTS.

LATER— ALONG A COUNTRY ROAD.
WOW! YOU CAN PAY YOUR SISTER BACK HER 2 BUCKS AND HAVE TEN LEFT OVER, LARRY!
NUTS TO HER!

STILL LATER.
THIS IS WHERE I LIVE.
GOSH, MODEL, IT'S SURE BEEN NICE SKATING WITH YOU. CAN I SEE YOU AGAIN?

ALL RIGHT— THERE'S THE PENNIES—THERE'S THE NICKELS, AND THERE'S THE DIMES.
WE'LL DRAW STRAWS.

THE LONGEST STRAW GETS THE DIMES, NEXT THE NICKELS, NEXT THE PENNIES.
DRAW.

MEANWHILE—
MODEL! YOU JUS' GETTIN' IN?
YES, MOTHER. IT'S ONLY ELEVEN.
CHESTER GOULD

R'MEMBER, YOU'VE GOT A JOB AND HAVE TO BE UP EARLY.
YEAH, AN' DON'T EVER FORGET THAT.

HE WAS WASHING BEHIND HIS EARS, TOO. HE'S NEVER DONE THAT BEFORE WITHOUT BEING TOLD.

SAY, I SMELL PERFUME—OR IS THAT HAIR STICKEM?
IT'S HAIR STICKEM.
CHESTER GOULD

IF I DIDN'T KNOW YOU SO WELL, I'D SAY YOU ACTED LIKE A GUY FALLING IN LOVE.
WHO, ME?

JUNIOR! YOU'RE POURING THE SYRUP IN THE SUGAR BOWL!

LARRY, MODEL DOESN'T GET PAID TILL MONDAY. HAVE YOU GOT ANY EXTRA DOUGH FOR YOUR MOM AND ME?
DOUGH?

SURE! TWO THOUSAND PENNIES! COUNT 'EM AND YOU CAN HAVE 'EM.
PENNIES? WHERE DID YOU GET PENNIES, SON?
PLOP

DON'T ASK SILLY QUESTIONS! COUNT 'EM UP! IT'LL GIVE YOU SOMETHING TO DO BETWEEN DRINKS.
TWO THOUSAND PENNIES!

MEANWHILE —
JUNIOR! YOU SHOULDN'T HAVE COME HERE TO THE STORE.
WHY NOT, MODEL? GOSH, I JUST HAD TO SEE YOU
CHESTER GOULD

GOSH, YOU SURE ARE A WONDERFUL GIRL, MODEL. I'D LIKE TO MEET YOUR FOLKS.

YOU'D BETTER NOT COME UP, JUNIOR. YOU SEE, DAD AND MOTHER WORK REAL HARD AND THEY GO TO BED EARLY.

CHESTER GOULD

HOW CAN I EVER TELL HIM?

GOT A GIRL, EH, KID?
YEAH, KINDA.

WHO IS SHE?
NAME'S MODEL JONES—SHE WORKS AT GIMMEL'S STORE.

SOUNDS LIKE A FINE GIRL. WHERE DOES SHE LIVE?
OUT ON LAKE STREET.

BRING HER TO THE HOUSE SOME TIME! THIS HOME IS FOR YOUR FRIENDS AS MUCH AS IT IS FOR OURS—EH, TESS?
OH, YES.
THANKS, FOLKS.

GOSH, MODEL'S A WONDERFUL GIRL! 'S FUNNY SHE NEVER INVITES ME IN. I ALWAYS HAVE TO LEAVE HER AT THE DOOR. DARN IT.

MEANWHILE, AT THE HOME OF MODEL JONES.
BUT, DADDY, I CALLED YOU 3 TIMES. I'VE GOT TO GO TO WORK. I'LL BE LATE AT THE STORE.

WHAT? AGAIN? SURELY, MODEL, YOU CAN TAKE TIME AT LEAST TO FIX YOUR FATHER A CUP OF COFFEE!
MOTHER! LOOK AT THE CLOCK. DO YOU WANT ME TO LOSE MY JOB?

I'VE GOT TO GO TO WORK! GOOD-BY.

LARRY! AT THIS HOUR?
CAN THE GAB! I KNOW WHAT YOU'RE THINKING—THAT I WON'T PAY YOU THE 2 BUCKS I BORROWED.

WELL, HERE IT IS! LOOK, LITTLE SIS, I'M LOADED!
WHAT? ALL IN NICKELS?

YEAH, IN NICKELS! DO YOU WANT YOUR DOUGH, OR DON'T YOU?

SIX MORE PARKING METERS—THAT MAKES A TOTAL OF 12.

YOU'D THINK SHE COULD FIX BREAKFAST FOR HER PARENTS BEFORE GOING TO WORK! SHE'S SO INCONSIDERATE!

AND AT THE FOOT OF THE STAIRS, MODEL MEETS HER BROTHER.

SO, NOW—I'VE PAID YOU BACK—ALL IN NICKELS.

YOU DIDN'T ANSWER MY QUESTION—**WHERE DID YOU GET THOSE NICKELS?**

AW, GO ON TO WORK AND MIND YOUR OWN BUSINESS! I'M GONNA SLEEP.

NICKELS? A WHOLE **BAG** OF NICKELS?

KEEP YOUR MITTS OFF 'EM, POP, BEFORE I BREAK YOUR WRISTS!

CHESTER GOULD

YES, I UNDERSTAND ABOUT THE NICKELS NOW, LARRY! I READ ALL ABOUT IT ON MY WAY TO WORK.

YOUNG PARKING METER THIEVES STRIKE AGAIN

NOW, I KNOW WHERE YOU **GOT** THEM.

WHAT ARE YOU TALKING ABOUT? YOU LITTLE FEMALE JERK!

WHY DON'T YOU GET YOUR **BABY-FACED BOY FRIEND** AND GO SKATING—AND KEEP YOUR NOSE **OUT** OF MY BUSINESS!

MEANWHILE—

GOSH, MODEL'S SUCH A FINE GIRL! BET SHE'S GOT WONDERFUL PARENTS. I'VE GOT TO MEET THEM.

CHESTER GOULD

THIS PARKING METER BANDITRY IS TAKING ON MAJOR PROPORTIONS, TRACY. WE'VE GOT TO GO AFTER THEM.

THE BOYS BROUGHT IN A LOG CHAIN THEY LEFT BEHIND. THEY SAY THEY'RE YOUNG KIDS—THREE OF 'EM.

MEANWHILE—

GOSH, MODEL, I'M CRAZY ABOUT YOU! BUT YOU DON'T ACT LIKE YOURSELF TONIGHT. WHAT'S WRONG?

OH—NOTHING

PARADISE

"INCIDENTALLY, I'VE MET ONLY YOUR BROTHER. I SURE WOULD LIKE TO MEET YOUR DAD AND MOTHER. HOW ABOUT IT?" ASKS JUNIOR.

CHESTER GOULD

HE LIKES ME—BUT HE DOESN'T KNOW THE TRUTH ABOUT MY FAMILY. I CAN'T FOOL HIM ANY LONGER!

IF HE STILL LIKES ME AFTER MEETING MY PARENTS, I'LL KNOW HE REALLY CARES.

MODEL IS COMING UP WITH A BOY FRIEND! THINK I'LL DUCK OUT THE BACK DOOR.

A **BOY FRIEND**? THE **NERVE** OF HER! IF SHE SHOULD GET MARRIED, WHAT WOULD MAW AND I DO? SHE'S OUR ONLY SUPPORT.

SO LONG.

CHESTER GOULD

STICK 'EM UP, BOYS! FINALLY, I'VE CAUGHT YOU PARKING METER THIEVES!

WAITED FOR YOU 5 NIGHTS—I KNEW YOU'D BE AROUND.

BANG

LARRY! YOU KILLED HIM!
LET'S GO.
CHESTER GOULD

JUNIOR, I'VE BEEN THINKING ABOUT YOU ALL DAY—THERE'S SOMETHING I'VE GOT TO TELL YOU.
AND I'VE BEEN THINKING ABOUT YOU, MODEL.

I'M CRAZY ABOUT YOU. I CAN'T THINK ABOUT ANYTHING ELSE.
SAY! YOU'RE SHAKING! AND ARE THOSE TEARS?

OH, JUNIOR!
MODEL, I LOVE YOU! I LOVE YOU AN AWFUL LOT! LET'S GET MARRIED!

MARRIED? NO—OH, NO! YOU—YOU DON'T KNOW ANYTHING ABOUT ME—OR MY FAMILY! BESIDES, OUR AGES—
WELL, I TRIED TO MEET YOUR DAD, BUT HE TOSSED ME DOWNSTAIRS.

ANYWAY—IT'S YOU I LOVE, MODEL. I DON'T CARE WHAT YOUR FAMILY THINKS OF ME! THEY'LL LEARN TO LIKE ME.
IT'S NOT THAT, JUNIOR—IT'S NOT THAT—

MEANWHILE, AT MODEL JONES'S HOME.
THAT'S ALL—JUST SEE TO IT THAT SISTER OF MINE KEEPS HER NOSE OUT OF MY BUSINESS!

LARRY, DON'T TALK THAT WAY ABOUT MODEL. WHY, SHE'S OUR BREAD AND BUTTER. WHAT IF SHE GETS MAD AND LEAVES HOME?

LISTEN, DON'T ASK ME ANY QUESTIONS—JUST KEEP HER OUT OF MY WAY! THIS TIME IT'S SERIOUS.
WHAT DO YOU MEAN, LARRY?

I HAD TO USE THIS TONIGHT.
PACK A BAG FOR ME, MAW. I'LL BE MINUS AROUND HERE FOR A COUPLE OF WEEKS.
WHAT?

I KNOW A STATE WHERE WE CAN GO AND GET MARRIED! WE'LL TAKE A BUS. I'VE GOT ENOUGH MONEY. I WANT TO MARRY YOU, MODEL.

OH, JUNIOR, LET'S GO! LET'S TAKE THE BUS RIGHT AWAY!

YOU MEAN YOU HAD TO SHOOT SOMEONE?
YOU HEARD ME, MAW! NOW, GET MY GRIP PACKED. I'VE GOT TO DISAPPEAR.
TSK TSK!

OH, LARRY, I WISH YOU'D BE MORE CAREFUL! WHAT WILL MODEL SAY? YOU KNOW HOW DAD AND I DEPEND ON HER.
NUTS TO MODEL!

MEANWHILE—
YES, JUNIOR, I'LL GO WITH YOU ANYWHERE—ANYWHERE AT ALL.
CHESTER GOULD

I CHECKED UP ON THE DIFFERENT STATES. THIS PLACE WE'RE GOING TO IS ONLY AN OVERNIGHT BUS RIDE. WE'LL GET MARRIED TOMORROW.

SO LONG, NOW. I'LL PHONE THAT BRAT SISTER OF MINE LATER WHERE SHE CAN MEET ME TO BRING ME DOUGH.

THEY'LL NEVER FIND ME.
Daily Paper
POLICEMAN SLAIN BY PARKING METER GOONS

GOING AWAY TO GET MARRIED! I NEVER KNEW IT COULD BE SO WONDERFUL.
ANOTHER $1.10 PLEASE.

HERE, I'VE GOT ALMOST TEN DOLLARS. HELP YOURSELF.
GOSH. THANKS, MODEL
CHESTER GOULD

A COUPLE OF EXCELLENT FOOTPRINTS IN THE SNOW. WHERE'S THE PLASTER CASTING OUTFIT?
IT'S IN THE TRUNK OF MY CAR AT HOME.

TESS, HAVE JUNIOR RUN DOWN TO HEADQUARTERS WITH MY PLASTER KIT.
JUNIOR ISN'T HERE, DICK. HE HASN'T BEEN HOME SINCE MORNING.

AND ON A CROSS-COUNTRY BUS—
I ONLY HOPE YOU'LL NEVER BE SORRY, JUNIOR, THAT YOU ASKED ME, TO MARRY YOU.
GOSH, MODEL, I'LL ALWAYS LOVE YOU.
CHESTER GOULD

JUST TO BE WITH YOU ALWAYS, AND AWAY FROM—FROM—
WE'LL GET AN APARTMENT. THEN LATER, WE'LL HAVE OUR OWN HOUSE.

GOSH, ANOTHER 4 HOURS AND WE'LL BE MR. AND MRS. TRACY.
IT SEEMS LIKE A DREAM.

I WISH WE WEREN'T EVER GOING BACK! I WANT TO BE JUST WITH YOU.
BUT WE'LL HAVE TO TELL YOUR PARENTS AND MY FOLKS.

MEANWHILE—
HE PROBABLY GOT SOME EXTRA WORK AT THE SUPER MARKET.
BUT HE ALWAYS CALLS WHEN HE WON'T BE HOME.

WHERE ARE YOU GOING NOW?
BACK TO THE LAB. WE'RE DOING A BALLISTICS CHECK ON THAT PARKING METER KILLING. SEE YOU ABOUT NINE.
CHESTER GOULD

FAR AS THE BUS GOES. TRANSFER FOR POINTS WEST.

IT'S AN HOUR BEFORE THE NEXT BUS. HOW ABOUT A SANDWICH?
YUMMY!
EATS

TO HECK WITH THE NEWS, CHARLIE. GET SOME MORE MUSIC.
OKAY, KID.
CHESTER GOULD

AND IN A RADIO STATION STUDIO.
IT'S THE LATEST POLICE BULLETIN ON THAT PARKING METER KILLING. WANT IT?
GIVE.

NEWS, NOTHING BUT NEWS.
GOSH, MODEL, WHAT ARE YOU THINKING, HONEY?

JUNIOR, AFTER WE'RE MARRIED, WILL YOU ALWAYS LOVE ME—NO MATTER WHAT HAPPENS?
WILL I? FOREVER AND EVER, HONEY!

AND NOW, FOR THE LATEST POLICE BULLETIN ON THE MURDER OF POLICEMAN MURPHY BY YOUNG PARKING METER BANDITS.
CHESTER GOULD

AN EYEWITNESS HAS BEEN FOUND, AN EMPLOYEE OF A LOCAL DAIRY COMPANY WHO SAW THE SHOOTING. IN JUST A MOMENT, A DESCRIPTION OF THE KILLER.
!

SCENE: A ROADSIDE STOPOVER ON A CROSS-COUNTRY BUS LINE.
I'M ABOUT FILLED UP, JUNIOR, BUT I COULD EAT A CINNAMON ROLL.
GAS
EATS

I'M GOING TO HAVE A CINNAMON ROLL, TOO, AND SOME ICE CREAM.
WE MUST BE SURE NOT TO FORGET THE BUS.

OH, WE WON'T! GOSH, MODEL, DEAR, JUST THINK, ANOTHER TWO HOURS BUS RIDE AND WE'LL GET MARRIED!

—AND A POLICEMAN WAS SHOT AND KILLED YESTERDAY EVENING BY YOUTHFUL PARKING METER BANDITS.

THESE PARKING METER THIEVES, OPERATING FOR SEVERAL WEEKS, WERE FINALLY CAUGHT RED-HANDED BY OFFICER TIM O'LANE, WHO WAS SUBSEQUENTLY SHOT TO DEATH.

AN EYE-WITNESS DESCRIBED THE GUNMAN AS BLOND WITH WAVY HAIR, AND ABOUT 5 FEET, FOUR INCHES IN HEIGHT.
MODEL! WHERE ARE YOU GOING?

HONEY!
JUNIOR, WE MUST GO BACK HOME!
WHAT?

I CAN'T MARRY YOU, JUNIOR—I JUST CAN'T! IT WOULDN'T BE FAIR!
WHAT WOULDN'T BE FAIR?

MODEL, HONEY, WHAT HAS MADE YOU CHANGE YOUR MIND? I LOVE YOU, MODEL—I LOVE YOU!

I LOVE YOU, TOO, JUNIOR, BUT WE CAN'T MARRY—WE CAN'T—
WHY, HONEY? WHY—WHY?

AND BACK IN THE CITY, UNAWARE OF THE INTERLOCKING NATURE OF EVENTS.
THERE ARE THE METERS, AND WE GOT TWO CASTS. SAY! WHAT'S EATING YOU?
JUNIOR'S NOT COMING HOME LAST NIGHT HAS KINDA GOT ME, I GUESS.
WHAT?

AND IN ANOTHER PART OF TOWN.
I'M AT THE CIGAR STORE. WHEN THAT NO-GOOD SISTER OF MINE GETS BACK, HAVE HER BRING ME SOME DOUGH—YEAH, HERE!

AS A DESCRIPTION OF THE PARKING METER KILLER COMES OVER THE RADIO, MODEL RUNS WILDLY FROM THE BUS STATION.

BUT WE WERE GOING TO GET MARRIED! WHAT MADE YOU CHANGE YOUR MIND?
ME MARRY YOU? AH, HA, HA!

UNAWARE THAT MODEL HAS JUST HEARD A RADIO DESCRIPTION OF HER BROTHER, JUNIOR IS AMAZED.
NO, I SEE IT ALL NOW! THIS IS SILLY!

ME? MARRY A LITTLE CRIMESTOPPER LIKE YOU? OH, HA, HA, HA! NO, IT'S ALL OFF. I'M GOING BACK HOME!
CHESTER GOULD

HA, HA! I CAN'T KEEP FROM LAUGHING, BUT IT JUST DAWNED ON ME MARRYING A KID LIKE YOU WOULD BE CRAZY.

BUT YOU'RE NOT REALLY LAUGHING, MODEL— THOSE ARE TEARS!
I'M LAUGHING SO HARD, I'M CRYING.

YOU SAID YOU LOVED ME! YOU SAID SO—YOU KNOW YOU DID! AND I LOVE YOU, MODEL!
CHESTER GOULD

GOOD-BY, SONNY!

YOU SAID YOU'D MARRY ME, MODEL! YOU KNOW YOU DID!

SO LONG, SQUIRT!

I HAD TO DO IT—I HAD TO DO IT!
CHESTER GOULD

I JUST COULDN'T GET YOU MIXED UP WITH THAT AWFUL FAMILY OF MINE! I-I LOVE YOU TOO MUCH! I'LL ALWAYS LOVE YOU— ALWAYS, ALWAYS, AND ALWAYS!

MY BROTHER A MURDERER! MY PARENTS DRUNKARDS. I COULDN'T MARRY YOU AND GET YOU MIXED UP WITH THEM. I COULDN'T!

PERHAPS, SOME DAY, YOU'LL KNOW—PERHAPS—

CHESTER GOULD

JUST A SQUIRT! THAT'S WHAT MODEL CALLED ME! SAID MARRYING A KID LIKE ME WOULD BE SILLY!

HOW CAN I TELL TRACY I WAS RUNNING AWAY TO GET MARRIED? HE'LL LAUGH AT ME, TOO.

AND BACK AT HEADQUARTERS.
THE MILK DRIVER WHO WAS EYEWITNESS TO THE METER KILLING IS HERE, TRACY.
CHESTER GOULD

HE'S GOING TO DESCRIBE THE KILLER, WHILE JUNIOR MAKES A SKETCH.
JUNIOR'S BEEN GONE SINCE YESTERDAY. I DON'T KNOW WHAT TO THINK, SAM.

JUNIOR!
HE STUMBLED IN HERE ABOUT 3 A.M. BEEN WALKING ALL NIGHT.

WHAT KIND OF SHENANIGANS HAS HE BEEN UP TO? WAKE HIM, MURPHY.

MODEL, IS THAT YOU?
(SOB) BOO-HOO-HOO! (SOB) BOO-HOO!

OH, BOO-HOO! (SOB) BOO-HOO-HOO!
CHESTER GOULD

WELL, IF YOU DON'T WANT TO TELL ME ABOUT IT, OKAY. BUT DON'T EVER GO AWAY LIKE THAT AGAIN WITHOUT LETTING US KNOW.

TESS WAS UP ALL NIGHT PACING THE FLOOR. I WAS WORRIED, TOO. TELL ME, WAS IT OVER A GIRL?
KINDA.

IS EVERYTHING ALL RIGHT? YOU'RE NOT IN TROUBLE?
NO, I'M FINE.

ALL RIGHT, THEN LET'S GO TO WORK.
THE EYEWITNESS WHO SAW THAT PARKING METER THIEF KILL A POLICEMAN IS INSIDE.

YOU DESCRIBE THE GUNMAN TO JUNIOR, AND HE WILL SKETCH HIM.
WELL, TO START WITH, HE HAD WAVY HAIR.

THE HAIR WASN'T PARTED, IT WAS JUST BRUSHED UP—

MEANWHILE—
BUT YOUR JOB! MAYBE YOU'LL LOSE YOUR JOB AND YOUR POOR SICK MOM AND I WILL STARVE.
WHAT DIFFERENCE WOULD IT MAKE? I WISH WE WERE ALL DEAD!

MODEL, WHAT ARE YOU SAYING?
AND YOUR BROTHER'S EXPECTING YOU TO BRING HIM SOME MONEY AT THE CIGAR STORE! MODEL, WHAT'S COME OVER YOU?

SEVERAL HOURS LATER—
AND NOW, THE DARK SHIRT!

THAT'S A DEAD RINGER FOR THE KILLER!
HUH? NO! OH, NO!

I MET HIM ONLY ONCE AT THE SKATING RINK, BUT THAT'S HIM! I DREW MODEL'S BROTHER!
WHAT AILS HIM?

SO THAT'S WHY SHE WOULDN'T MARRY ME! THAT NEWSCAST IN THE HAMBURGER STAND—I SEE IT ALL NOW! GOSH, MODEL, YOU REALLY DO LOVE ME—
HEY, KID!

AS THE EYEWITNESS TALKS JUNIOR SKETCHES, THEN SUDDENLY REALIZES HE HAS SKETCHED MODEL'S BROTHER!

ALL I KNOW IS I WAS TALKING, WHEN HE SUDDENLY GOT UP AND RAN OUT ON THE FIRE ESCAPE.

NOW, WHAT SHALL I DO? SHALL I TELL THEM IT'S THE BROTHER OF THE GIRL I **LOVE**?

I MUST BE **SURE** FIRST! I MUST HAVE PROOF! I'LL GO AND **ASK** MODEL!

CHESTER GOULD

I'LL GO TO MODEL AND ASK HER IF HER BROTHER REALLY IS THE PARKING METER KILLER.

BUT I WON'T TELL TRACY OR ANY OF 'EM WHAT I THINK TILL I'M **SURE**.

JUNIOR! HEY—

MEANWHILE, MODEL, BROKEN AND DESPONDENT, GETS ORDERS FROM HER DRUNKEN FATHER.

YOU'VE GOT TO MEET YOUR BROTHER AND GIVE HIM SOME MONEY.

CHESTER GOULD

HE NEEDS DOUGH. HE SAID HE'D BE WAITING FOR YOU AT THE CIGAR STORE.

ALL RIGHT, BUT THIS IS THE LAST TIME. I **HATE** HIM! I HATE **ALL** OF YOU!

ORDERED TO MEET HER FUGITIVE BROTHER TO GIVE HIM MONEY, MODEL APPROACHES THE APPOINTED PLACE.

I WISH I WERE DEAD—

CIGARS & TOBACCO

Smoke

WHERE?

CHESTER GOULD

HERE IN THE PHONE BOOTH, YOU DOPE!

WHERE'S THE DOUGH?

MODEL MEETS HER FUGITIVE BROTHER, ANGERED AND HEARTBROKEN.

TWO BUCKS? IS THAT ALL YOU'VE GOT?

THAT'S ALL.

LARRY, WHY DON'T YOU GIVE YOURSELF UP BEFORE IT'S TOO LATE—BEFORE THE POLICE KILL YOU?

I OUGHT TO SMACK YOU, MODEL. I ASKED YOU TO BRING ME **DOUGH**, AND YOU BRING ME A LECTURE! **WHY, YOU LITTLE—**

MEANWHILE, JUNIOR KNOCKS ON THE DOOR OF MODEL'S PARENTS' APARTMENT.

SHE'S GOT TO TELL ME.

WHOSH THERE? (HIC)

CHESTER GOULD

WHAT CHA WANT?
I'D LIKE TO SEE MODEL. I'M JUNIOR TRACY.

WAIT, MR. JONES. I'LL HELP YOU TO A CHAIR.
MODEL AIN'T HOME. WHO'D Y'SAY Y'ARE?

I'M JUNIOR TRACY.
JUNER JACY? YOU'RE A GOOD BOY JUNER—GOOD BOY.

MEANWHILE, MODEL IS RETURNING HOME FROM THE MEETING WITH HER BROTHER, LARRY.
I'LL PACK A FEW THINGS AND TAKE A BUS TO THE COAST! I'LL RUN AWAY FROM ALL THIS.
CHESTER GOULD

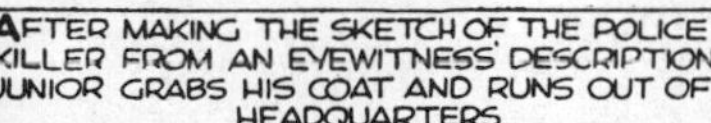
AFTER MAKING THE SKETCH OF THE POLICE KILLER FROM AN EYEWITNESS' DESCRIPTION, JUNIOR GRABS HIS COAT AND RUNS OUT OF HEADQUARTERS.

I CAN'T UNDERSTAND IT!
HE SAID NOTHING, HE JUST RAN OUT.

DID THE SKETCH REMIND HIM OF SOMEONE? WHY WOULD HE BE SO AFFECTED?

MEANWHILE—
BUT I ONLY WANT TO SEE MODEL FOR JUST A MINUTE. WHEN WILL SHE BE BACK?

I TOL' YOU MODEL AIN'T HERE—'AT'S ALL—SHE AIN'T HERE—
THEY TOLD ME AT THE STORE SHE'D QUIT HER JOB—OH! I HEAR SOMEONE ON THE STAIRS.

MODEL!

I UNDERSTAND EVERYTHING NOW.
JUNIOR! OH, JUNIOR!

I'VE NO TIME TO LOSE—I MUST ASK YOU ONE QUESTION—
IS YOUR BROTHER THE POLICE KILLER?

YES, JUNIOR! YES! MY FAMILY'S NO GOOD! YOU SHOULDN'T HAVE COME HERE!
WHAT'S GOING ON HERE?

AN EYEWITNESS DESCRIBED THE KILLER AND I SKETCHED HIM. BUT BEFORE I TOLD TRACY, I DECIDED I'D HAVE TO MAKE SURE.

WHAT WILL THEY DO NOW?
THEY'LL GET HIM AND PUT HIM WHERE HE BELONGS—AND YOU'D HAVE TO HELP, MODEL.

WHERE IS YOUR BROTHER? HUH? WHERE?

WHERE IS HE, MODEL? YOU'LL HAVE TO TELL US! WHERE IS HE?
GET OUT!

THEN YOU WON'T TELL ME WHERE YOUR BROTHER IS?
I SAID GET OUT!

MODEL, YOU KNOW I **LOVE** YOU, AND YOU LOVE ME! WON'T YOU HELP US CATCH YOUR BROTHER?
GET OUT!

DO YOU THINK MY DAUGHTER'S A STOOL PIGEON? **WANT ME TO SOCK 'IM**, MODEL?
FATHER!

CHESTER GOULD

GET OUT!
YEAH-GIT OUT!

OUT!

NOW, MODEL—

JUNIOR WAS RIGHT! I **SHOULD** TELL HIM WHERE LARRY IS STAYING! I SHOULD HELP THE POLICE GET LARRY!

CHESTER GOULD

I SHOULD HAVE THE POLICE TAKE **YOU**, TOO; YOU'RE NOT REAL PARENTS—YOU'RE BUMS! YOU'RE TO BLAME FOR LARRY'S FIX. YOU— **YOU TWO!**
NOW, MODEL—

YOU **TWO** ARE TO BLAME FOR LARRY'S FIX. YOU'RE **NOT FIT** TO RAISE CHILDREN!

PARENTS LIKE YOU ARE THE CAUSE OF BOYS LIKE LARRY GOING WRONG—

NO DAUGHTER O'MINE CAN TALK **LIKE THAT** ABOUT HER **FATHER!**

MEANWHILE—
YES, HER BROTHER **IS** THE PARKING METER KILLER, ALL RIGHT, BUT MODEL WON'T TELL ME WHERE HE'S HIDING.

CHESTER GOULD

SCENE: ROOMING HOUSE IN AN OLD PART OF TOWN—
NOT A BAD HIDEOUT, BUT IF THAT STUPID SISTER OF MINE DOESN'T BRING ME SOME DOUGH AND CLEAN CLOTHES, I'LL—

—I'LL GO BACK AND CLEAN OUT THE OLD MAN AND THE OLD LADY AND **HER**, TOO!

MEANWHILE—
YOU WILL GET YOUR OLD JOB BACK, WON'T YOU, MODEL? PLEASE SAY YOU WILL!
I'M SORRY I HIT YOU, MODEL. I FEEL TERRIBLE.

CHESTER GOULD

AND AT HEADQUARTERS—
WE'LL GO OUT TO HER HOUSE AND START FROM THERE.

THERE, I'VE WRAPPED LARRY'S OTHER SUIT AND SOME SHIRTS. NOW, WHEN YOU LEAVE FOR WORK, MODEL—

WHERE DID SHE **GO?**
I DUNNO—

AND DOWNSTAIRS.
OKAY. LET'S GO UP.

SHE MUSTA GONE DOWN TO THE MAIL BOX —AND THE LOCK SNAPPED.
MODEL, IS THAT **YOU?**

CHESTER GOULD

I'LL TALK TO HIM ONCE MORE! AFTER ALL, HE IS MY BROTHER. IF I CAN PERSUADE HIM TO GIVE UP, IT MAY SAVE HIS LIFE.

LARRY

NO BUNDLE OF CLOTHES? AND WHERE'S THE MONEY?
DIDN'T BRING ANY!

MEANWHILE—
YOU KNOW WHAT WE WANT, AND YOU CAN HELP US. WHERE IS HE?
HEY, TRACY!

YES. IT'S ME.
YOU'RE LUCKY YOU DIDN'T GET SHOT. I THOUGHT YOU SAID YOU WERE NEVER GOING TO COME NEAR ME AGAIN, LITTLE SISTER.

I JUST HAD TO! NO, I DIDN'T BRING YOUR OTHER CLOTHES LIKE YOU ASKED ME. I'VE COME TO SAVE YOU FROM YOURSELF, LARRY.
YEAH?

WHAT KIND OF TALK IS THAT? DON'T TRY TO GET CUTE WITH ME, MODEL, OR I'LL—

LARRY, I WANT YOU TO GIVE YOURSELF UP BEFORE IT'S TOO LATE. FOR DAD AND MOTHER'S SAKE— FOR MY SAKE— BEFORE POLICE BULLETS END YOUR LIFE!
HA, HA! WHY, YOU LITTLE JERK!

DID YOU COME HERE JUST TO GIVE ME A LAUGH? NOW, GET OUT OF HERE.

MEANWHILE, ON JUNIOR'S INFORMATION, DICK TRACY AND SAM CATCHEM HAVE CALLED ON MODEL'S PARENTS.
A MAN'S SUIT— HURRIEDLY WRAPPED. THIS IS NO ACCIDENT.
A YOUNG MAN'S SUIT.
GET OUTA MY PLACE.

THIS SCRIBBLED ADDRESS ON THE PAPER COULD BE JUST WHAT WE'RE LOOKING FOR! THE HANDWRITING LOOKS FEMININE.
LET'S GO!

TWENTY MINUTES LATER.
LARRY, PLEASE! BEFORE IT'S TOO LATE.
HEY! WHAT'S THIS?

YOU'VE LED THE COPS HERE! YOU'VE DOUBLE-CROSSED YOUR OWN BROTHER!
LARRY— I DIDN'T—

I'LL BEAT 'EM TO THE DRAW! I'LL PLUG 'EM AS THEY GET OUT OF THEIR CAR!

GET YOUR HANDS OFF ME, YOU—

TURN LOOSE OF THAT GUN—
BANG

LARRY THREATENS TO FIRE AT TRACY AND CATCHEM—
BANG!
I TOLD YOU NOT TO GRAB MY GUN—WHY DID YOU DO IT?
HEY, SIS! IT WAS AN ACCIDENT!
CHESTER GOULD
AND DOWN BELOW—
YEAH—I HEARD IT, TOO, SAM.
DO YOU SUPPOSE THE KID BUMPED HIMSELF OFF?

PLEASE, LARRY—GIVE YOURSELF UP—BEFORE THEY KILL YOU—
WON'T OPEN. EH?
GIVE TO CONQUER CANCER
AMERICAN CANCER SOCIETY
CHESTER GOULD

THAT WAS GLASS CRASHING!
OH—H—
HE DUCKED. I MAY HAVE HIT HIM.
LIKE HECK, I DID!
CHESTER GOULD
IT HURTS—

IT WAS AN ACCIDENT—HE DIDN'T MEAN TO—
THIS IS A RUSH, BOYS. A BULLET HOLE THROUGH THE NECK—LOOKS LIKE THE JUGULAR. I WON'T MOVE HER—
2-WAY WRIST RADIO
IF I CAN MAKE THIS NEXT ROOF, I'LL BE—
CRACK!
CHESTER GOULD

I WAS **SURE** I HIT HIM! I SAW HIM **DROP**—BUT WHERE IS HE?
SWOOSH
AND BELOW, IN LARRY'S ROOM—
BLEEDING VERY HEAVY. THAT'S WHY I PUT THE TOWELS THERE.
JUGULAR.
NOT GOOD! NOTIFY HER PARENTS.

SHE WAS ABLE TO SAY A FEW WORDS. SHE AND HER BROTHER WERE QUARRELING. SHE WANTED HIM TO GIVE HIMSELF UP.

HEY, TRACY! COME HERE QUICK!
THAT'S OFFICER COLE'S VOICE.
I'LL GO, TRACY.

WE'VE GOT A FIGHT ON OUR HANDS TO SAVE HER, CHIEF. YES, THE CITY HOSPITAL.
Fight CANCER

AND AT HEADQUARTERS.
MODEL?
CHESTER GOULD

SHOT THROUGH THE NECK— SHE'S BLEEDING BADLY.
SHE AND LARRY WERE QUARRELING.

SHE WAS TRYING TO TALK HER BROTHER INTO SURRENDERING.

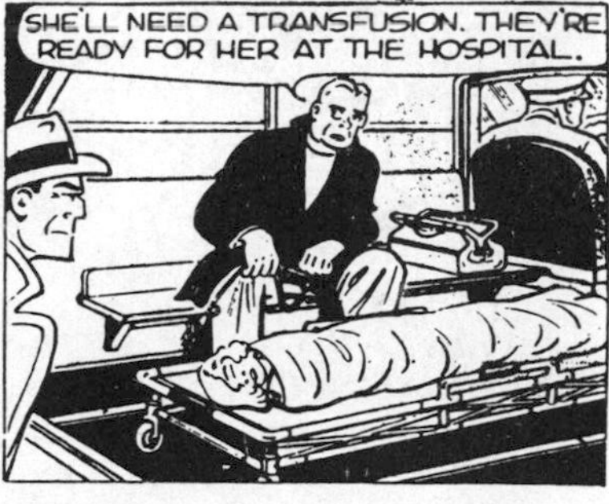
SHE'LL NEED A TRANSFUSION. THEY'RE READY FOR HER AT THE HOSPITAL.

I TELL YOU, SAM, AFTER I FIRED AT LARRY ON THE ROOF, HE JUST DISAPPEARED.

NOT QUITE, TRACY. LISTEN.
THAT'S HIS VOICE.
HELP HELP HELP

HE'S IN A ROOM INSIDE.
THERE'S NO ROOM DOWN THERE. THAT'S THE BASE OF AN ABANDONED CHIMNEY.

HE'S RIGHT. IT'S AN OLD CONDEMNED CHIMNEY. THIS STEEL ONE NEXT TO IT IS THE REAL ONE NOW.
GET SOME SLEDGE HAMMERS, BOYS.

HE MUST HAVE CLIMBED ON TOP OF THE OLD CHIMNEY TO REACH THE BUILDING NEXT DOOR WHEN YOU SHOT! AND HE FELL INSIDE.

AND AT THE HOME OF MODEL'S PARENTS.
—AND HER CONDITION IS GRAVE. YOU'RE TO COME AT ONCE.

LATER, AT THE HOSPITAL.
SHE SACRIFICED HERSELF TO MAKE HER BROTHER COME CLEAN.

AND THAT'S WHY SHE BROKE OFF WITH ME. SHE DIDN'T WANT ME TO GET MIXED UP WITH A FAMILY LIKE HERS! OH, MODEL, WHY DID YOU DO IT?

IT'S CHIEF PATTON. THE HOSPITAL REPORTS — NOT A CHANCE.

LUCKILY, THAT OLD CHIMNEY'S BEEN ABANDONED IN FAVOR OF THE STEEL STACK. WHEN I FIRED, LARRY DROPPED IN.

PRESSING AGAINST THE SIDES WOULD BREAK HIS FALL, BUT HE'S PROBABLY SKINNED UP AND WOUNDED.

AND AT THE HOME OF MODEL'S PARENTS.

IT'S ALL MY FAULT! I NEGLECTED MY CHILDREN! DRINK—DRINK—**DRINK!**

"SHE'S VERY LOW. THEY WANT YOU TO COME RIGHT AWAY," SAYS THE POLICEMAN. "I'M THE ONE WHO OUGHT TO DIE," SAYS THE FATHER.

NO PULSE AT ALL

CHESTER GOULD

THAT'S THE FOURTH BOTTLE OF PLASMA.

HER SKIN IS COLD—WON'T WARM UP.

NO PULSE—AND I CAN BARELY PICK UP A HEART-BEAT—VERY FAINT.

WHAT'S HER BLOOD PRESSURE?

A MEASLY 30.

I'LL SEE IF YOU CAN COME IN.

CHESTER GOULD

GIVE US A HAND.

CAN YOU STAND UP, LARRY?

YEAH—SHOULDER HURTS.

AND AT THE HOSPITAL—

BETTER GET ANOTHER CYLINDER OF OXYGEN.

CHESTER GOULD

SKIN'S STILL COLD—GETTING COLDER.

BETTER BRING THE PARENTS IN.

SHE'S IN PROFOUND SHOCK. SHE WON'T BE ABLE TO HEAR YOU.

THIS ISN'T MY SON'S FAULT—IT'S **MINE!** I'M THE GUILTY ONE. I NEGLECTED MY CHILDREN.

I DID THIS JUST AS SURELY AS IF I HAD FIRED THE GUN! MODEL—MY BABY!

CHESTER GOULD

MAYBE IT MIGHT HELP HER WAKE UP—IF **I** COULD JUST SPEAK TO HER.

YOU'RE NEXT.

MODEL! IT'S ME.

HER HAND! IT'S ICE COLD.

IT'S JUST A MATTER OF MINUTES.

IF SHE'D ONLY RALLY ENOUGH TO RECOGNIZE ME—AND SPEAK.

CHESTER GOULD

MEANWHILE—

EMERGENCY TREATMENT AND A SHOWER—THEN **LOCK** HIM UP.

MY SISTER! WHAT **ABOUT** HER?

THERE'S STILL A HEART-BEAT, BUT IT'S BARELY PERCEPTIBLE.

CHESTER GOULD

MODEL'S FATHER AND MOTHER, DEEP IN REMORSE, KEEP VIGIL AT MODEL'S BEDSIDE.

THE OLD MAN BROKE ALL HIS BOTTLES HE'S TAKING THIS PLENTY HARD.
ONLY HE'S STARTING TOO LATE, SAM.

I DON'T BLAME LARRY. THE FAULT IS MINE. I DIDN'T HAVE TIME FOR MY KIDS. I'VE BEEN A RAT.
I THINK YOU'RE RIGHT. PARENTS MUST SET AN EXAMPLE FOR THEIR CHILDREN.

MEANWHILE, AT THE COUNTY JAIL.
HOW IS SHE?
NOT TOO GOOD, LARRY.

I DIDN'T MEAN TO DO IT! MY OWN SISTER!

SHE'S CALLING FOR SOMEBODY.
—JUNIOR—

FIFTEEN MINUTES LATER.

THAT'S THE ONLY WORD SHE'S SPOKEN!
THIS MAY BE—

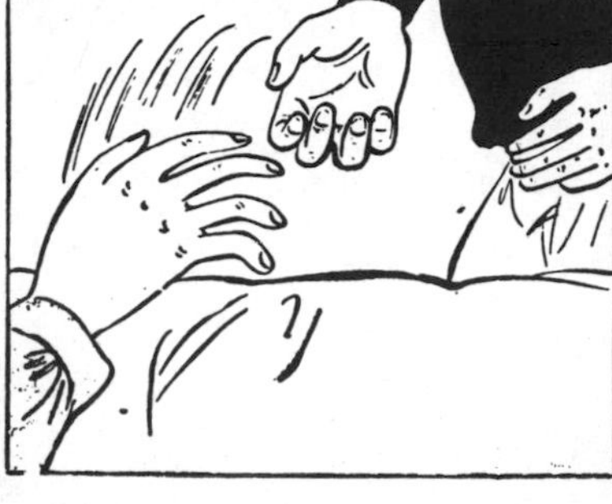

SHE SPOKE HIS NAME AND TRIED TO RISE, THEN—

SHE'S GONE—MODEL'S GONE.

DICK! WHEN DID IT HAPPEN?

AT 10:26, TESS.

THAT'S THE WAY IT IS, KID. LIFE DEALS 'EM THAT WAY ONCE IN A WHILE.

WHY DID IT HAVE TO BE MODEL? HER PARENTS—HER BROTHER—THEY WERE THE GUILTY ONES.

THEY'RE THE ONES WHO OUGHT TO PAY.

THEY'RE PAYING NOW.

MODEL, I'LL ALWAYS LOVE YOU.

THE 1960s

SPOTS

by Chester Gould

8/3/60–11/30/60

The 1960s were by no one's yardstick the glory years for Chester Gould's *Dick Tracy.* Gould's diatribes against hippies and his "Law and Order First" campaign made the once cutting-edge strip seem to some readers crankily, creakily Establishment-oriented. (Ironically, many counterculture "underground" cartoonists—including Art Spiegelman, Kim Deitch, Gilbert Shelton, and Robert Crumb, who visited Gould's Tribune Tower office in the late sixties—continued to extol the virtues of *Tracy's* creator, both for his storytelling and his graphic mastery.)

Gould's decision to take Tracy to the moon pleased few of his fans, though Chet himself loved these sequences. Marrying Junior Tracy off to the exotic Moon Maid seemed, to some of the faithful, a mistake of major proportions: In the late forties and the fifties, Gould had clearly set events in motion so that Junior would one day marry Sparkle Plenty (whom Moon Maid resembled in some regards). And outfitting Tracy and crew in flying magnetic moon buckets violated Gould's stated intention to keep Tracy only one simple remove away from reality. Taking Tracy into outer space, and giving him science fiction gadgetry, went well beyond the Two-Way Wrist Radio, satellite television hookups, and openheart surgery, to name a few of Gould's one-step-ahead-of-the-times visions.

In fact, Tracy didn't beat Neil Armstrong to the moon by *that* many years, did he?

Nonetheless, the moon sequences represent Gould's wonderful imagination at its least disciplined. Editors and readers were as uncomfortable with Tracy in a Space Coupe as they'd have been with Buck Rogers or Flash Gordon in a squad car.

Also, Gould's wonderfully tight storylines of the 1940s, and especially of the early 1950s, had begun to meander. Gould did not plot ahead, and felt if he didn't know what was going to happen next, neither would the reader; this philosophy served him well for decades. And the stories of the 1960s remained very effective, taken in daily doses; but when read in one sitting, they are less successful.

The strengths of the 1960s, in fact, are not in the area of story; where the sixties shine is in the artwork. These years might be described as Gould's pop-art period; his dramatic use of striking black-and-white composition hit its peak around 1968. (The assistants during this period were the two artists who would later, individually, take over the *Tracy* art chores: coeditor Dick Locher and Rick Fletcher.) Particularly in his depiction of weather and terrain, Gould was (as Richard Marschall has described him) a "wildly successful" Expressionist. The strip had never looked better, particularly the dynamic, stunningly designed Sunday pages. This is the period that influenced Warhol, Lichenstein, and other purveyors of pop art.

We have chosen a sequence that merges some of these pop-art tendencies with the last, pre-moon gasp of Gould's better writing. Spots is a terrific villain, who somewhat resembles the earlier thirties fiend the Blank, and the doggerel-spouting poet Ogden represents Gould's zany humor at its most offbeat. And the demise of Spots is particularly memorable.

Coeditor Locher was Gould's assistant at the time of this continuity; he and Gould also collaborated on an extensive sequence in 1958, which resulted in the strip's first National Cartoonists Society Reuben award.

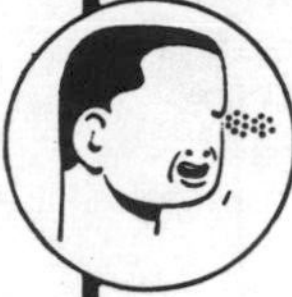

TRACY, I'M GLAD YOUR HAWAIIAN CASE TURNED OUT SO WELL. IT'S GOOD TO HAVE YOU BACK.
THANKS, SAM.
WHAT ARE YOU DOING WITH THE BATTERY-POWERED TV PORTABLE CAMERA?
A JEWELER WANTS IT PUT ON HIS SAFE FOR A FEW NIGHTS. HE'S HAD A COUPLE OF STICK-UPS.
GOLLY, WE'VE BEEN USING THIS ATOMIC-POWERED PORTABLE TV CAMERA OF DIET SMITH'S SINCE SEPTEMBER OF 1948.
WEIGHT, 9 LBS.
POWER COMPLETELY SELF-CONTAINED, RANGE LIMITLESS.
SELF-CONTAINED ATOMIC LIGHT
REMEMBER THE TIME WE FLOATED ONE INTO A LARGE STORM SEWER AND LOCATED A MURDERER NAMED "RUGHEAD"?
I SURE DO, SAM. THAT WAS IN 1955.
CHESTER GOULD

WELCOME, SIR, WON'T YOU COME IN?
ONE SIDE, KID!
SPOTS!
YOU DOUBLE-CROSSER!
OH, HALAKAHIKI, THIS IS MY ATTORNEY, MR.-ER-SMITH.
PLEASED TO MEET YOU, SIR.
CHESTER GOULD

OKAY, SPOTS– SHE'S OUT OF THE ROOM. NOW–
YOU CAN'T BACK OUT OF THIS DEAL. THAT KID IS WORTH $100,000! AND WE WANT THAT MONEY.
MY MOUTHPIECE IN HONOLULU IS AIR-MAILING PAPERS FOR YOU TO SIGN, MAKING YOU HER CUSTODIAN. IT'S JUST THAT EASY!
NO, SPOTS.
I'M BEGGING OFF. MY MOTHER INSTINCTS HAVE ME OVER A BARREL. I LIKE THE KID TOO MUCH. YOU CAN PLAY THIS ONE ALONE.
CHESTER GOULD

*MAKUAHINE HANAUNA, YOU SEEM SAD.
OH—I'M ALL RIGHT, HALAKAHIKI. I'M JUST SLEEPY.
*AUNT

IT'S EASY TO SEE WE ARE RELATED—WE BOTH HAVE THE SAME TATTOO.
OUCH!

DON'T TOUCH IT! IT'S SORE—VERY, VERY SORE!
YOUR TATTOO IS SORE?

—STILL SORE? ???
CHESTER GOULD

WELL, TRACY, THAT HAWAIIAN CASE HAD A REAL HAPPY ENDING. CONGRATULATIONS.
THANKS, CHIEF.

YES, LITTLE PINEAPPLE WAS ORPHANED BY THE TIDAL WAVE, BUT WE FOUND HER AUNT AND EVERYBODY'S HAPPY.

AND DON'T FORGET THOSE DESPICABLE CHARACTERS, FLYFACE AND FIFTH, MET THEIR JUST DESERTS.
YES, BUT YOU CAN'T BE REALLY SURE THEY'RE DEAD. THE BODIES NEVER WERE FOUND.

ANYWAY, LI'L PINEAPPLE'S HAPPY—AND HAS A NICE HOME.
WHAT'S NEW, CHIEF?

SPEAKING OF LI'L PINEAPPLE—
HALAKAHIKI, WOULD YOU PLAY IN THE LIVING ROOM A FEW MINUTES WHILE I TALK WITH MY ATTORNEY?
YES, MA'AM.

THANK YOU.

LOOK, THESE PAPERS FROM HONOLULU MUST BE SIGNED BEFORE YOU CAN GET YOUR HANDS ON ONE CENT OF THAT 100 GRAND! NOW, SIGN!

I SAID SIGN!
NO, NO, SPOTS, I CAN'T.

SHE'S TOO SWEET! SHE'S TOO WONDERFUL! I CAN'T! I KNOW I'M YOUR WIFE, BUT I CAN'T GO ALONG WITH YOU ON THIS, SPOTS.

SIGN!
NO!

PUT YOUR NAME TO THAT PAPER, OR YOU AND THE LITTLE GIRL WILL NEVER LEAVE THIS APARTMENT ALIVE.

—I'LL SIGN.
CHESTER GOULD

I'LL SIGN—I'LL SIGN!

SIGN YOUR FULL NAME.

MY MOUTHPIECE WILL FLY THIS DOCUMENT TO HONOLULU TOMORROW. THAT 100 GRAND IS GETTING CLOSER BY THE MINUTE.

OUR KEEPING YOU HERE, HAS NOT FILLED US WITH GLEE, SO WHEN WE GET THE MONEY, MA'AM, YOU SHALL GO FREE. —TALLSTOY.

CHESTER GOULD

IMAGE McIMAGE TATOOIST

$1

McIMAGE, WHAT DO YOU FIND SO INTERESTING IN THE PAPER? I DIDN'T KNOW YOU COULD READ.

H'M?? I'M JUST ADDING.

A TATTOO DOES IT!

$100,000 WAIF UNITED WITH AUNT!

ADDING?

YEAH—I'M PUTTING TWO AND TWO TOGETHER.

$100,000!! —AND TO THINK I DID THAT PINEAPPLE TATTOO FOR $17.50!

IMAGE McIMAGE

CHESTER GOULD

SO I GOT $17.50, PLUS A TIP—FOR A $100,000 JOB.

IMAGE McIMAGE, YOU'RE DRUNK!

LET'S SEE, THE REAL DAME WAS LYING BOUND UP ON THE COUCH. THEY HAD ME TATTOO THE FAT DAME. H'M! SOME GAME THEY'RE PLAYING.

THERE SHOULD BE A COURT ORDER BY FRIDAY.

THEN WE WILL HAVE THE GOLDEN FLEECE, AND YOU CAN JOIN YOUR LITTLE NIECE. —RUSKIN

YES, I KNOW NOW. I KNOW YOU'RE NOT MY REAL AUNT.

CHESTER GOULD

THE OTHER DAY WHEN YOU SAID YOUR TATTOO WAS SORE, I KNEW.

—I KNEW SOMETHING WAS WRONG---TATTOOS ARE SORE ONLY WHEN THEY'RE NEW.

CHESTER GOULD

OH, HALAKAHIKI! (SOB, SOB, SOB)

I—I'M SO ASHAMED.

SO YOU JERKS DON'T BELIEVE ME??

I'M TELLIN' THE TRUT'! I CAN PUT THAT GANG BEHIND BARS!
BARS? HA, HA!
WHAT'S WRONG WITH THIS BAR? HAVE 'NOTHER DRINK, IMAGE.

ARE YOU REALLY GLAD I FOUND YOU OUT?

WHILE WE WAIT FOR COURT ORDERS, A QUESTION, IT SEEMS, IS, CAN YOUR WIFE BE TRUSTED TO NOT SPILL THE BEANS?
—KBATS
SHUT UP!

THA'S ALL I'M GONNA TELL YU—

IMAGE McIMAGE, THE GABBIEST TATTOOIST IN NORTH AMERICA! WHAT DOES HE KNOW ABOUT THIS HAWAIIAN KID? NOTHIN'!
THAT'S RIGHT— NOTHIN'!

I SUPPOSE NEXT HE'LL TELL US HE PUT THE ORIGINAL PINEAPPLE TATTOO ON OLD KING KAMEHAMEHA!
AHA, AHA!

SCUM!

MEANWHILE
I'M GLAD! I'M GLAD YOU KNOW THE TRUTH, HALAKAHIKI.

AFTER WHAT I HEARD AND SAW, I KNEW YOU WERE NOT MY REAL AUNT.
BUT I LOVE YOU ANYWAY.

I SHALL SEE THAT YOU ARE UNITED WITH YOUR REAL AUNT, IF IT'S THE LAST THING I EVER DO! YOU CAN DEPEND ON THAT, HALAKAHIKI.

AND AT SPOTS' APARTMENT—
HOW LONG, DO YOU FIGURE, BEFORE YOUR WIFE GETS HER HANDS ON THAT 100 GRAND, SPOTS?
MY MOUTHPIECE IS CALLING TONIGHT—I'LL ASK—
WHO'S THAT?

IMAGE McIMAGE!
HOW JA DO?

I GOTTA TALK TO YOU.

WHAT ABOUT? WHAT ARE YOU BACK HERE FOR? I PAID YOU.
AHA! THAT YOU DID— THAT YOU DID! —$17.50.
—PLUS A NICE TIP.

$17.50 FOR ONE PINEAPPLE TATTOO IS THE ORDINARY RATE. BUT FROM WHAT I'VE BEEN READING, THIS WAS NO ORDINARY JOB! —UH— I WANT A GRAND.
A GRAND?

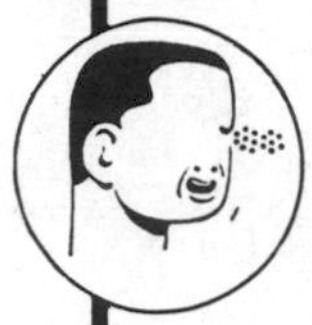

THEN THIS IS A SHAKEDOWN, EH?

NO-O-O. I WOULDN'T CALL IT A SHAKEDOWN. I'M JUST ASKING FOR APPROPRIATE PAY FOR HELPING PUT OVER A $100,000 JOB.

YOU WANT A GRAND, EH?
YEAH— A GRAND.

McIMAGE, YOUR NERVE HAS A DISTINCT AROMA. I FEAR YOU'LL END UP IN A CEMENT KIMONA.
—WHITTIER

THAT GUN DON'T FRIGHTEN ME. YOU WOULDN'T DARE HAVE A MURDER RAP ON YOUR HANDS, TOO.

HE WOULDN'T? MY FRIEND, LET ME GIVE YOU ADVICE— WHERE HIS HEART OUGHT TO BE IS A CHUNK OF DRY ICE.
—DICKENS

SMACK

HE HAS A VERY HARD FACE—LET 'IM HAVE IT, SPOTS.
OKAY— ONE, TWO—

DON'T SHOOT! I'LL CUT THAT THOUSAND TO 500—HONEST, I WILL.

McIMAGE, YOU'RE A LAUGH! YOU PUT THE PINEAPPLE TATTOO ON MY WIFE'S ANKLE. YOU'RE AS MUCH OF A CONSPIRATOR AS WE ARE. WHY, I COULD TURN YOU OVER TO THE COPS—
OH, NO!

CROOK!

IT'S NOT LIKE SPOTS TO FREE A MAN WHO'S TRIED TO SHAKE HIM DOWN. DEPART THIS FLAT—BEGONE, I SAY. BEST YET, GET OUT OF TOWN.
—TENNYSON

DO YOU UNDERSTAND NOW? I'LL LEAVE YOU IN THIS DRUG STORE PHONE BOOTH FOR ABOUT 10 MINUTES.
YES.

FIRST, I'LL PASTE THIS STICKER ON THE PHONE BOOTH DOOR SO NO ONE WILL TRY TO USE THE PHONE.
AND I HIDE INSIDE ON THE FLOOR?
OUT of ORDER

RIGHT!
THE APARTMENT WHERE YOUR REAL AUNT IS, IS NEXT DOOR AND TWO FLIGHTS UP.
OUT of ORDER

AND YOU WILL BRING MY AUNT TO ME?
IF IT'S THE LAST THING I EVER DO!

OH, HALAKAHIKI, IF THIS DOESN'T WORK, WE'LL BOTH DIE—
DON'T BE FRIGHTENED. I'M NOT.

LET'S SEE, I'LL NEED MY APARTMENT KEY AND A PAIR OF SCISSORS TO CUT YOUR AUNT'S BONDS—AND THE SIGN.

I DO NOT UNDERSTAND HOW ALL THIS CAME ABOUT —BUT I AM MOST THANKFUL THAT YOU ARE GOING TO BRING ME, AT LAST, TO MY REAL AUNT.

A FEW MINUTES LATER
GET IN THERE. SQUAT DOWN AND STAY PUT.

OGDEN, HAVE YOU GOT YOUR RADIO ON?
YES.

WELL, TURN IT OFF —I KEEP THINKING I HEAR NOISES.

SH-SH SH-

QUICKLY- THE WRISTS FIRST-
CHESTER GOULD

SH-SH! DON'T ASK ANY QUESTIONS— JUST FOLLOW ME.

SH-SH-SH!!

TWO FLIGHTS DOWN— QUICKLY—QUICKLY!

BUT WHO-?
DON'T WORRY ABOUT WHO I AM. JUST HURRY.

OGDEN, DID YOU HEAR SOMETHING?
HUH??

THE SECOND PHONE BOOTH IN THIS ALL-NIGHT DRUG STORE.
TAXI

COME—THERE'LL BE TIME ENOUGH FOR THAT LATER.
Beauty Sal
50¢

GET OUT OF HERE AS FAST AS YOU CAN. GO TO THE FIRST POLICE STATION—THEY'LL KNOW WHAT TO DO.
TAXI

OKAY, CABBIE. YOU HEARD ME. NOW, GIT!
TAXI

CHESTER GOULD

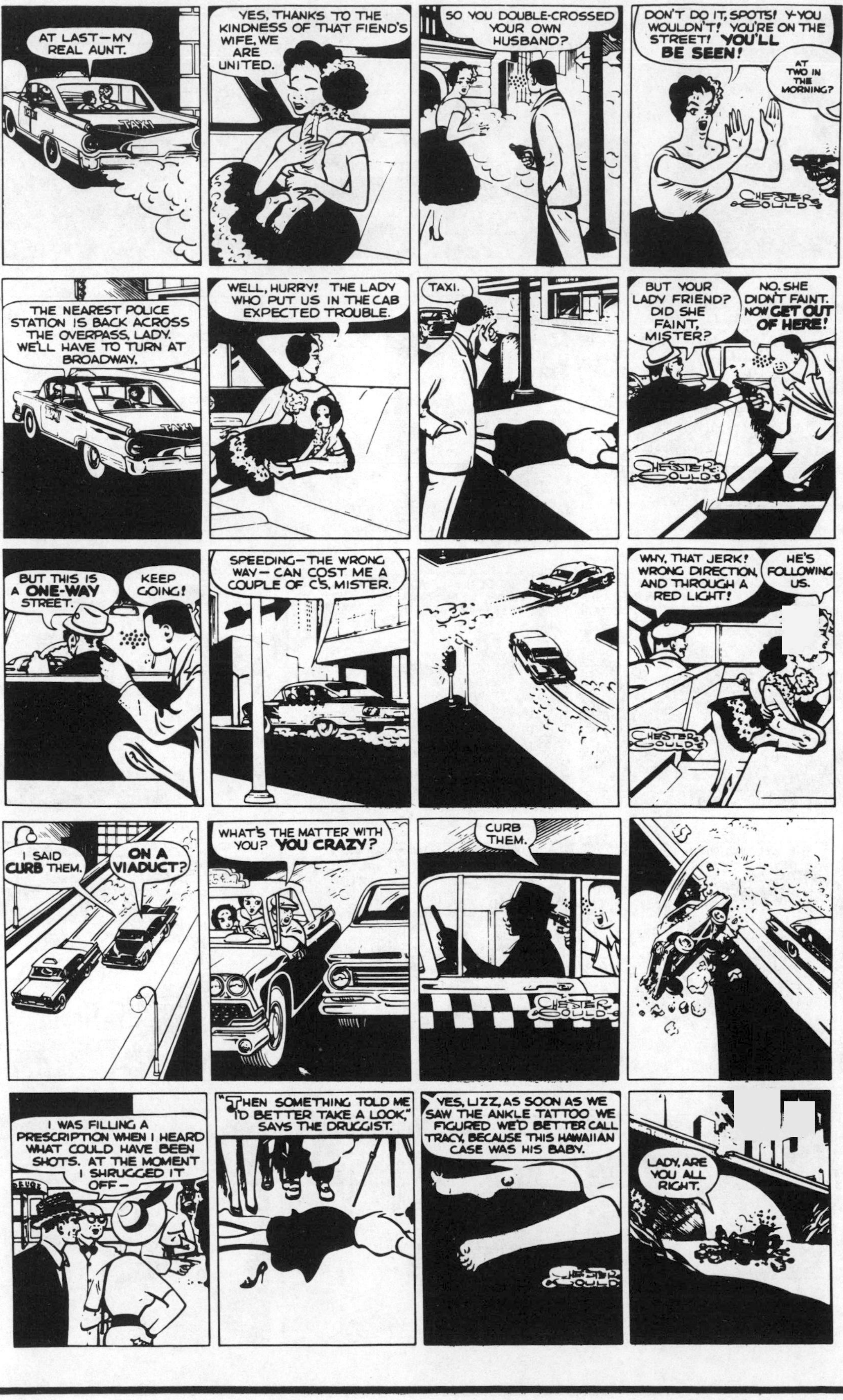

AT LAST—MY REAL AUNT.

YES, THANKS TO THE KINDNESS OF THAT FIEND'S WIFE, WE ARE UNITED.

SO YOU DOUBLE-CROSSED YOUR OWN HUSBAND?

DON'T DO IT, SPOTS! Y-YOU WOULDN'T! YOU'RE ON THE STREET! **YOU'LL BE SEEN!**

AT TWO IN THE MORNING?

CHESTER GOULD

THE NEAREST POLICE STATION IS BACK ACROSS THE OVERPASS, LADY. WE'LL HAVE TO TURN AT BROADWAY.

WELL, HURRY! THE LADY WHO PUT US IN THE CAB EXPECTED TROUBLE.

TAXI.

BUT YOUR LADY FRIEND? DID SHE FAINT, MISTER?

NO, SHE DIDN'T FAINT. NOW **GET OUT OF HERE!**

CHESTER GOULD

BUT THIS IS A **ONE-WAY** STREET.

KEEP GOING!

SPEEDING—THE WRONG WAY—CAN COST ME A COUPLE OF C'S, MISTER.

WHY, THAT JERK! WRONG DIRECTION, AND THROUGH A RED LIGHT!

HE'S FOLLOWING US.

CHESTER GOULD

I SAID **CURB** THEM.

ON A VIADUCT?

WHAT'S THE MATTER WITH YOU? **YOU CRAZY?**

CURB THEM.

CHESTER GOULD

I SAID, ARE YOU ALL RIGHT?
OH-H-H-
I THINK SO.

THERE'S A CUSHION OR SOMETHING ON MY BACK.

THE LITTLE GIRL? WHERE IS THE LITTLE GIRL?

MY RIGHT ARM MUST BE BROKE —CAN'T USE IT.
HELP!

YOU'RE THE OPERATOR OF THAT ALL-NIGHT DRUG STORE?
RIGHT. ABOUT 2:15 I HEARD SHOTS. I RAN OUT AND SAW HER ON THE SIDEWALK.
DRUGS

I CALLED THE POLICE. THAT'S ALL I KNOW ABOUT IT.
TRACY, THERE'S NO QUESTION ABOUT IT.

THAT IS THE LITTLE GIRL'S AUNT. LOOK! THERE'S THAT PINEAPPLE TATTOO.

THIS IS FANTASTIC! THEN WHERE IS THE LITTLE GIRL? WHERE IS THE LITTLE GIRL?

YES, SHE WOULD HAVE BEEN WITH HER AUNT.
DID ANYONE SEE A LITTLE GIRL?

ANSWERING TRACY'S QUESTION, WE SHIFT TO A SCENE SEVERAL MILES AWAY.
HE CROWDED ME RIGHT INTO THE RETAINING WALL.

THAT OTHER CAB FORCED US THROUGH THE RAILING. HIS PASSENGER WAS HOLDING A GUN ON HIM. I SAW IT.
YES— I SAW IT, TOO, DRIVER.

ARE YOU HURT, LADY?
DON'T WORRY ABOUT ME. THE REAL TROUBLE'S IN THERE.

MY NIECE— MY NIECE!

I CAN'T MOVE HER— WE NEED HELP. GO UP AND FLAG A CAR.
MY RADIO'S GONE DEAD.

WELL?

YOU'RE WHITE AS A SHEET —SPILL IT.
START PACKING.
CHESTER GOULD

BUT IT'S 2:30 A.M.!

YOU HEARD ME, OGDEN, I SAID START PACKING!
WHAT HAPPENED, SPOTS?

PLENTY! WE'VE GOT TO MOVE! START PACKING!
WHAT A GOSH-AWFUL HOUR TO CHANGE ONE'S ADDRESS! WE HAVE NO PLACE TO GO. AND I DON'T WANT TO DRESS.
—KEATS
CHESTER GOULD

YOU ONCE TOLD ME YOU HAD A STUDIO WHERE YOU OCCASIONALLY HID AWAY TO WRITE POETRY —HOW ABOUT THAT??
OH—THAT?

BUT, SPOTS, YOU WOULDN'T LIKE MY STUDIO AS A HIDEOUT.
I'D LIKE ANY PLACE AS A HIDE-OUT.

I JUST SLAPPED DOWN MY WIFE AND THEN FORCED A CAB FULL OF PEOPLE OVER A VIADUCT.
Y-Y-YOU MEAN—YOU—YOU—YOUR OWN WIFE?

THEN YOU ARE THE REAL AUNT?
YES, THE MURDERED WOMAN WAS AN IMPOSTOR FORCED INTO THIS CONSPIRACY BY HER GANGSTER HUSBAND.

LITTLE PINEAPPLE—CAN YOU HEAR ME?
CHESTER GOULD

GO EASY GETTING HER ON THAT STRETCHER.
IS SHE BREATHING?
BARELY.

WHAT AN ORDEAL FOR A LITTLE GIRL.
FIRST SHE WENT THROUGH A TIDAL WAVE, THEN THIS.

THE CITY'S BEST DOCTORS ARE WAITING FOR HER AT THE HOSPITAL.
YEEEEEE

MALIA, YOU'LL BE OUR KEY WITNESS IN THIS CASE. WE'LL NEED ALL THE HELP YOU CAN GIVE US.
I'LL TELL YOU EVERYTHING I KNOW, MR. TRACY.
CHESTER GOULD

OGDEN, YOU MUST BE MIGHTY ASHAMED OF YOUR "STUDIO," NOT TO WANT ME TO USE IT AS A HIDE-OUT.
I'M NOT ASHAMED. I WANT YOU TO USE IT.

ALL I SAID WAS, YOU WON'T LIKE IT.

WHAT IS IT A BASEMENT DUNGEON—OR SOMETHING?
OH, NO, INDEED, SPOTS.

IT'S HIGH AND DRY AND IT'S QUITE TALL, BUT THERE'S ONE FAULT, —INSIDE IT'S SMALL.
—BURNS
CHESTER GOULD

THIS WORLD-WAR TWO TANK IS YOUR STUDIO?
YES.

IT HAS RUNNING WATER AND ELECTRICITY. I'LL TELL YOU ABOUT IT WHEN WE GET INSIDE. IT'S A LONG STORY.

BUT THIS IS A PUBLIC PARK.
IT'S A LITTLE-USED PARK—FLOODS OUT EVERY YEAR. CITY'S GOING TO ABANDON IT.

STEP ON THAT HOOK AND HANG ON!
CHESTER GOULD

AND YOU COME HERE TO WRITE POETRY?
YES, SPOTS.

I COME TO SIT ALONE
AND THINK,
MY VERSES TO DEVISE.
THERE'S PEACE AND QUIET
IN THESE WALLS,
TO LINGER HERE IS WISE.
—WORDSWORTH

YOU WANTED A PLACE TO HIDE OUT FROM THE COPS—SO!

—LAFAYETTE WE ARE HERE!
UGH!

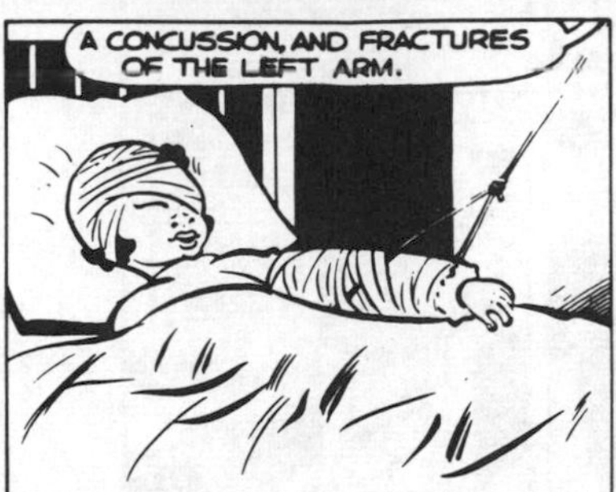
A CONCUSSION, AND FRACTURES OF THE LEFT ARM.

IF ONLY I COULD HAVE BEEN THE ONE TO GET THE INJURIES, INSTEAD OF HALAKAHIKI.

WELL, THEY HAD US FOOLED! WHEN I SAW THE TATTOO ON THE OTHER WOMAN'S ANKLE IT CONVINCED EVERYBODY SHE WAS THE AUNT.

POOR MRS. SPOTS! SHE PAID WITH HER LIFE FOR HELPING ME AND THE LITTLE GIRL.

AND NOW, INSTEAD OF A CONSPIRACY CASE, WE HAVE A MURDER ON OUR HANDS—HIS OWN WIFE.

THE BOYS REPORT SPOTS' APARTMENT ABANDONED. NOTHING BUT EMPTY ROOMS.

SCENE: ONE OF THE CITY'S LITTLE-USED PUBLIC PARKS—WHERE A MEMENTO OF WORLD WAR TWO RESTS ON A CONCRETE PEDESTAL.

HERE?
WHY NOT? IT HAS ELECTRICITY AND RUNNING WATER. IT'S MY PRIVATE STUDIO.

I PUT IN BUNKS WHERE THE MOTORS AND TURRET USED TO BE—THERE'S A STOCK OF FOOD.

YOU SEE, SPOTS—I FIXED THIS UP ON THE QT YEARS AGO, AS A PLACE TO COME TO BE ALONE AND WRITE POETRY.

WHEN I WRITE POETRY I LIKE SOLITUDE. I SNEAKED DOWN HERE AT NIGHTS AND PUT IN PLUMBING AND WIRING MYSELF.

WITH THIS REVOLVING PERISCOPE, YOU SEE THE COUNTRYSIDE,
OH, YES, IT'S JUST MY STUDIO
BUT WHAT A PLACE TO HIDE!
—MILTON
UGH! GIVE ME ANOTHER COFFEE.

YES, YOU CAN USE THE PERISCOPE TO LOOK AROUND. WE HAVE A RADIO. THERE'RE PLENTY OF PROVISIONS—
IT MAKES A LOVELY HOME, SPOTS.
UM!
I DON'T SEE ANY DIFFERENCE BETWEEN THIS AND A CELL IN THE PENITENTIARY!
WHAT?
OH, GRATITUDE'S NOT IN YOUR SOUL, YOU SNEER AND SNARL NO END. BUT JUST REMEMBER HOW THIS BEATS THE 'LECTRIC CHAIR, MY FRIEND.
—WHITTIER.
CHESTER GOULD

SHE'S REGAINED CONSCIOUSNESS, BUT SHE'S UNDER SEDATION.
POOR LITTLE PINEAPPLE.
MALIA, THE TATTOOIST INVOLVED IN THIS COULD BE A BIG HELP TO US. WOULD YOU KNOW HIM IF YOU SAW HIM?
I CERTAINLY WOULD.
HERE'S THE LIST OF ALL KNOWN TATTOOISTS DOING BUSINESS IN THE CITY—
THANKS, SAM.
"I THINK," SAYS TRACY, "MALIA AND I ARE GOING ON A LITTLE 'TOUR OF THE TATTOO SHOPS.'"
IMAGE McIMAGE TATTOOIST
CHESTER GOULD

IT'S 90° IN HERE, OGDEN! I'M DYING OF THE HEAT!
WHY DIDN'T YOU AIR-CONDITION THIS IRON MONSTER WHILE YOU WERE AT IT?
OH, SIMMER DOWN, SPOTS.
LET THIS DEVICE I HOLD IN HAND BE ANSWER TO YOUR QUESTION. DON'T JUMP THE GUN, RELAX, MY BOY, LEST YOU GET INDIGESTION.
CHESTER GOULD
NICE?
UGH.

ACROSS THE STREET.
TATTOOIST
YES—INDEED— TATTOOS, ANYONE?
CHESTER GOULD
HOW ARE YOU AT DOING PINEAPPLES?

JUST KIDS PRACTICING FOOTBALL. QUIT WORRYING!
BUT YOU TOLD ME THIS PARK WASN'T USED.
I SAID THE PARK BOARD OFFICIALLY CLOSED IT BECAUSE IT FLOODS EVERY SPRING.
HEY, DON'T SMOKE!
IF THE KIDS SMELL CIGARETTE SMOKE AND START SNOOPING, WE'LL BE SUNK.
CHESTER GOULD

HEY! TOSS ME A PASS!

—SH-SH— DON'T MAKE COFFEE WHILE THE KIDS ARE AROUND! THE AROMA MAY GET OUT!

DON'T TALK! SH-SH-SH— DON'T DROP ANYTHING! AND LET'S TURN OFF THE FAN— IT MAKES A HUM.

A-AND DON'T STRIKE ME. IF MY BODY FALLS— IT'LL MAKE A NOISE — AND THEY'LL HEAR IT— SH-SH—
CHESTER GOULD

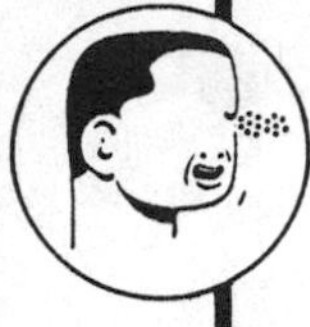

I'VE TRIED MY BEST, SPOTS, TO MAKE YOU COMFORTABLE—BUT WHAT HAPPENS?

ALL I GET FROM YOU IS ABUSE.
THIS HEAT! THIS AWFUL HEAT! I'M SUFFOCATING.

AHA! BUT IT ISN'T THE KIND OF HEAT YOU'D GET FROM SITTING IN THE ELECTRIC CHAIR.
REMEMBER YOU'RE A MURDERER.

AS YOUR TRUE FRIEND, I BROUGHT YOU HERE TO HIDE YOU FROM THE LAW. INSTEAD OF THANKS I GET A CURSE, I OUGHT TO BREAK YOUR JAW.
WHEW!

DEATH IN SOLITARY COULDN'T BE WORSE WHAT DOES THAT THERMOMETER SAY?
IT'S 106°.

HEY, SPOTS I JUST NOTICED! YOUR GUN IS GONE!
WHAT? WHY I HAD IT WHEN I CAME IN HERE.

WHAT WAS THAT?
PLUNK

AND AT THE MORGUE
YOU ARE THE MAN. I SAW YOUR FACE FROM WHERE I LAY BOUND UP ON THAT COUCH.
I ADMIT IT, LADY. I DID THE TATTOO.
AUTOPSY

SURE, MR. TRACY. THAT'S MY WORK. I DID IT BECAUSE I WAS SCARED. THE GUY HAD A GUN.

THE "GUY" WAS THE DEAD WOMAN'S HUSBAND. HE'S WANTED FOR MURDER. COULD YOU DESCRIBE HIM?
WELL, UH, WU-ER—

DID HE LOOK LIKE THIS?
HE SURE DID! WHERE DID YOU GET THAT?

I HAD TO STRIKE YOU ON THE KNOB— 'TIS ALL FOR YOUR OWN GOOD. YOU CAN'T GO OUT TO FIND THAT GUN WHILE THERE'S KIDS IN THE NEIGHBORHOOD.
—KEATS
CHESTER GOULD

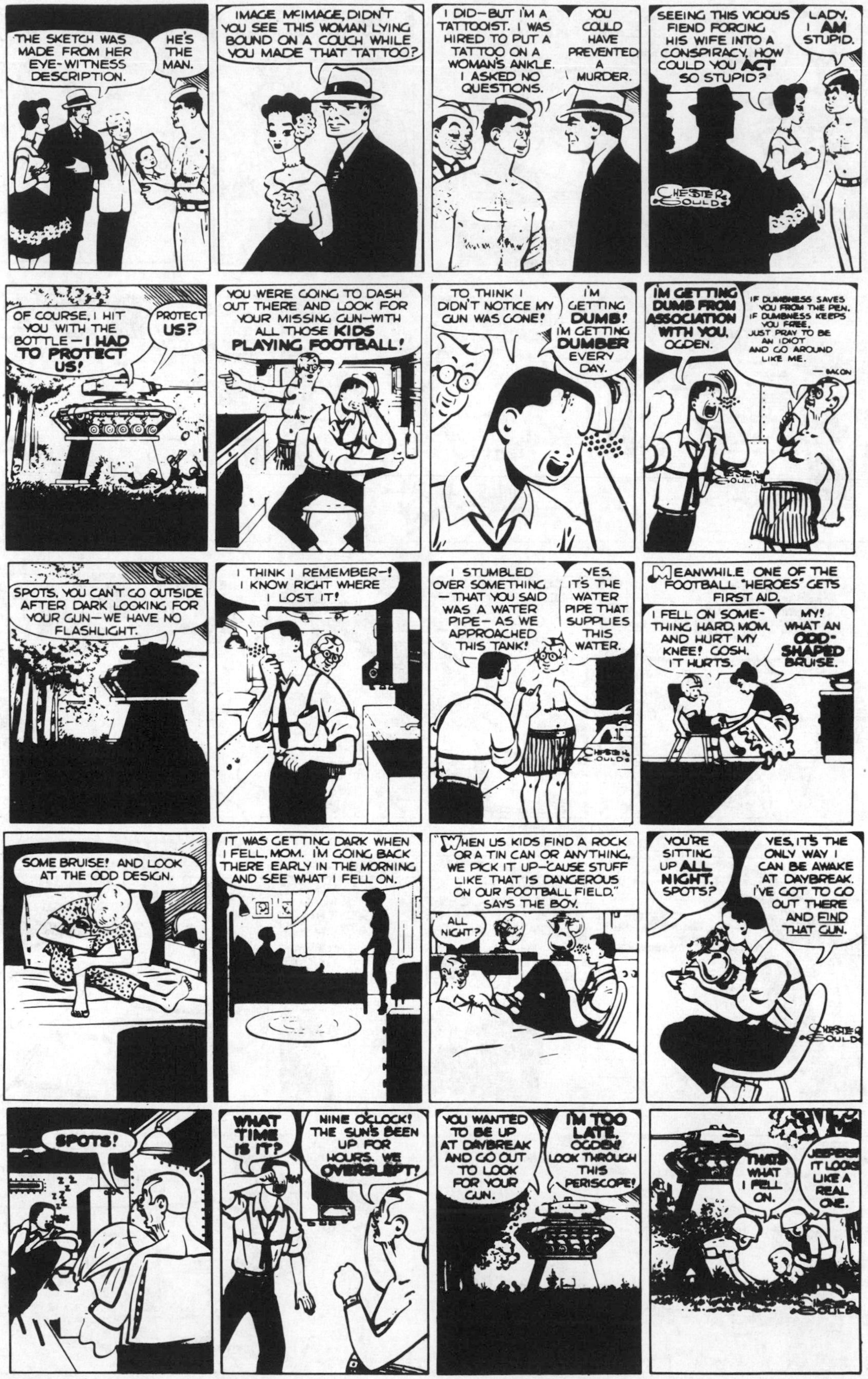

THE SKETCH WAS MADE FROM HER EYE-WITNESS DESCRIPTION.
HE'S THE MAN.
IMAGE McIMAGE, DIDN'T YOU SEE THIS WOMAN LYING BOUND ON A COUCH WHILE YOU MADE THAT TATTOO?
I DID—BUT I'M A TATTOOIST. I WAS HIRED TO PUT A TATTOO ON A WOMAN'S ANKLE. I ASKED NO QUESTIONS.
YOU COULD HAVE PREVENTED A MURDER.
SEEING THIS VICIOUS FIEND FORCING HIS WIFE INTO A CONSPIRACY, HOW COULD YOU **ACT** SO STUPID?
LADY, I **AM** STUPID.
OF COURSE, I HIT YOU WITH THE BOTTLE—**I HAD TO PROTECT US!**
PROTECT **US?**
YOU WERE GOING TO DASH OUT THERE AND LOOK FOR YOUR MISSING GUN—WITH ALL THOSE **KIDS PLAYING FOOTBALL!**
TO THINK I DIDN'T NOTICE MY GUN WAS GONE!
I'M GETTING **DUMB!** I'M GETTING **DUMBER** EVERY DAY.
I'M GETTING DUMB FROM ASSOCIATION WITH YOU, OGDEN.
IF DUMBNESS SAVES YOU FROM THE PEN, IF DUMBNESS KEEPS YOU FREE, JUST PRAY TO BE AN IDIOT AND GO AROUND LIKE ME. —BACON
SPOTS, YOU CAN'T GO OUTSIDE AFTER DARK LOOKING FOR YOUR GUN—WE HAVE NO FLASHLIGHT.
I THINK I REMEMBER—! I KNOW RIGHT WHERE I LOST IT!
I STUMBLED OVER SOMETHING —THAT YOU SAID WAS A WATER PIPE—AS WE APPROACHED THIS TANK!
YES, IT'S THE WATER PIPE THAT SUPPLIES THIS WATER.
MEANWHILE ONE OF THE FOOTBALL "HEROES" GETS FIRST AID.
I FELL ON SOMETHING HARD, MOM, AND HURT MY KNEE! GOSH, IT HURTS.
MY! WHAT AN **ODD-SHAPED** BRUISE.
SOME BRUISE! AND LOOK AT THE ODD DESIGN.
IT WAS GETTING DARK WHEN I FELL, MOM. I'M GOING BACK THERE EARLY IN THE MORNING AND SEE WHAT I FELL ON.
"WHEN US KIDS FIND A ROCK OR A TIN CAN OR ANYTHING, WE PICK IT UP—'CAUSE STUFF LIKE THAT IS DANGEROUS ON OUR FOOTBALL FIELD." SAYS THE BOY.
ALL NIGHT?
YOU'RE SITTING UP **ALL NIGHT,** SPOTS?
YES, IT'S THE ONLY WAY I CAN BE AWAKE AT DAYBREAK. I'VE GOT TO GO OUT THERE AND FIND THAT GUN.
SPOTS!
WHAT TIME IS IT?
NINE O'CLOCK! THE SUN'S BEEN UP FOR HOURS. WE **OVERSLEPT!**
YOU WANTED TO BE UP AT DAYBREAK AND GO OUT TO LOOK FOR YOUR GUN.
I'M TOO LATE, OGDEN! LOOK THROUGH THIS PERISCOPE!
THAT'S WHAT I FELL ON.
JEEPERS! IT LOOKS LIKE A REAL ONE.

IS IT REAL?
SURE, IT IS!

I SEE BULLETS IN THE CHAMBER.

HEY, WE'D BETTER GET A POLICEMAN.
YEAH– LET'S GET OFFICER HANLEY.

"OR BETTER YET, LET'S TAKE THIS TO OFFICER HANLEY," SAYS ONE BOY. "WHY NOT?" ASKS THE OTHER.
THAT DIRTY BRAT! HE'S GOT YOUR GAT.

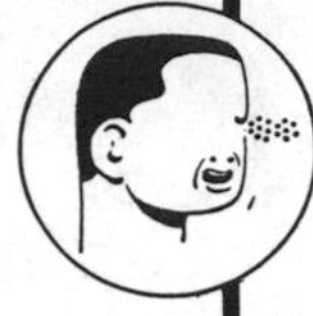

AND YOU FOUND IT?
YES, OFFICER HANLEY, WE FOUND IT IN THE OLD PARK.

THIS IS A BRILLIANT THING YOU'VE DONE, LADS. WHERE DID YOU LEARN TO HANDLE SUSPICIOUS FIREARMS LIKE THIS?
AT THE POLICE YOUTH TRAINING BUREAU. THAT'S WHERE.

CONGRATULATIONS, KIDS. YOU'VE BEEN TAUGHT WELL. YOU'LL HEAR FROM HEADQUARTERS FOR THIS.

MAY I HAVE MY SHOELACE BACK, OFFICER HANLEY?

OH, YES. AND BY THE WAY, LAD, SHOW ME NOW—JUST WHERE DID YOU FIND THIS GUN?

AND IN THE PARK—
IF YOU HADN'T SOCKED ME WITH THAT BOTTLE, I'D HAVE MY GUN BACK NOW.
I HAD TO STOP YOU, SPOTS.

IF YOU HAD GONE OUT THERE AND BEEN SEEN BY THOSE KIDS, WE'D BE HEADED FOR THE HOT SEAT.
IT DOES NOT PAY, YOU DUNDERHEAD, TO GO PLUMB NUTS AND LOSE YOUR HEAD.
–BURNS

WHY WORRY ABOUT THE GUN? NOBODY CAN PROVE IT'S YOURS.
THOSE KIDS! I SAW THEM FIND IT.

SO—LET'S USE SENSE AND PLAY IT SAFE. DON'T RANT AND SCREAM AND YAP AND CHAFE.
–THACKERAY

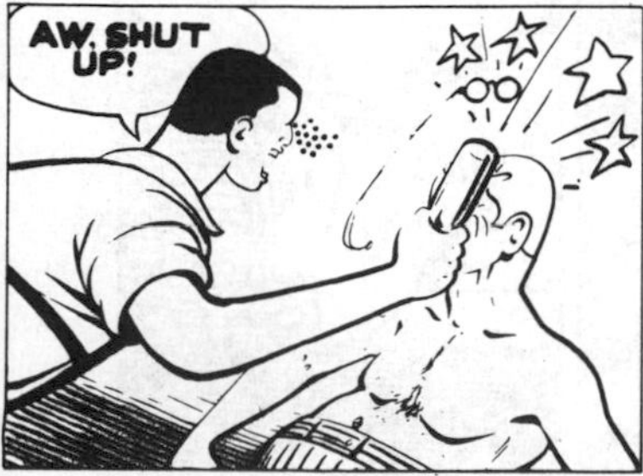
AW, SHUT UP!

PLUNK

HEY, OGDEN! GET UP AND LOOK! QUICK, OGDEN! OGDEN!
CHESTER GOULD

OGDEN! THE COPS ARE HERE! WE'RE SUNK!—UH?

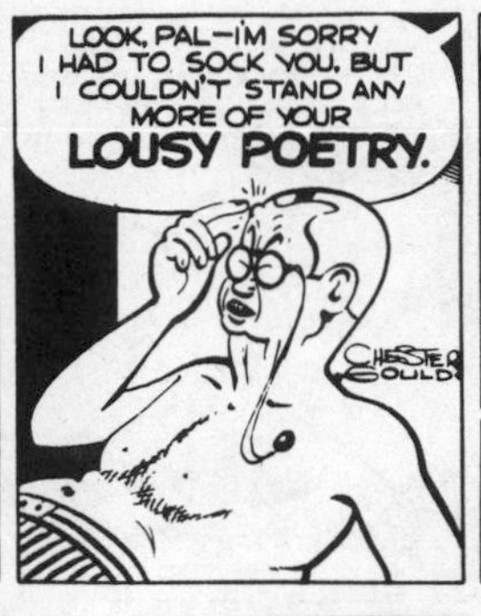

LOOK, PAL—I'M SORRY I HAD TO SOCK YOU, BUT I COULDN'T STAND ANY MORE OF YOUR LOUSY POETRY.
CHESTER GOULD

OFFICER HANLEY, DID YOU HEAR VOICES?
YES—I THOUGHT I DID.

PROVIDENCE M. OGDEN—YOU PHONY! WAKE UP! WE MAY HAVE TO FIGHT OUR WAY OUT OF HERE! SAY SOMETHING!
YOU STRUCK ME DOWN TO END MY VERSE, OH, LET'S GIVE UP AND CALL THE HEARSE. —POE

THERE'S A MUSIC SHOP ACROSS THE PARK THAT HAS A SIDEWALK LOUDSPEAKER.
THAT MUST BE WHERE THE VOICES CAME FROM.

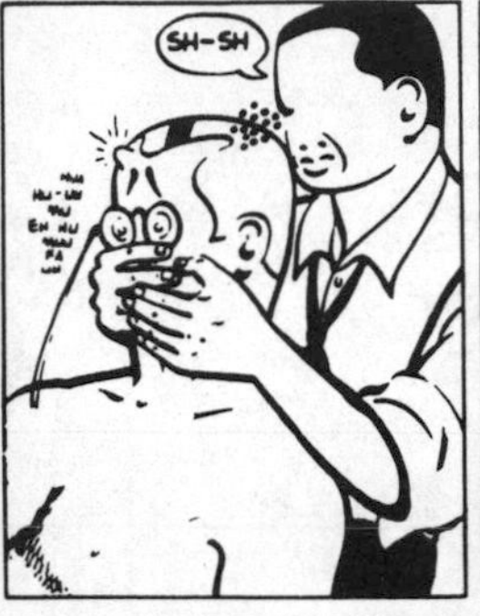

SH—SH

THEY'RE RIGHT OUTSIDE —LOOKING THIS PLACE OVER.

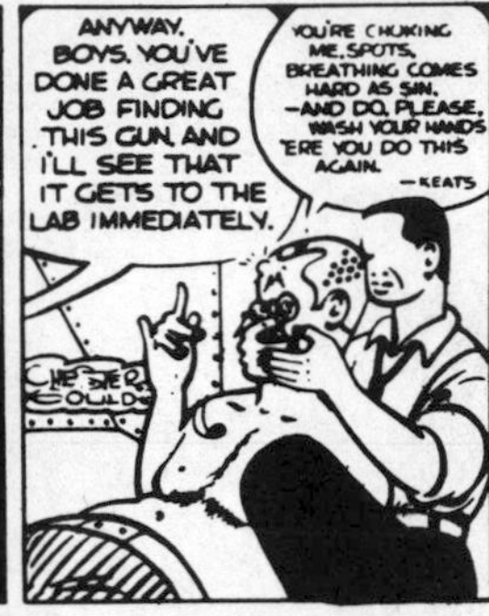

ANYWAY, BOYS, YOU'VE DONE A GREAT JOB FINDING THIS GUN, AND I'LL SEE THAT IT GETS TO THE LAB IMMEDIATELY.
YOU'RE CHOKING ME, SPOTS, BREATHING COMES HARD AS SIN. —AND DO, PLEASE, WASH YOUR HANDS 'ERE YOU DO THIS AGAIN. —KEATS
CHESTER GOULD

WELL, AGAIN LI'L PINEAPPLE PREPARES TO LEAVE THE HOSPITAL.
CHESTER GOULD

MALIA, WILL YOU USE ANY OF HER $100,000 FOR HER EDUCATION?
WILL YOU GO BACK TO YOUR JOB AT THE GIFT SHOP?
WILL YOU TAKE HER BACK TO HAWAII?

THAT COP AND THE KIDS ARE STILL HANGING AROUND.
WHAT EVER GOT US IN THIS MESS?

A LITTLE HAWAIIAN NAMED 'APPLE LOST GRAMP IN A TIDAL WAVE GRAPPLE. THE RICH OLD GALOOT LEFT THE KID ALL HIS LOOT, THIEVING YOU, TRIED TO TAKE THE KID'S CAPITAL. —KEATS
REMEMBER?

SAM, SOME SHARP LITTLE KIDS IN EDGEPARK RAN ONTO THIS IN THE GRASS.

H'M! IT OUGHT TO BE DUSTED FOR PRINTS—AND MAYBE GIVEN A FIRING IN THE SHOOT-BOX.

"LEAVE IT ON THE TABLE. I'LL CALL TRACY," SAYS SAM.

DO THESE "LOST" GUNS EVER SOLVE CASES, SAM?
OH, YES. BULLET COMPARISON TESTS ARE MOST IMPORTANT, ESPECIALLY WHERE WE CAN ESTABLISH OWNERSHIP OF THE GUN.
CHESTER GOULD

WE DISCUSS PLANS, BOTH YOU AND I, I ALWAYS HEAR YOU THROUGH, BUT WHEN I TALK, YOU RAISE A SQUAWK, MY PLANS WILL NEVER DO. —KEATS

I TAKE ABUSE, I TAKE THE BLAME, I TAKE THE BIG SHELLAC, YOU TAKE THE GLORY AND THE DOUGH, AND HAND ME TROUBLE BACK.

OH, WHEN WILL ALL THIS END, PRAY TELL? WHEN WILL THINGS EVER CHANGE? I FEEL JUST LIKE A HOMELESS CUR, WITH FLEAS AND TICKS AND MANGE. —SHELLY

THE GUN FOUND NEAR THE WAR TANK IS BEING TESTED.
THE PAPER PIECES ARE TO HELP LOCATE THE BULLET QUICKLY.

THE SLUG WILL ALWAYS BE FOUND BETWEEN THE LAST PIERCED PAPER AND THE NEXT ONE.

IN REGARD TO THIS GUN, HANLEY, HAS THERE BEEN ANY UNSOLVED STICK-UPS OR SHOOTINGS IN YOUR DISTRICT?
NONE.

SO THEY FOUND THIS GUN IN THE OLD PARK, EH?

YES, THAT LITTLE-USED OLD PARK THAT FLOODS OUT EVERY YEAR.

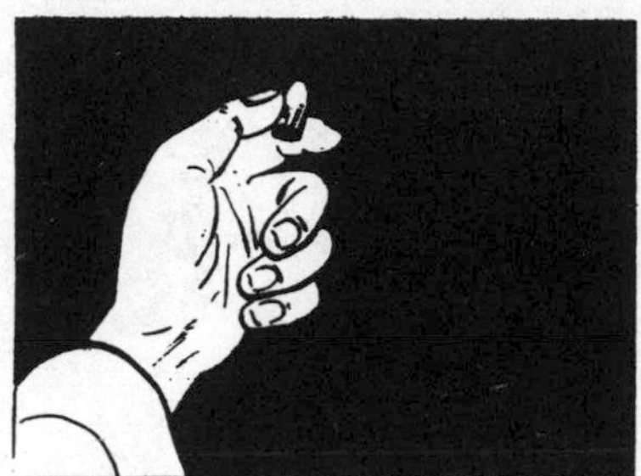

RUN THE USUAL FIREARMS IDENTIFICATION TEST ON THIS, SAM, TO SEE IF IT CHECKS WITH ANY OF OUR UNSOLVED SHOOTING CASES.

AND BACK AT THE TANK—
SPOTS! WILL YOU STOP PACING THE FLOOR?

WHAT AILS ME?—ME, WHO USED TO HAVE GUTS—HIDING OUT WITH A COWARDLY POET IN A TIN CAN?

EVERY TIME I'VE LISTENED TO YOU I'VE BEEN WORSE OFF. IT WAS YOUR IDEA TO NAB THAT LITTLE HAWAIIAN GIRL'S DOUGH IN THE FIRST PLACE! YOU STARTED ALL THIS!

I'VE DONE MY BEST TO SAVE YOUR HIDE BY SHARING MY SMALL NEST. IF YOU'RE FED UP, DEPART ALONE. I'LL STAY, WITHOUT MY GUEST.
—BACON

AND ABOUT 300 FEET AWAY AT THE PARK MAINTENANCE BARN.
I NEVER NOTICED THAT BEFORE.
WHAT?
A PLASTIC WATER LINE AND AN ELECTRIC CABLE.

HEY! IS SOMEBODY STEALING WATER AND JUICE FROM THE PARK? RIP IT OUT!

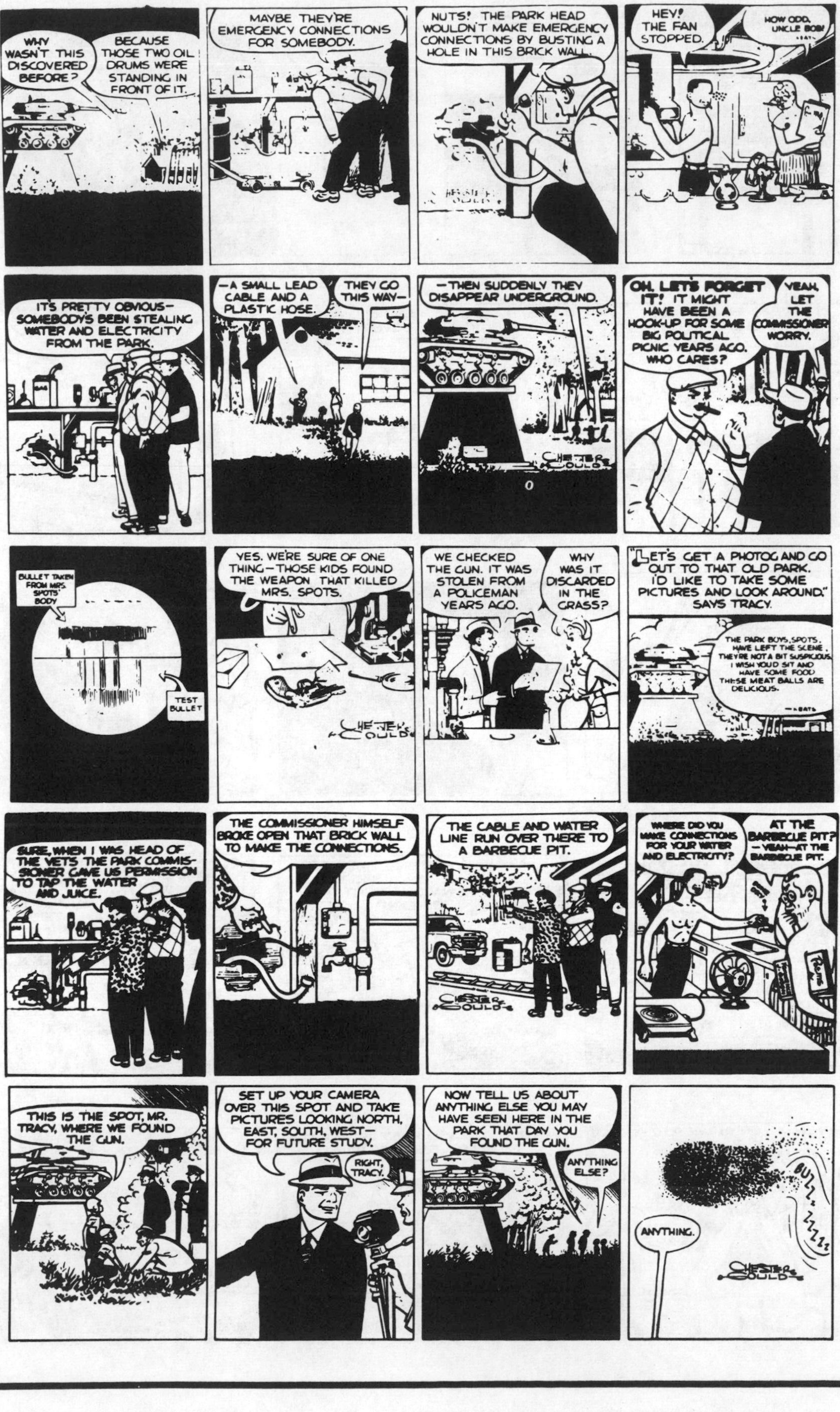

WHY WASN'T THIS DISCOVERED BEFORE?
BECAUSE THOSE TWO OIL DRUMS WERE STANDING IN FRONT OF IT.
MAYBE THEY'RE EMERGENCY CONNECTIONS FOR SOMEBODY.
NUTS! THE PARK HEAD WOULDN'T MAKE EMERGENCY CONNECTIONS BY BUSTING A HOLE IN THIS BRICK WALL.
HEY! THE FAN STOPPED.
HOW ODD, UNCLE BOB!

IT'S PRETTY OBVIOUS—SOMEBODY'S BEEN STEALING WATER AND ELECTRICITY FROM THE PARK.
—A SMALL LEAD CABLE AND A PLASTIC HOSE.
THEY GO THIS WAY—
—THEN SUDDENLY THEY DISAPPEAR UNDERGROUND.
OH, LET'S FORGET IT! IT MIGHT HAVE BEEN A HOOK-UP FOR SOME BIG POLITICAL PICNIC YEARS AGO. WHO CARES?
YEAH, LET THE COMMISSIONER WORRY.

BULLET TAKEN FROM MRS. SPOTS' BODY
TEST BULLET
YES. WE'RE SURE OF ONE THING—THOSE KIDS FOUND THE WEAPON THAT KILLED MRS. SPOTS.
WE CHECKED THE GUN. IT WAS STOLEN FROM A POLICEMAN YEARS AGO.
WHY WAS IT DISCARDED IN THE GRASS?
"LET'S GET A PHOTOG AND GO OUT TO THAT OLD PARK. I'D LIKE TO TAKE SOME PICTURES AND LOOK AROUND," SAYS TRACY.
THE PARK BOYS, SPOTS, HAVE LEFT THE SCENE. THEY'RE NOT A BIT SUSPICIOUS. I WISH YOU'D SIT AND HAVE SOME FOOD. THESE MEAT BALLS ARE DELICIOUS.

SURE, WHEN I WAS HEAD OF THE VETS THE PARK COMMISSIONER GAVE US PERMISSION TO TAP THE WATER AND JUICE.
THE COMMISSIONER HIMSELF BROKE OPEN THAT BRICK WALL TO MAKE THE CONNECTIONS.
THE CABLE AND WATER LINE RUN OVER THERE TO A BARBECUE PIT.
WHERE DID YOU MAKE CONNECTIONS FOR YOUR WATER AND ELECTRICITY?
AT THE BARBECUE PIT? —YEAH—AT THE BARBECUE PIT.

THIS IS THE SPOT, MR. TRACY, WHERE WE FOUND THE GUN.
SET UP YOUR CAMERA OVER THIS SPOT AND TAKE PICTURES LOOKING NORTH, EAST, SOUTH, WEST—FOR FUTURE STUDY.
RIGHT, TRACY.
NOW TELL US ABOUT ANYTHING ELSE YOU MAY HAVE SEEN HERE IN THE PARK THAT DAY YOU FOUND THE GUN.
ANYTHING ELSE?
ANYTHING.
BUZZ
ZZZZZ

A PLAINCLOTHESMAN! I SEE HIS CALL BOX KEY HANGING ON HIS BELT.

AND THOSE PARK MAINTENANCE MEN ARE COMING OUT AGAIN. WE'RE SUNK OGDEN.

OH, WEAKEN NOT! LET COURAGE REIGN, BE BRAVE AND STRONG AND STOUT. REMEMBER BALL GAMES NE'R ARE O'ER TILL THAT LAST MAN IS OUT.

BY JOVE! WHAT'S THAT BUZZING?
JUST THE SCREWS IN YOUR IDIOT HEAD, PROVIDENCE J. OGDEN!
ZZZ
BZZZ
CHESTER GOULD

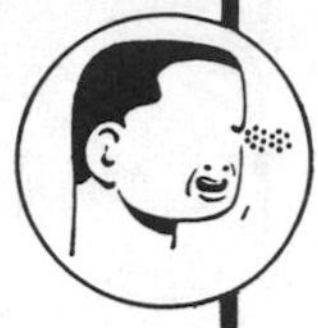

THE PARK SUPERINTENDENT GAVE THE SERVICEMEN PERMISSION TO TAP IN FOR POWER AND WATER FOR THEIR PICNICS.

THOSE LINES GO OVER TO THE PICNIC TABLE AND BARBECUE PIT.

BETTER PLUG THEM IN AGAIN TILL AFTER THE FALL POWWOW NEXT WEEK.

HEY, SPOTS! THE WATER JUST CAME ON—AND THE FAN STARTED!

WHO CARES? TAKE A GANDER THROUGH THIS PERISCOPE, OGDEN.

PLAIN-CLOTHESMEN! AND THEY'RE TALKING TO THE KIDS THAT FOUND MY GUN.

I'M LEAVING THIS PLACE AS SOON AS IT GETS DARK.
RESTRAIN YOURSELF, RAISE NOT YOUR VOICE, IF THOSE ARE COPS OUT THERE. BREATHE NOT A SOUND, LEST YOU BE FOUND BEFORE YOU TAKE THE AIR. —KEATS.

BESIDES THAT OLD TANK, WHAT ELSE IS IN THIS PARK?
NOTHING, MISTER, 'CEPT THE VETERANS' BARBECUE TABLE AND PIT DOWN THERE.

HEY—WHAT'S THAT?
THAT BUZZING?
BZZZ ZZZZZ

BEES?
BEES?
YES, SOMEBODY LOST A HIVE OF BEES.
BZZZ

AND THEY'RE LOOKING FOR A PLACE TO SWARM.

THEY FOUND A PLACE.
BOY! I'M STAYING AWAY FROM THERE.
CHESTER GOULD

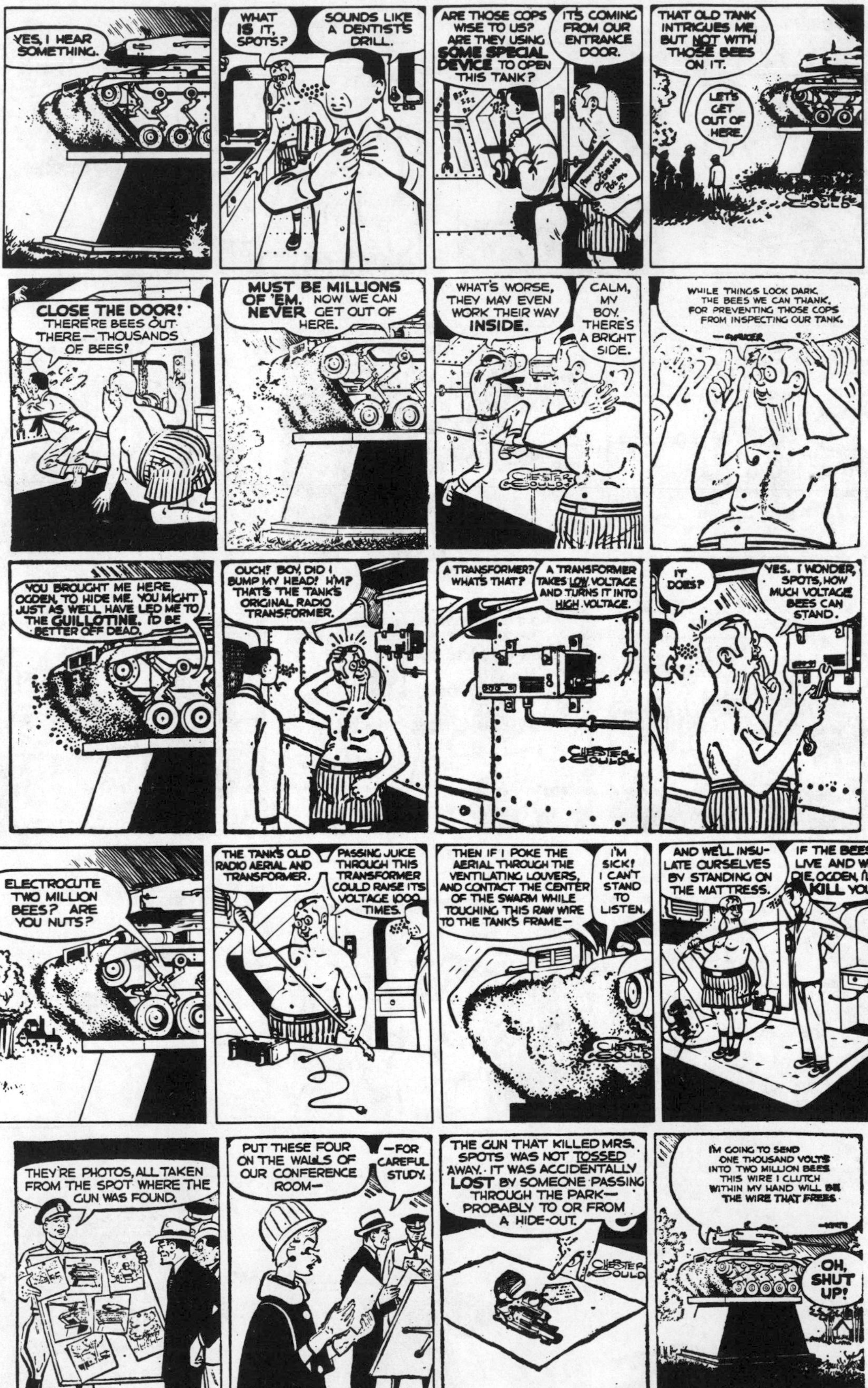

YES, I HEAR SOMETHING.
WHAT IS IT, SPOTS?
SOUNDS LIKE A DENTIST'S DRILL.
ARE THOSE COPS WISE TO US? ARE THEY USING SOME SPECIAL DEVICE TO OPEN THIS TANK?
IT'S COMING FROM OUR ENTRANCE DOOR.
THAT OLD TANK INTRIGUES ME, BUT NOT WITH THOSE BEES ON IT.
LET'S GET OUT OF HERE.
CHESTER GOULD

CLOSE THE DOOR! THERE'RE BEES OUT THERE—THOUSANDS OF BEES!
MUST BE MILLIONS OF 'EM. NOW WE CAN NEVER GET OUT OF HERE.
WHAT'S WORSE, THEY MAY EVEN WORK THEIR WAY INSIDE.
CALM, MY BOY. THERE'S A BRIGHT SIDE.
CHESTER GOULD
WHILE THINGS LOOK DARK, THE BEES WE CAN THANK, FOR PREVENTING THOSE COPS FROM INSPECTING OUR TANK.

YOU BROUGHT ME HERE, OGDEN, TO HIDE ME. YOU MIGHT JUST AS WELL HAVE LED ME TO THE GUILLOTINE. I'D BE BETTER OFF DEAD.
OUCH! BOY, DID I BUMP MY HEAD! H'M? THAT'S THE TANK'S ORIGINAL RADIO TRANSFORMER.
A TRANSFORMER? WHAT'S THAT?
A TRANSFORMER TAKES LOW VOLTAGE AND TURNS IT INTO HIGH VOLTAGE.
CHESTER GOULD
IT DOES?
YES. I WONDER, SPOTS, HOW MUCH VOLTAGE BEES CAN STAND.

ELECTROCUTE TWO MILLION BEES? ARE YOU NUTS?
THE TANK'S OLD RADIO AERIAL AND TRANSFORMER.
PASSING JUICE THROUGH THIS TRANSFORMER COULD RAISE ITS VOLTAGE 1000 TIMES.
THEN IF I POKE THE AERIAL THROUGH THE VENTILATING LOUVERS, AND CONTACT THE CENTER OF THE SWARM WHILE TOUCHING THIS RAW WIRE TO THE TANK'S FRAME—
I'M SICK! I CAN'T STAND TO LISTEN.
CHESTER GOULD
AND WE'LL INSULATE OURSELVES BY STANDING ON THE MATTRESS.
IF THE BEES LIVE AND WE DIE, OGDEN, I'LL KILL YOU!

THEY'RE PHOTOS, ALL TAKEN FROM THE SPOT WHERE THE GUN WAS FOUND.
PUT THESE FOUR ON THE WALLS OF OUR CONFERENCE ROOM—
—FOR CAREFUL STUDY.
THE GUN THAT KILLED MRS. SPOTS WAS NOT TOSSED AWAY. IT WAS ACCIDENTALLY LOST BY SOMEONE PASSING THROUGH THE PARK—PROBABLY TO OR FROM A HIDE-OUT.
CHESTER GOULD
I'M GOING TO SEND ONE THOUSAND VOLTS INTO TWO MILLION BEES. THIS WIRE I CLUTCH WITHIN MY HAND WILL BE THE WIRE THAT FREES.
OH, SHUT UP!

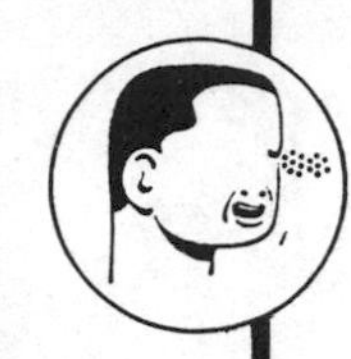

I HOPE TO EARN YOUR DEEP RESPECT BY WHAT I PLAN TO DO, ELECTROCUTE TWO MILLION BEES, OR MAKE THEM ALL SKIDOO. —KEATS
PERHAPS I SHOULD EXPLAIN TO YOU EXACTLY HOW THIS WORKS. 'LECTRICITY OFT IS HARD TO DIG, BY GOOFS AND SAPS AND JERKS. —BACON

WHO'S A JERK?
CALM DOWN. I'M ONLY KIDDING. TUT-TUTTY TUT-TUT.
BUZZ BZZ BZZ

OH, WHAT'S THE USE? I'M A BROKEN MAN! CARRY ON, OGDEN. ANYTHING YOU SAY. JUST GET US OUT OF HERE. THAT'S ALL—OUT-OUT—
CHESTER GOULD

WE'VE GOT TO ELECTROCUTE THOSE BEES—TO GET OUT. BESIDES, THEY MAY SWARM INSIDE NEXT.

THE TANK'S ORIGINAL RADIO TRANSFORMER AND THIS AERIAL FROM WAR DAYS OUGHT TO DO IT.

THE JUICE THAT COMES OUT OF HERE WILL BE MUCH HIGHER VOLTAGE, SO NOW WHEN I TOUCH THIS RAW WIRE TO THE TANK—

STAND ON THE MATTRESS AND DON'T TOUCH THE TANK. READY?

WHILE AT HEADQUARTERS
FOUR VIEWS. NORTH, EAST, SOUTH, WEST.
EAST
SOUTH

TAKEN FROM THE EXACT SPOT WHERE THE GUN WAS FOUND.
EAST

THAT OLD WAR TANK FASCINATES ME. I WONDER IF THE BEES ARE STILL ON IT.

TRACY—HOW MUCH TIME ELAPSED BETWEEN THESE TWO PHOTOS?
TIME? DON'T KNOW, SAM, MAYBE A MINUTE OR TWO. WHY?

IN THIS PICTURE THERE SEEMS TO BE SOMETHING PROJECTING FROM THE TOP OF THE TANK.
IN THE BIG PICTURE —NO.

THAT'S FUNNY, THERE IS SOMETHING PROJECTING FROM THE TOP OF THIS ONE.
WHAT WOULD IT BE?
CHESTER GOULD

LIZZ, CALL THE FIFTH ARMY ARMORED DIVISION AND ASK THEM TO SEND US A TANK EXPERT.

SIZZLE
SIZZLE
SIZZLE
SIZZLE
SIZZLE

DON'T STEP OFF THAT MATTRESS! I'M GOING TO GIVE 'EM ANOTHER SHOT.

THERE! NOW, SPOTS, YOU CAN OPEN THE DOOR.
OPEN THE DOOR?? DO YOU THINK I'M NUTS?

CHESTER GOULD

YES, THIS IS A PERISCOPE.
IT HADN'T BEEN RAISED WHEN THE FIRST PICTURE WAS TAKEN.

THOSE OLD WAR TANKS HAD WONDERFUL PERISCOPES WITH BUILT-IN BINOCULARS. SOMEBODY WAS INSIDE THIS TANK.

YOU'RE RIGHT, OGDEN—THE BEES ARE DEAD.
OBOY! LET'S GET OUT OF HERE.

FIRST, TAKE THIS AERIAL OFF MY NECK,
AND APOLOGIZE, YOU CAD.
MY PLAN YOU SPOOFED,
YOU SAID I GOOFED,
YOU'RE WRONG, AND AM I GLAD.
-SHELLY

CHESTER GOULD

NOW?
NO WAIT, SPOTS, THERE'S A CAR OUT THERE.

A CAR?
YEAH! JUST A CAR.

EXPENSIVE LOOKING, TOO—A 1960 JOB—

AN UTTERLY ABANDONED SPOT! THIS WILL BE JUST THE PLACE TO LEAVE IT.

CHESTER GOULD

I SAID THIS LOOKS LIKE A GOOD PLACE TO LEAVE IT.

NO, NO, I CAN'T! I JUST CAN'T!
FRESH, OBEY YOUR MOTHER. LEAVE IT HERE!

IS THE CAR STILL THERE, OGDEN?
YES.

WHAT ARE THEY DOING?
SEARCH ME! —UNDOUBTEDLY, LOVERS BILLING AND COOING. BE PATIENT, SPOTS, BE PATIENT.

CHESTER GOULD

NO MATTER WHAT YOU SAY, FRESH, WE'RE NOT LEAVING HERE TILL YOU ABANDON IT.

MOTHER, HOW CAN YOU ASK ME TO DO SUCH A THING?

FRESH, THE FAMILY NAME OF UPP IS A PROUD NAME, AND WE'VE NEVER HAD A BLOT ON IT. NOW DO AS I SAY.

WAIT! I'LL TURN THE CAR AROUND SO WE CAN MAKE A QUICK GETAWAY AFTER YOU LEAVE IT.
OH, MOTHER!

CHESTER GOULD

HURRY, FRESH! WE MUST GET OUT OF HERE.

GOT ALL YOUR BELONGINGS, SPOTS?
YEP, I'M READY TO GO.

OH, LITTLE, HUMBLE, RUSTY TANK,
YOU'VE BEEN A HOME SO TRUE.
WE BID YOU BYE,
WE HEAVE A SIGH,
AS WE SAY FOND ADIEU.
—CHAULEN

CHESTER GOULD

IT TOOK TWO JOLTS, SPOTS, BUT WE FINALLY ELECTROCUTED THE BEES.

LOOK THROUGH THAT PERISCOPE AND SEE IF THE COAST'S CLEAR SO WE CAN GET OUT OF HERE.

WAIT! DON'T OPEN THAT HATCH YET.
WHY?

SH! — SOMEONE'S COMING TOWARD THE TANK — A WOMAN!

SHE'S CARRYING SOMETHING — AND THERE'S A CAR WAITING —

IS IT A POLICE CAR?
NO. THERE'S A WOMAN AT THE WHEEL — AND I CAN SEE THEIR LICENSE PLATE.

THEY'RE LEAVING.
GOOD. SO ARE WE.

HEY, SPOTS, WAIT—
LET'S SEE WHAT THAT WOMAN—

COME ON, YOU DOPE, LET'S GET OUT OF HERE.
HUH??
A BABY?
WA-A WA WA-A-

A BABY?
CHESTER GOULD

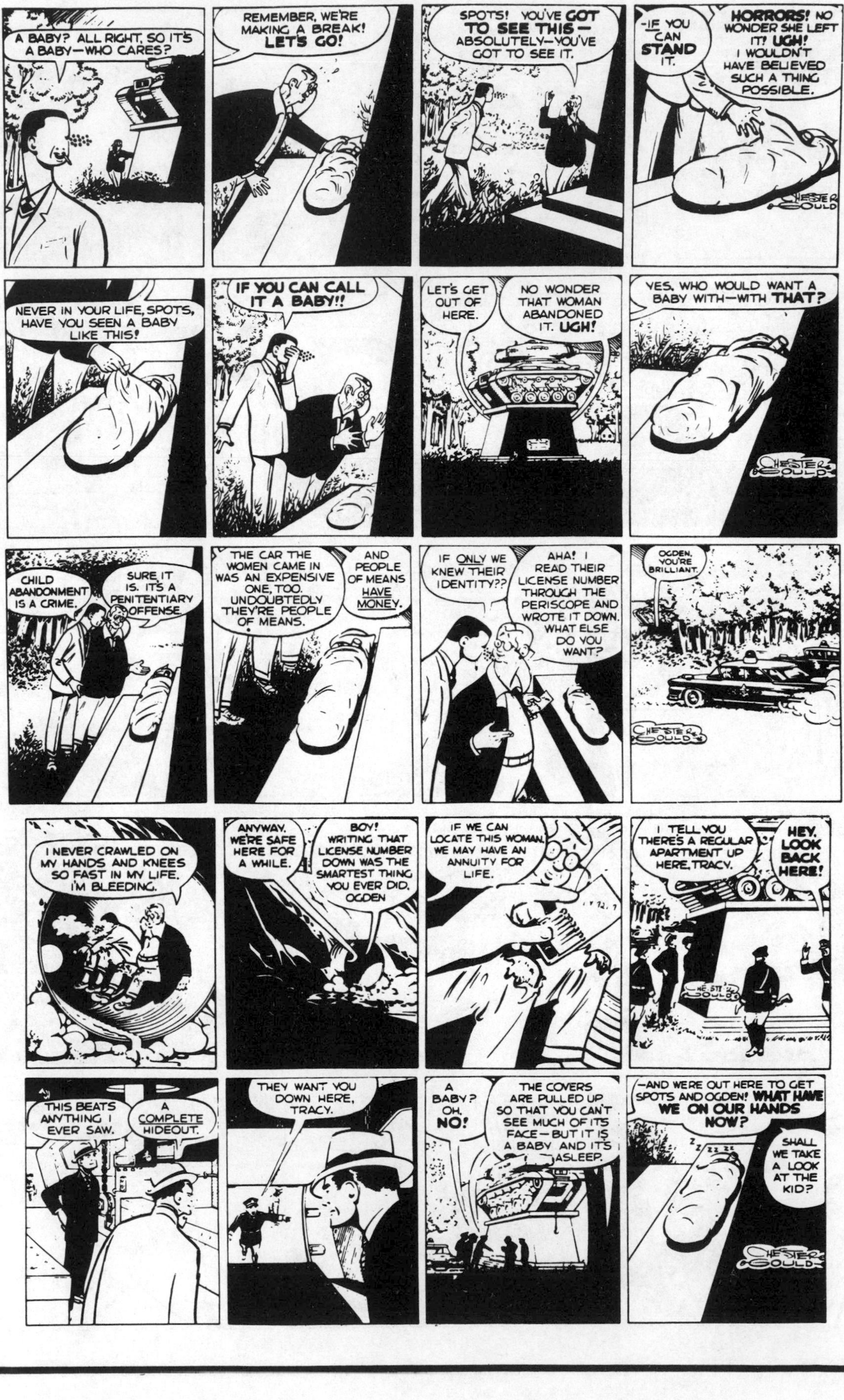

A BABY? ALL RIGHT, SO IT'S A BABY—WHO CARES?
REMEMBER, WE'RE MAKING A BREAK! **LET'S GO!**
SPOTS! YOU'VE **GOT TO SEE THIS**— ABSOLUTELY—YOU'VE GOT TO SEE IT.
-IF YOU CAN **STAND** IT.
HORRORS! NO WONDER SHE LEFT IT? **UGH!** I WOULDN'T HAVE BELIEVED SUCH A THING POSSIBLE.
CHESTER GOULD

NEVER IN YOUR LIFE, SPOTS, HAVE YOU SEEN A BABY LIKE THIS!
IF YOU CAN CALL IT A BABY!!
LET'S GET OUT OF HERE.
NO WONDER THAT WOMAN ABANDONED IT. **UGH!**
YES, WHO WOULD WANT A BABY WITH—WITH **THAT?**
CHESTER GOULD

CHILD ABANDONMENT IS A CRIME.
SURE IT IS. IT'S A PENITENTIARY OFFENSE.
THE CAR THE WOMEN CAME IN WAS AN EXPENSIVE ONE, TOO. UNDOUBTEDLY THEY'RE PEOPLE OF MEANS.
AND PEOPLE OF MEANS HAVE MONEY.
IF ONLY WE KNEW THEIR IDENTITY??
AHA! I READ THEIR LICENSE NUMBER THROUGH THE PERISCOPE AND WROTE IT DOWN. WHAT ELSE DO YOU WANT?
OGDEN, YOU'RE BRILLIANT.
CHESTER GOULD

I NEVER CRAWLED ON MY HANDS AND KNEES SO FAST IN MY LIFE. I'M BLEEDING.
ANYWAY. WE'RE SAFE HERE FOR A WHILE.
BOY! WRITING THAT LICENSE NUMBER DOWN WAS THE SMARTEST THING YOU EVER DID, OGDEN
IF WE CAN LOCATE THIS WOMAN, WE MAY HAVE AN ANNUITY FOR LIFE.
I TELL YOU THERE'S A REGULAR APARTMENT UP HERE, TRACY.
HEY, LOOK BACK HERE!
CHESTER GOULD

SHOULD WE PULL THOSE COVERS BACK AND TAKE A LOOK AT THE CHILD?
WAIT. IT MIGHT WAKE UP.

LET IT **SLEEP** WHILE WE MAKE A FEW OBSERVATIONS.

THE WEEDS SHOW A CAR HAD DRIVEN UP OVER THERE.
AND SOMEONE APPARENTLY WALKED TO THAT SPOT WHERE THE BABY LIES.

DID THAT SAME CAR TAKE SPOTS AND OGDEN AWAY???
CAN THERE BE ANY CONNECTION?
ZZ
THAT SLEEPING CHILD! WHAT SHOCKING SURPRISE DOES IT HOLD FOR TRACY AND SAM?
CHESTER GOULD

IT'S DONE! THAT'S ALL THERE IS TO IT. **IT'S DONE!** NOW STOP CRYING, FRESH.

BUT, MOTHER, IT ALL SEEMED SO COLD-BLOODED. THERE MUST HAVE BEEN ANOTHER WAY.

WILL YOU STRAIGHTEN UP? WE HAVE MANY THINGS TO THINK ABOUT NOW.

—AND THEY'RE ALL PLEASANT—YOU HAVEN'T A WORRY IN THE WORLD, FRESH. COME HAVE A NICE, COOL COLA.

AND AT THE PARK—
THERE'S NO QUESTION ABOUT IT—THE TANK'S BEEN LIVED IN—AND THE OCCUPANTS HAVEN'T BEEN GONE VERY LONG, FROM THE SMELL OF CIGARETTE SMOKE IN THERE.

IT'S EASY TO SEE WHY THEY FLED. THEY SAW OUR EVERY MOVE THROUGH THE TANK'S PERISCOPE! THAT'S UNDERSTANDABLE, BUT—

—THIS NEW MYSTERY HAS ME **ABSOLUTELY BAFFLED!**

AN ABANDONED CHILD? WHAT CONNECTION COULD THERE BE? WHAT COULD THIS POSSIBLY HAVE TO DO WITH **SPOTS AND OGDEN?** WHAT? WHAT?

PERFECTLY HAPPY, A BEAUTIFUL CHILD. BLUE EYES—ROSY CHEEKS. PULL THAT BLANKET DOWN SO WE CAN SEE THE REST OF ITS FACE.

HEY!
OH, **NO!**

DO YOU SEE THAT?
IMPOSSIBLE!
I DON'T BELIEVE IT.

A BEARD?
CHESTER GOULD

A BEARD?
YES, A BEARD.

A REAL BEARD?!
WA
WA WA
WA
WA WA
WA

AS SURE AS MY NAME IS BURPIE UPP, YOU'LL NEVER REGRET THIS FRESH.
BUT WHAT WOULD MY POOR HUSBAND SAY—WERE HE ALIVE—KNOWING I'VE ABANDONED OUR BABY?
TSH! TSH! MOTHAW KNOWS BEST.
A BABY WITH A BEARD! UGH!

YES, IT'S REAL! YOU CAN COMB IT!

WELL, WE CAN'T LEAVE IT HERE.
BETTER TAKE IT TO THE CITY HOSPITAL FOR A PHYSICAL CHECK-UP.

ROPE OFF THIS ENTIRE AREA.
WE'VE GOT TO MAKE FURTHER EXAMINATION OF THE TANK AND GROUNDS.

GOLLY! IT'S AS SOFT AS SILK.

I REPEAT—WHO WANTS A BABY WITH A BEARD?
W-W-WE—COULD HAVE SHAVED HIM.

THE HOSPITAL GAVE HIM A CLEAN BILL. HE'S IN PERFECT HEALTH.

WE DON'T KNOW HIS REAL NAME. WE'LL HAVE TO GIVE HIM ONE.

AND IT CERTAINLY WILL NOT BE "BEARDSLEY"! HAH!
WELL, I HOPE NOT, LIZZ. THAT'S MY UNCLE'S NAME.

MEANWHILE
VERDA, GET ME A LICENSE CHECK ON PLATE LY-921-9.

AREN'T THOSE PENCIL MARKS?

YES—WRITING—LOOKS LIKE NUMBERS. THEY'VE BEEN SMEARED.

GIVE ME YOUR FLASHLIGHT, SAM.

"LITTLE BOY BEARD!"
HEY! THAT'S NOT A BAD NAME.

THAT WAS A KNOCK.
WERE YOU EXPECTING ANYONE?

A MESSAGE FROM THE DESK, MA'AM.
THE DESK?

EEK!
JUST WHO ARE YOU?

WE'VE COME HERE TO TALK, MA'AM, WITH YOU AND YOUR DAUGHTER. YOU'VE BEEN DOING THINGS, MA'AM, THAT YOU HADN'T OUGHTER. —POE
WHO IS THIS HORRID CREATURE?

FOUND ABANDONED AT THE FOOT OF THE OLD WAR TANK, THE BABY BOY WITH THE BEARD HAS CAUSED A SENSATION.
NOTHING LIKE HIM IN MEDICAL HISTORY.

NEVER BEFORE IN PROFESSIONAL ANNALS HAS A BABY BEEN REPORTED BORN WITH A BEARD.

WHAT ABOUT SPOTS AND OGDEN? YOU WENT THERE TO GET THEM.
CHIEF, THERE SEEMS TO BE NO CONNECTION BETWEEN THEIR OCCUPYING THAT TANK AND THE ABANDONMENT OF THIS CHILD.

YOU MEAN IT WAS PURELY COINCIDENTAL THAT THE KID WAS ABANDONED AT THAT SPOT?
SO IT SEEMS, CHIEF.
OH, THAT BEARD'S REAL, ALL RIGHT.

THE HOSPITAL EXAMINATION SHOWS HE'S IN PERFECT HEALTH. WE TOOK HIS FOOTPRINTS FOR POSSIBLE IDENTIFICATION.

HAVE YOU ANY LEADS ON WHAT HAPPENED TO SPOTS AND OGDEN?
YES, WE HAVE SOME CLUES.

SPEAKING OF OGDEN AND SPOTS—
YOU AWFUL CREATURES— FORCING YOUR WAY IN HERE! WHO ARE YOU?

WHAT MATTERS? WE KNOW WHO YOU ARE. YOU'RE BURPIE UPP AND THAT'S YOUR DAUGHTER, FRESH. YOU DROVE A CAR INTO A CITY PARK AND ABANDONED A BABY.

WE SAW! WE COPIED YOUR LICENSE NUMBER. WE HAD A LADY CLERK CHECK IT IN THE LICENSE REGISTRATION BUREAU.

WHY ARE YOU HERE, YOU HORRID MEN?
TUT, TUTTY. DON'T PANIC. OUR PLOT IS TITANIC. —BURNS

WE DON'T WANT TO KNOW ANY DETAILS. WE JUST WANT TO MAKE A BUSINESS DEAL WITH YOU.
BUSINESS DEAL —INDEED!

IT'S OBVIOUS, YOU AND YOUR DAUGHTER SO FAIR ARE PULLING A FAST LITTLE SCHEME. WE WON'T TELL A SOUL. KEEPING MUM IS OUR GOAL. IF YOU'LL JUST MEET OUR TERMS WITH LONG GREEN.
CHESTER GOULD

BLACKMAIL ME? WHY, YOU MORONS! **LEAVE MY APARTMENT AT ONCE!**

OH, YOU SOCIETY DAMES CAN BE SO CUTE!

SMACK

CHESTER GOULD

HEY! THAT SLAP HURT. BOTH CHEEK AND PRIDE.
YOU STRUCK ME ON MY FACE.
NOW TILL WE GET JUST WHAT WE WANT,
WE'LL NEVER LEAVE THIS PLACE.
—MCCAULY

WHAT RIGHT HAVE YOU TWO TO—

KEEP QUIET, FRESH! MOTHAW WILL HANDLE THIS.

LOOK. WE SAW HER ABANDON THE BABY—WE SAW YOU AT THE WHEEL OF THE CAR. WE WROTE DOWN YOUR LICENSE NUMBER. NOW WE WANT MONEY.

YOU ROTTERS! YOU STINKERS!

KEEP YOUR DIRTY LITTLE EPITHETS TO YOURSELF, BURPIE UPP. JUST PAY.

I THINK ONE FINDS IT AWFULLY HARD,
TO FACE THE FACTS, WITHAL.
HOWEVER, THAT'S THE FINEST COURSE
WHEN ONE'S BACK'S TO THE WALL.
-CHAUCER

CHESTER GOULD

LITTLE BOY BEARD.

WHAT A NAME! LITTLE BOY BEARD!

DID YOU NOTICE THAT?

WHAT?

I HANDED HIM A PACKAGE OF CIGARETTES AND HE CRUSHED THEM LIKE THEY WERE SOAP BUBBLES.

THIS KID'S GOT A GRIP OF IRON!

WHAT TH-?? HUH?

CHESTER GOULD

WELL, WE WON'T LEAVE THIS APARTMENT TILL WE'VE MADE A DEAL, BURPIE UPP.

SIT DOWN, OGDEN.

OH, THANK YOU SO MUCH.
WHAT A LUSH PLACE TO LOAF,
WHILE WE TRY TO DO BUSINESS
WITH THIS LADY OAF.
—TOLSTOY

CHESTER GOULD

REFRESHMENTS! HOW NICE!

HELP YOURSELF—THAT ONE HAS THE STRYCHNINE IN IT.

BLACKMAIL ME? **NEVER!** YOU'RE JUST WASTING YOUR TIME.

YUM-YUM

HAVE ANOTHER CANTALOUPE?

INDEED, I WILL! I LOVE CANTALOUPE.

TEN THOUSAND DOLLARS WOULD SEAL OUR LIPS FOREVER, BURPIE.

YOUR FEARS
WOULD BE O'ER
WHEN WE LEFT
YOUR DOOR.
—POE

MOM!

LITTLE BOY BEARD

CHESTER GOULD

FIRST PHOTOS OF LITTLE BOY BEARD.

THE ABANDONED WAIF THAT IS CAUSING COMMENT FROM COAST TO COAST.

WAS HE ABANDONED BY HIS PARENTS? WAS HE A VICTIM OF KIDNAPPERS? WHO IS LITTLE BOY BEARD?
MY BABY!

WHILE TRACY BEGINS A TEDIOUS CHECK OF MATERNITY WARDS.
DO YOUR RECORDS SHOW A BABY BOY BEING BORN HERE WITH A BEARD?
WITH A WHAT?

POLICE ARE ATTEMPTING TO LOCATE THE PERSON OR PERSONS WHO ABANDONED THIS CHILD.
MY BABY!

CHILD ABANDONMENT IS A FELONY PUNISHABLE BY A TERM IN THE PENITENTIARY.

HE'S TALKING TO YOU, MRS UPP! THAT'S WHAT'S AHEAD FOR YOU AND YOUR DAUGHTER IF WE SQUEAL—

OH-BOO-HOO-HOO— MY LITTLE BABY.

WILL YOU SHUT UP?
OH, I WISH I HAD BEEN KILLED IN THAT CAR WITH MY HUSBAND JOHNNY.

THEN THIS IS JUST PLAIN OLD BLACKMAIL—FOR $5,000—IS THAT WHAT YOU WANT?
YES, BURPIE UPP.
INDEED, OH, YES! HOW RIGHT YOUR GUESS. —KEATS

IN CASH!
NATURALLY, DAHLING.

MEANWHILE, DICK TRACY HAS BEEN CALLING ON HOSPITAL MATERNITY WARDS.
A BEARD? A BABY WITH A BEARD??—NO, OUR RECORDS SHOW NO SUCH BIRTH.

—A BEARD?? HEY! A FATHER WALKED IN HERE SEVERAL WEEKS AGO WITH A BABY THAT HAD A BEARD.
SHE'S RIGHT!

THAT'S RIGHT! THE CHILD WASN'T BORN HERE—BUT THE FATHER BROUGHT HIM HERE TO SEE WHAT COULD BE DONE ABOUT THE BEARD.

HE WAS TOLD NOTHING COULD BE DONE.
WHAT WAS THE FATHER'S NAME?
I DON'T THINK WE HAVE A RECORD OF HIS NAME.
CHESTER GOULD

A BABY WITH A BEARD! WHAT WON'T YOU DETECTIVES HAVE TO WORRY ABOUT NEXT?
YOU NAME IT!
THAT'S THE BABY!

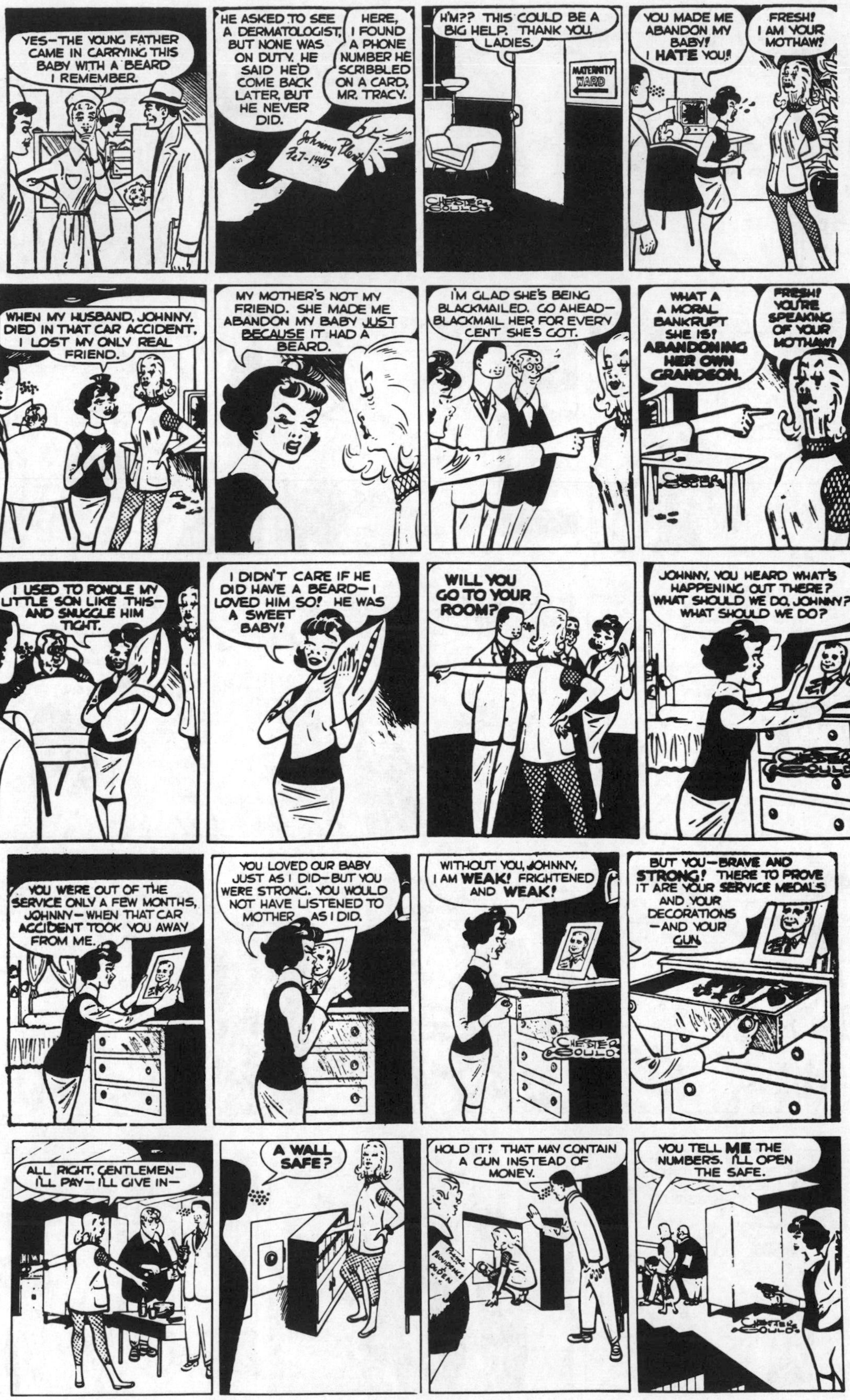

YES—THE YOUNG FATHER CAME IN CARRYING THIS BABY WITH A BEARD I REMEMBER.

HE ASKED TO SEE A DERMATOLOGIST, BUT NONE WAS ON DUTY. HE SAID HE'D COME BACK LATER, BUT HE NEVER DID.

HERE, I FOUND A PHONE NUMBER HE SCRIBBLED ON A CARD, MR. TRACY.

Johnny Plens Fe7-1415

H'M?? THIS COULD BE A BIG HELP. THANK YOU, LADIES.

MATERNITY WARD

YOU MADE ME ABANDON MY BABY! I **HATE** YOU!

FRESH! I AM YOUR MOTHAW!

WHEN MY HUSBAND, JOHNNY, DIED IN THAT CAR ACCIDENT, I LOST MY ONLY REAL FRIEND.

MY MOTHER'S NOT MY FRIEND. SHE MADE ME ABANDON MY BABY JUST BECAUSE IT HAD A BEARD.

I'M GLAD SHE'S BEING BLACKMAILED. GO AHEAD—BLACKMAIL HER FOR EVERY CENT SHE'S GOT.

WHAT A MORAL BANKRUPT SHE IS! **ABANDONING HER OWN GRANDSON.**

FRESH! YOU'RE SPEAKING OF YOUR MOTHAW!

I USED TO FONDLE MY LITTLE SON LIKE THIS—AND SNUGGLE HIM TIGHT.

I DIDN'T CARE IF HE DID HAVE A BEARD—I LOVED HIM SO! HE WAS A SWEET BABY!

WILL YOU GO TO YOUR ROOM?

JOHNNY, YOU HEARD WHAT'S HAPPENING OUT THERE? WHAT SHOULD WE DO, JOHNNY? WHAT SHOULD WE DO?

YOU WERE OUT OF THE SERVICE ONLY A FEW MONTHS, JOHNNY—WHEN THAT CAR **ACCIDENT** TOOK YOU AWAY FROM ME.

YOU LOVED OUR BABY JUST AS I DID—BUT YOU WERE STRONG. YOU WOULD NOT HAVE LISTENED TO MOTHER AS I DID.

WITHOUT YOU, JOHNNY, I AM **WEAK!** FRIGHTENED AND **WEAK!**

BUT YOU—**BRAVE** AND **STRONG!** THERE TO PROVE IT ARE YOUR **SERVICE MEDALS** AND YOUR DECORATIONS —AND YOUR GUN.

I SAID PUT 'EM UP-ALL OF YOU!

YES, YOU TOO! DON'T MOVE.
FRESH! I AM YOUR MOTHAW.

YOU'RE NOT MY "MOTHAW." YOU'RE A MORAL PAUPER AND A FIEND.

SHE MADE ME ABANDON MY BABY.
NOW, I'M GOING TO HOLD COURT AND PASS JUDGMENT ON ALL OF YOU.
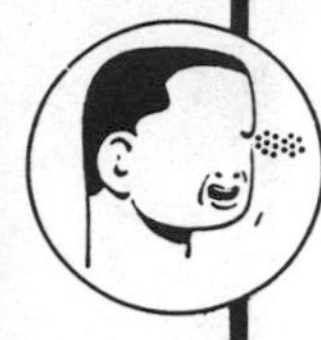

I REMEMBERED MY HUSBAND'S GUN THAT HE GOT A WEEK BEFORE HE DIED—SO THE BABY AND I WOULD HAVE PROTECTION WHEN HE WAS AWAY.

NOW HE IS DEAD AND I HAVE NO BABY—JUST THIS PILLOW.

MY OWN MOTHER MADE ME ABANDON MY BABY! MY OWN WRETCHED, WICKED MOTHER.

—FORCED HER OWN DAUGHTER TO ABANDON HER BABY SON JUST BECAUSE IT WAS BORN WITH A BEARD!
HOW I HATE YOU.

YOU'RE THREE OF A KIND! A VICIOUS, CRUEL MOTHER, A BLACKMAILING GANGSTER AND A BLOOD-SUCKING GANGSTER'S ACCOMPLICE! UGH!

FRESH—REMEMBER, I AM YOUR MOTHAW. AND MOTHAW KNOWS BEST, FRESH. YOU MUST LISTEN TO MOTHAW.

THE CYLINDER OF THIS .38 HOLDS THREE BULLETS—JUST ENOUGH IF I USE THEM RIGHT.

THREE PEOPLE—THREE BULLETS—THREE CORPSES.

AND GOOD RIDDANCE! JUSTICE WOULD BE DONE AND MY BABY WOULD BE AVENGED.

FRESH—YOU'RE MAD! YOU'D HAVE THIS ON YOUR HANDS THE REST OF YOUR LIFE. YOU'LL—
AH, HA, HA, HA!

YOU CRINGING, UNCLEAN, STUPID-LOOKING COWARDS!

FRESH!
CHESTER GOULD

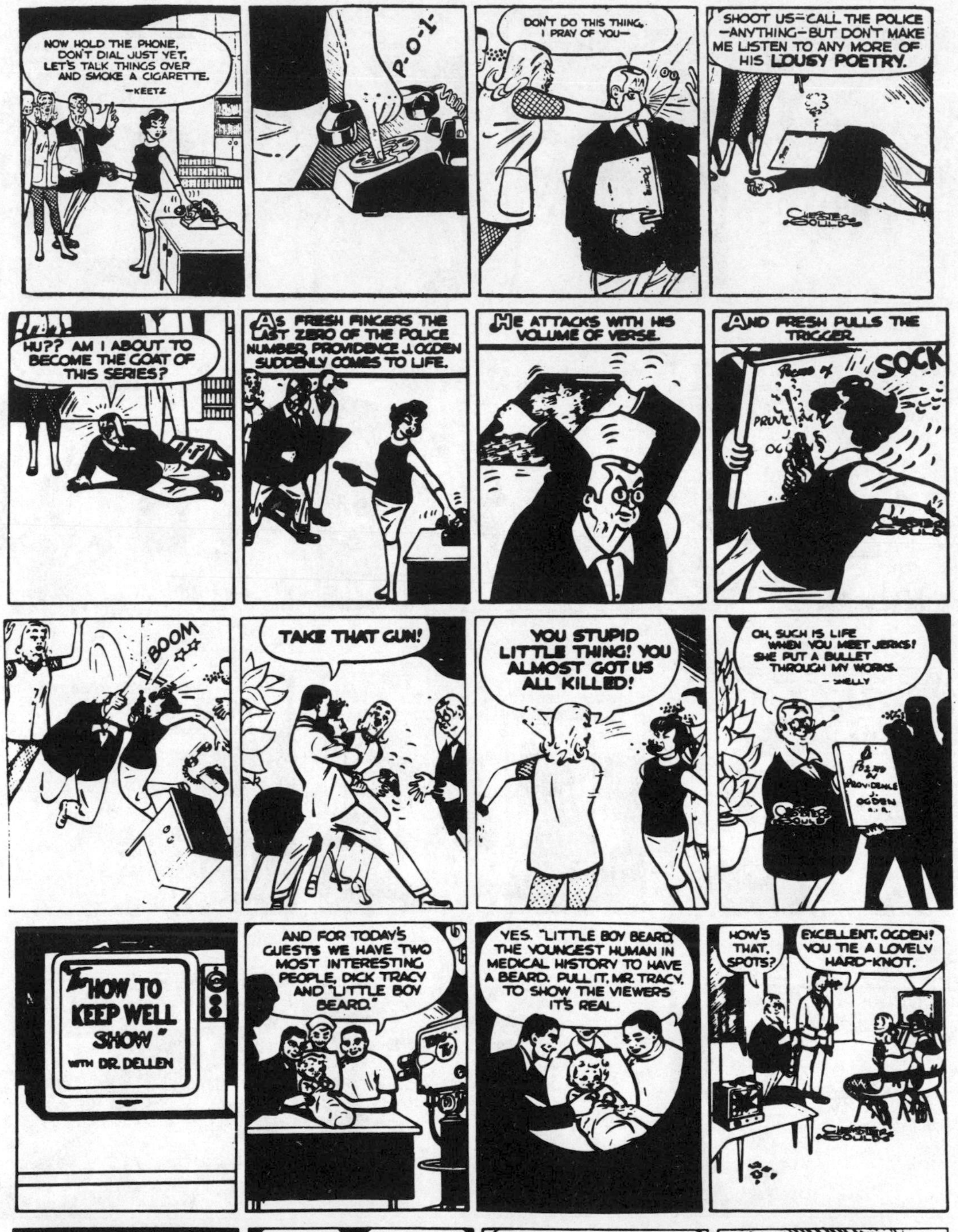

NOW HOLD THE PHONE, DON'T DIAL JUST YET, LET'S TALK THINGS OVER AND SMOKE A CIGARETTE. —KEETZ

P-O-1-

DON'T DO THIS THING, I PRAY OF YOU—

SHOOT US—CALL THE POLICE —ANYTHING—BUT DON'T MAKE ME LISTEN TO ANY MORE OF HIS **LOUSY POETRY.**

HU?? AM I ABOUT TO BECOME THE GOAT OF THIS SERIES?

AS FRESH FINGERS THE LAST ZERO OF THE POLICE NUMBER, PROVIDENCE J. OGDEN SUDDENLY COMES TO LIFE.

HE ATTACKS WITH HIS VOLUME OF VERSE.

AND FRESH PULLS THE TRIGGER.

SOCK

BOOM

TAKE THAT GUN!

YOU STUPID LITTLE THING! YOU ALMOST GOT US ALL KILLED!

OH, SUCH IS LIFE WHEN YOU MEET JERKS! SHE PUT A BULLET THROUGH MY WORKS. —SHELLY

The "HOW TO KEEP WELL SHOW" WITH DR. DELLEN

AND FOR TODAY'S GUESTS WE HAVE TWO MOST INTERESTING PEOPLE, DICK TRACY AND "LITTLE BOY BEARD."

YES. "LITTLE BOY BEARD," THE YOUNGEST HUMAN IN MEDICAL HISTORY TO HAVE A BEARD. PULL IT, MR. TRACY, TO SHOW THE VIEWERS IT'S REAL.

HOW'S THAT, SPOTS?

EXCELLENT, OGDEN! YOU TIE A LOVELY HARD-KNOT.

WHERE ARE YOU, MOTHER? THIS BABY BOY NEEDS YOU.

DOCTOR DELLEN, YOU HAVE EXAMINED "LITTLE BOY BEARD." WILL YOU TELL THE VIEWERS WHAT YOU'VE FOUND?

MY LITTLE BABY—

AH! BUT WE TARRY. COME, SPOTS, LET US DEPART.
ERE THAT KIDDIE'S GOATEE. GROWS CLEAR DOWN TO HIS KNEE.

IT'S "LITTLE BOY BEARD" AND TRACY, BEING INTERVIEWED ON TV BY DR. DELLEN OF THE CHILDREN'S CLINIC.

MOTHER OF "LITTLE BOY BEARD," WHEREVER YOU ARE, I WANT YOU TO KNOW THAT YOU HAVE A WONDERFUL HEALTHY CHILD.

IF YOUR CONCERN IS THIS LITTLE FELLOW'S BEARD, FORGET IT.

AS HE GROWS OLDER AND BEGINS TO SHAVE—THIS BEARD WILL BE NO PROBLEM, ANYWAY.

YES, WHOEVER YOU ARE, MOTHER OF THIS CHILD, COME BACK AND CLAIM YOUR BABY. THE POLICE WILL BE GLAD TO HELP YOU.

GAA GOO OOF UUGA

WHILE AT BURPIE UPP'S APARTMENT THE SITUATION IS SUDDENLY REVERSED.

I FOILED YOU WITH MY VOLUME RARE,
BUT IT IS NONE THE WORSE.
THOUGH YOU FIRED THROUGH MY POETRY BOOK,
JUST NAUGHT DESTROYS GOOD VERSE.
POEMS BY PROVIDENCE OGDEN

ADIEU, LADIES. WE LEAVE NOW.
BUT WE WILL BE BACK. MEANWHILE, THANKS FOR THE $5000 CASH. WE'LL RETURN FOR MORE LATER.

YOU HAVE JUST VIEWED THE WORLD'S MOST FAMOUS BABY—"LITTLE BOY BEARD." WHERE IS HIS MOTHER?

YOUR FRIENDS WHO MAY HAVE MISSED THIS PHENOM, CAN SEE "LITTLE BOY BEARD" ON THE ED SULLIMUN SHOW LATER TODAY.

WHERE IS HIS MOTHER?

REMEMBER—HALF OF THAT FIVE GRAND IS MINE, SPOTS.
YOU'LL GET YOURS, OGDEN.

HEY! SOME DOPEY TRUCK DRIVER PARKED HIS TRUCK SO WE CAN'T GET OUT.
WE'RE HEMMED IN, FORE AND AFT.

HECK, IT'S ONLY A RENTED CAR— LET'S LEAVE IT AND TAKE A CAB.

NOTHING DOING! I'LL MAKE THIS JERK MOVE.

MOVE THIS TRUCK SO I CAN GET OUT, YOU—

'RAISE 'EM, SPOTS.

BANG BANG
DROPPING TO THE GROUND, SPOTS ROLLS UNDER THE TRUCK.

THERE. YOUR WRISTS ARE FREE.

I HEARD SHOTS.

IF THAT'S THE POLICE— YOU AND I ARE GOING TO THE ROOF.

TAKE THAT— YOU TIN-STAR FL—
HE DIDN'T EVEN GET TO FINISH.

PITTING HIS CRIMINAL CUNNING AGAINST DICK TRACY'S UNFAILING MARKSMANSHIP, SPOTS COMES OUT A POOR SECOND.

OW—MY SHOULDER.
YOU'RE JUST LUCKY, POET!

AND INSIDE
BUT THE POLICE ARE ON OUR SIDE, MOTHER.
NOT MY SIDE —THEY'RE NOT! COME, CHILD —THE ROOF.

WE'VE GOT TO GET AWAY FROM THE POLICE! YOU AND I ARE GOING TO THE ROOF.

WHAT WILL WE DO UP THERE— SEE WHO CAN THROW THE OTHER OFF THE ROOF?

FRESH, HOW CAN YOU SAY SUCH A THING? HOW CAN YOU?
HOW CAN I?? I HATE YOU!

AFTER WHAT YOU MADE ME DO TO MY BABY, A TWENTY-FIVE STORY FALL IS TOO GOOD FOR YOU.
FRESH! GET YOUR HAND AWAY FROM MY THROAT—

THE EMERGENCY AMBULANCE AND THE STRETCHER CREW! --10-4.
2-WAY WRIST RADIO

YES—I THINK THE STEAM IS ALL OUT OF OUR BOY SPOTS.

CHESTER GOULD

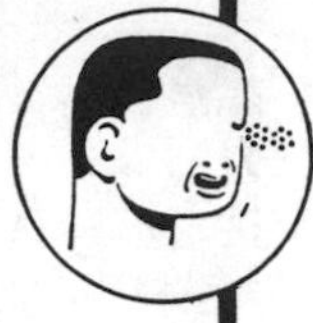

SPOTS! THE GANGSTER WHO MURDERED HIS WIFE IN COLD BLOOD—

—BECAUSE SHE REFUSED TO JOIN IN A CONSPIRACY TO SEIZE LI'L PINEAPPLE'S $100,000 ESTATE.

HOW DID YOU TRAIL US HERE?
WE CAME HERE TO SEE BURPIE UPP, WHOSE LICENSE NUMBER WAS SCRAWLED ON THE PERISCOPE IN THAT TANK— WE JUST HAD GOOD LUCK— THAT'S ALL.

BUT WE SAW YOU ON TELEVISION TWO MINUTES AGO.
SAP! THAT SHOW WAS TAPED YESTERDAY.

WHAT'S UPSTAIRS?
THE TV'S ON.
TWO PEOPLE APPARENTLY WERE TIED TO CHAIRS ONLY MOMENTS AGO.

"THEY COULDN'T HAVE GONE VERY FAR," SAYS TRACY.

BUT I WANT THE POLICE TO FIND ME. I WANT MY BABY!

THAT MISERABLE LITTLE THING WITH THE BEARD? LOOK, DEAR, YOUR MOTHAW KNOWS BEST.
DON'T YOU TOUCH ME! I'LL RUN MY OWN LIFE—

FRESH!
I'M WARNING YOU—

FRESH!

CHESTER GOULD

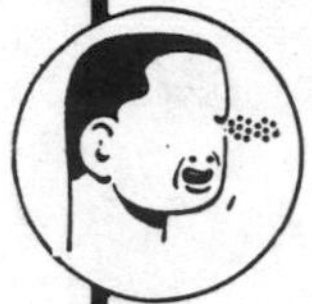

DON'T COME ANY CLOSER TO ME!
FRESH, I AM YOUR MOTHAW.
I'M RUNNING AWAY FROM YOU FOREVER.
YOU CAN'T DO THIS! BESIDES, WHERE WILL YOU RUN TO UP HERE?
ANYWHERE! —JUST SO I LIVE TO TESTIFY AGAINST YOU IN COURT.
YOU'LL NEVER GET AWAY FROM YOUR MOTHAW.
CHESTER GOULD
COME BACK HERE BEFORE I BREAK EVERY BONE IN YOUR BODY.
MOTHER—IT'S YOU OR ME—
IT'S TWENTY-FIVE STORIES DOWN THERE.
YOU LITTLE WITCH.
CHESTER GOULD
MY BABY HAS BEEN AVENGED!
CHESTER GOULD

THE 1970s

BIG BOY'S OPEN CONTRACT

by Max Allan Collins and Rick Fletcher

6/12/78–12/30/78

Chester Gould's final years on *Tracy* were marked by continued artistic excellence. The artwork slipped somewhat, however, from the superb sixties visuals, especially when the Tribune Syndicate handed Gould a new Sunday page format in 1974, forcing him to abandon the full-page tabloid-style originals he'd done since 1931 in favor of a smaller half-page format.

If the stories still suffered from a tendency to meander, the moon sequences had all but disappeared (despite Moon Maid's continued occasional presence) and there was a refreshing infusion of topical material—record counterfeiting, obscene phone calls, a feminist bank robbery ring, a Watergate-style crooked politician. A last burst of strong villains included the Button, Pucker Puss, and the Pouch. A rather unfortunate attempt by Gould to make Tracy seem up-to-date resulted in an unflattering longer hairstyle and a mustache that was wholly inappropriate—a fact that Gould came to recognize, as seen when the regular cast eventually held Tracy down for an enforced shave!

In 1977 Gould retired, and turned the artistic reins over to his longtime assistant Rick Fletcher. The coeditor of this volume, Max Allan Collins, was selected to write the strip after submitting a sample story ("Dick Tracy Meets Angeltop"), which became the new team's first continuity. For a time, Gould's name remained on the strip (with Collins and Fletcher); but Chet's only role was that of informal consultant to the writer.

The continuity included here—a long two-part one, actually—is the third Collins/Fletcher offering. It was the writer's wish to bring the strip full circle, providing, finally, a conclusion to the very first story: the return, and eventual demise, of Big Boy.

Also, although the moon had played an increasingly small role in Chester Gould's universe, writer Collins wished to send a message to the editors and readers by removing, once and for all, that aspect of the story—making it clear that Dick Tracy operated not out of a flying magnetic bucket, but a squad car; bringing the strip solidly back to earth. Rather than simply pretending the moon sequence had never happened, the *Tracy* continuity addressed it head-on with the violent removal of a sympathetic character (a long-standing Gould tradition).

The fan mail ran strongly in favor of the removal of this character, incidentally, although a vocal few continue to express their dissenting votes.

Additionally, a parallel subplot was designed to get the Sparkle Plenty character back on track—and in a position to eventually marry Junior Tracy—through the departure of her cartoonist husband Vera Alldid (an uninspired Gould creation of the seventies) by way of an offstage divorce. The bittersweet love affair between Sparkle and a hitman was an effort to invoke the poignance of the Model/Junior tragedy.

One of the reasons this story was chosen for inclusion here is the strength of Fletcher's artwork. While Rick did a craftsmanlike job throughout his run on the strip, it's generally agreed that his first year or so represents his finest work—crisp, modern, and sufficiently Gould-like, without smothering Fletcher's native, rather more illustrative style.

GOULD
Fletcher
COLLINS
HE WAS THE CRIME CZAR OF THE CENTURY—THE GODFATHER OF GODFATHERS—BIG BOY.

BUT THAT WAS THE BIG BOY OF YESTERDAY. TODAY? TODAY HE IS DYING.
COME CLOSER.

WEALTH IS MINE. RESPECT. POWER? THAT HAS FALLEN TO YOUNGER HANDS.
GOULD
Fletcher
COLLINS

CONTROL OF THE APPARATUS* WAS FOREVER LOST TO ME WHEN, OVER 20 YEARS AGO, A ROOKIE DETECTIVE SENT ME UP...
*THE NATIONWIDE CRIME SYNDICATE

DICK TRACY!

18 YEARS IN PRISON. 18 YEARS OF HUMILIATION. 18 DEGRADING YEARS. BECAUSE OF ONE MAN.

THE APPARATUS* HAD A SEAT ON THE COUNCIL, WAITING FOR ME... ONE VOTE. BIG BOY GETS... ONE VOTE.
*CRIME SYNDICATE
GOULD
Fletcher
COLLINS

THAT WAS HIS FAULT TOO... DICK TRACY. NOW I'M DYING. SO MUST HE.

I'M DYING, THE DOCS SAY... BUM TICKER, BUM EVERYTHING. SIX MONTHS TO A YEAR, I GOT.
GOULD
Fletcher
COLLINS

BUT THAT'S TIME ENOUGH—TIME ENOUGH TO SEE MY FINAL WISH COME TRUE.
DAILY DAILY
HAF-AND-HAF CAPTURED

HIT TRACY. HIT THE COP.
DAILY DAILY
HAF-AND-HAF CAPTURED

BIG BOY—EXCUSE ME, BUT... THE APPARATUS AIN'T GONNA STAND FOR KILLING TRACY OR ANY COP...

I KNOW THAT—BUT THIS ISN'T GOING TO BE AN APPARATUS HIT.
GOULD
Fletcher
COLLINS

AN OPEN CONTRACT—SPREAD THE WORD. OPEN CONTRACT ON DICK TRACY.

GOULD Fletcher COLLINS
KILLING TRACY'S BEEN TRIED BEFORE...FLATTOP, PRUNEFACE, THE BROW—THEY ALL TRIED AND ENDED UP HAMBURGER. EVEN THE APPARATUS TRIED AND FAILED.

FACE IT, BIG BOY—THAT SHOVEL-JAWED COP IS HARD TO KILL.

THAT'S BECAUSE BEFORE NOBODY EVER OFFERED A MILLION BUCKS TO GET THE JOB DONE...

$1,000,000 "OPEN CONTRACT" ON DICK TRACY—
I CAN AFFORD IT. I'M RICH—AND I'M DYIN'.

BIG BOY—EVERY CHEAP HOOD IN THE COUNTRY'S GOING TO TRY TO COLLECT...

YEAH—AIN'T IT GRAND? OPEN SEASON ON DICK TRACY. NOW GET OUTTA HERE!

"SPREAD THE WORD ON THE STREETS!" BIG BOY SAYS. And at HQ—
ZELDA, WE'RE PRESSING NO CHARGES.

HOW CAN I THANK YOU?
BY KEEPING OUT OF TROUBLE—

HAF-AND-HAF'S BACK WHERE HE BELONGS, AND YOU AND HE SHOULD BE SAFE FROM EACH OTHER. SO LONG, ZELDA.
GOULD Fletcher COLLINS

IT'S NICE TO HAVE THE PRESSURE OFF, FOR A CHANGE.

ON THE STREET, the WORD IS OUT—
NO PARKING THIS SIDE
BEER
WHISKEY 20
GOULD Fletcher COLLINS

$1,000,000 OPEN CONTRACT ON DICK TRACY.

LOAN SHARKS'LL START BREAKING BONES, IF I DON'T PAY UP... IT'S EITHER WIN THE LOTTERY, OR HIT DICK TRACY — AND I CAN'T AFFORD A LOTTERY TICKET...
RACING

SPARKLE PLENTY! HAVEN'T SEEN YOU IN OVER A YEAR...
Dick

DICK, SPARKLE AND I ARE HAVING A LITTLE "WOMAN-TO-WOMAN" CHAT... GIVE US SOME TIME ALONE TOGETHER, PLEASE?

GOULD Fletcher COLLINS

HI-HONEY, I...OH! SPARKLE! I THOUGHT YOU WERE MY WIFE...

GOULD Fletcher COLLINS
SLAP!

WHAT...?

WHAT'S WITH SPARKLE? I TOUCHED HER SHOULDER—MISTOOK HER FOR MY WIFE, SAME BLOND HAIR, YOU KNOW... SLAPPED ME.

JUNIOR, SPARKLE'S BEEN THROUGH A TRAUMATIC TIME.
GOULD Fletcher COLLINS

HER HUSBAND, VERA ALLDID, THE CARTOONIST, RAN OFF TO MEXICO FOR A "QUICKIE" DIVORCE.

JUNIOR, I'M...I'M SORRY-I SHOULDN'T HAVE SLAPPED YOU.
IT'S OKAY. SORRY TO HEAR ABOUT YOU AND VERA.

SUCCESS WENT TO VERA'S HEAD-WASN'T ANY ROOM FOR ME IN THE LIFE OF A MAN OBSESSED ONLY WITH MAKING MONEY.
GOULD Fletcher COLLINS

BUT THAT'S OVER. I HAVE A MORE IMMEDIATE PROBLEM...

I HOPED TO GO BACK HOME, AND LIVE WITH MY PARENTS. BUT I'M NOT WELCOME THERE.

WHY? YOUR FATHER NEVER APPROVED OF THE MARRIAGE, ANYWAY...
HE APPROVES LESS OF THE DIVORCE.
GOULD
Fletcher
COLLINS

ELSEWHERE IN the BUILDING-
POLICE
Dept
MAINTENANCE

YOU AND VERA DIVORCED? SPARKLE, I'M SORRY.
VERA COULDN'T HANDLE FAME, MR. TRACY. HE BECAME OBSESSED WITH MONEY.
HE ALSO HAD AN INTEREST IN WINE, WOMAN AND SONG- ONLY SPARKLE WASN'T THE WOMAN.
CELL BLOCK 3

HER IMMEDIATE PROBLEM, DICK, IS HER PARENTS.
B.O. PLENTY AND GRAVEL GERTIE?

B.O. WON'T LET SPARKLE MOVE BACK IN. SAYS, "B.O. PLENTY HAS NO DAUGHTER."
THAT OLD HYPOCRITE...

YOU CAN MOVE IN WITH ME FOR NOW.
OH, LIZZ... THANKS.

BUT JUST TILL I GET A JOB, AND MY OWN APARTMENT.

POLICE
Dept
MAINTENANCE
CELL BLOCKS
GOULD
Fletcher
COLLINS

GERTIE, IF YOU WANT TO CONTACT SPARKLE, SHE'LL BE STAYING WITH LIZZ.
THOUGHT YOU'D LIKE TO KNOW.

THANK YOU, MR. TRACY.
GERTRUDE, GIVE ME THAT CONSARNED PHONE—
I AIM TO GIVE THAT MACY A PIECE OF MY MIND!

ARE YOU SURE YOU CAN SPARE IT, B.O.?
GOULD Fletcher COLLINS

BOO-HOO-
BRACY, THE PLENTY FAMILY DON'T COTTON TO DIVORCE— SPARKLE MARRIED THAT NO-GOOD VARMINT, AND SHOULDA STUCK WITH HIM.
6-27 78

B.O.—VERA DIVORCED SPARKLE—SHE CAN'T DO ANYTHING ABOUT THAT. REMEMBER, SHE'S YOUR DAUGHTER—

DON'T GOT A DAUGHTER—AND FROM HERE ON OUT, KINDLY MIND YER OWN BIZNESS, MR. MACY.
GOULD Fletcher COLLINS
PATOO

TRACY PHONES B.O. PLENTY, re: SPARKLE'S RECENT DIVORCE.
LISTEN, YOU OLD REPROBATE—GET OFF YOUR HIGH HORSE! YOU—CLICK! HUNG UP ON ME, THE OLD...
GOULD Fletcher COLLINS

THANK YOU FOR TRYING, MR. TRACY.

HE'LL COME AROUND, SPARKLE... YOU'LL SEE.
POLICE Dept MAINTENANCE

SEE YOU TOMORROW, GANG!
THINK I'LL HEAD FOR HOME, TOO, DICK— HOW 'BOUT YOU?
NOT JUST YET—I WANT TO FINISH UP THIS REPORT ON HAF-AND-HAF'S CAPTURE FIRST...
POLICE Dept MAINTENANCE
GOULD Fletcher COLLINS

RING

"THIS IS TRACY—"
THIS IS SWEEPLY, MAINTENANCE, MR. TRACY—WE'VE FOUND ONE OF OUR MEN BOUND AND GAGGED...
POLICE Dept MAINTENANCE

...AND STRIPPED DOWN TO HIS SHORTS AND SOCKS!"
GOULD Fletcher COLLINS

OOF!

GOULD
Fletcher
COLLINS

A PHONE CALL WARNS TRACY THAT A BOGUS MAINTENANCE MAN MAY BE IN THE BUILDING—

GOULD
Fletcher
COLLINS

YE GODS—

JUST HEARD, DICK—CAN'T BELIEVE IT! A GUY TRIED TO KILL YOU—AT HEADQUARTERS?

THAT'S RIGHT. HERE'S WHAT'S LEFT OF HIM, AFTER FALLING FROM THE SQUAD ROOM WINDOW.

HEY-I KNOW THIS GUY!
GOULD
Fletcher
COLLINS

DON'T YOU REMEMBER? WE BUSTED HIM A COUPLE TIMES FOR RUNNIN' A FLOATIN' DICE GAME... USED TO HAVE A MUSTACHE...

LOUIE SMALL! PETTY GAMBLER. BUT WHAT...

WHAT WOULD MAKE A SMALL-TIMER, WITHOUT SO MUCH AS A PRIOR FOR CARRYING A CONCEALED WEAPON, TRY TO HIT DICK TRACY?
POLICE
GOULD
Fletcher
COLLINS

THE MEDIA WILL HAVE A FIELD DAY WITH THIS ONE-ARMED KILLER ENTERS POLICE STATION UNSEEN-HAS NO TROUBLE REACHING THE SQUAD ROOM...
GOULD
Fletcher
COLLINS

...WHERE CHIEF OF DETECTIVES TRACY OBLIGINGLY THROWS HIM TO HIS DEATH FROM A WINDOW!

THAT'S WHY I'VE CALLED A PRESS CONFERENCE.

I DECIDED TO CALL YOU GOOD PEOPLE OF THE PRESS IN IMMEDIATELY—BEFORE WE EVEN HAD A CHANCE TO REPLACE THE BROKEN WINDOW.
GOULD
Fletcher
COLLINS

WHY SO ACCOMMODATING, MR. TRACY? THE INCIDENT IS BOUND TO EMBARRASS THE DEPARTMENT. THINK BUTTERING US UP WILL HELP?

LOUIS SMALL ENTERED THIS PUBLIC BUILDING, UNNOTICED—WAITED TILL EVENING, WITH LESS STAFF ON DUTY, AND ASSAULTED A JANITOR, STOLE HIS UNIFORM, THEN TRIED TO KILL ME—

AND, REGRETFULLY, WAS HIMSELF KILLED.
"REGRETFULLY"? GOING SOFT, TRACY?

NO, I REGRET ANSWERS TO SO MANY QUESTIONS DYING WITH HIM.
GOULD
Fletcher
COLLINS

GOULD
Fletcher
COLLINS
WAS SMALL'S PAST RECORD ONE OF VIOLENT CRIME? WAS HE ON DOPE OR ALCOHOL AT THE TIME OF THE ASSAULT?
NO...NO.
PRESS

SMALL'S RECORD MAY NOT BE VIOLENT, MR. TRACY, BUT YOURS IS—AS YOUR ENEMIES IN THE D.A.'S OFFICE WELL KNOW. DO YOU ANTICIPATE PRESSURE "FROM UPSTAIRS" FOR YOUR RESIGNATION?
PRESS

TRACY HOLDS A PRESS CONFERENCE at HQ—
NO OTHER POLICE OFFICER IN THE CITY'S HISTORY HAS BEEN INVOLVED IN SO MUCH BLOODSHED—

I'M SENIOR DETECTIVE ON THE FORCE—HAVE OVER 20 YEARS IN. MY RECORD'S NOT SO UNUSUAL.

YOUR ENEMIES IN THE D.A.'S OFFICE WILL BE PRESSING FOR YOUR RESIGNATION...

I HAVE NO ENEMIES IN THE D.A.'S OFFICE—THE ENEMY IS CRIME IN THE STREET.
AND IN THE SQUAD ROOM?

WHY A PETTY GAMBLER WOULD ARM HIMSELF AND INVADE OUR TURF IS A MYSTERY TO ME...

"A MYSTERY," TRACY SAYS, "I INTEND TO SOLVE." While—
TELEPHONE, BIG BOY.

TRIED TO KILL HIM, AT HEADQUARTERS!
HA!

"A FAILURE? NOT AT ALL," BIG BOY SAYS. "OTHERS'LL BE TRYING SOON—MORE THE MERRIER!"
GOULD
Fletcher
COLLINS

WHILE BIG BOY GLOATS OVER TURNING AN UNSUSPECTING DICK TRACY INTO A TARGET, VIA A $1,000,000 OPEN CONTRACT—
TRIED TO KILL HIM, AT HEADQUARTERS!
HA!

ANOTHER WOULD-BE MILLIONAIRE PREPARES FOR A GRAB at the "COPPER" RING—

And at HQ—
TRACY ISN'T GOING TO LIKE THIS—
GOULD Fletcher COLLINS

DID YOU SEE WENDY WICHEL'S TRASHY COLUMN, DICK? CALLS YOU—
CRIME in the STREETS
Dick Tracy Style

"... A RELIC OF A DAY WHEN POLICE BRUTALITY WAS AN ACCEPTED PRACTICE, A DAY WHEN CIVIL LIBERTIES OF SUSPECTS WERE FLAGRANTLY IGNORED AS A MATTER OF COURSE."
I SAW IT.

While—
211* IN PROGRESS-POSSIBLE HOMICIDE. REQUEST DICK TRACY.
GOULD Fletcher COLLINS
2-WAY WRIST TV
*211: ROBBERY

WENDY WICHEL RAKED ME OVER THE COALS. BUT THE MEDIA OTHERWISE WAS FAIR TO ME.
PRESS CONFERENCE WAS A GOOD IDEA.
CRIME in the STREETS
Dick Tracy Style

GROOVY JUST CALLED IN—GAS STATION STICK-UP, MANAGER SHOT—FEW BLOCKS FROM HERE...

"LET'S GO!" TRACY SAYS.
While
GOULD Fletcher COLLINS

TRACY AND SAM CATCHEM RUSH TO THE SCENE OF A GAS STATION STICK-UP/HOMICIDE—
IS GROOVY ALREADY ON THE SCENE?
POLICE

NO. WE MAY BEAT HIM THERE—HE WAS OFF DUTY, AT HOME—GOT A PHONE TIP.
GOULD Fletcher COLLINS

"THAT SEEMS STRANGE," TRACY SAYS.

GOULD Fletcher COLLINS
GROOVY GOT THE CALL ABOUT THIS GAS STATION STICK-UP AT HOME? MUST'VE BEEN SOMEBODY WHO KNEW HIM, THEN...

I GUESS SO. BUT THEY DIDN'T GIVE THEIR NAME.

"IT WAS AN ANONYMOUS TIP?" TRACY ASKS. "AT HIS HOME? SOMETHING'S SCREWY HERE—"

YES, SAM–I'M ON THE SCENE, BUT IT'S A FALSE ALARM–NO ROBBERY, NO HOMICIDE.
SUPER

TELL HIM TO WAIT THERE FOR US. SOMETHING'S WRONG ABOUT THIS...
POLIC

GOULD Fletcher COLLINS

TRACY AND SAM ARE ON THE WAY TO THE SCENE OF A REPORTED GAS STATION STICK-UP/HOMICIDE–
YOW-W-W
POLICE

BANG!

POLICE

WHERE IS HE?
HE WAS IN THAT WINDOW UP THERE–I SAW HIM! –GONE NOW–

"COVER THE FRONT," TRACY SAYS. "I'LL TAKE THE BACK."

CODE 9*–WE GOT A SNIPER TRAPPED IN A BUILDING...
2-WAY WRIST TV
GOULD Fletcher COLLINS
*CODE 9–ASSISTANCE REQUESTED

YOU! HOLD IT RIGHT THERE–

GOULD
Fletcher
COLLINS
THE AFTERMATH of the SNIPER'S BULLET— ONE SHATTERED WINDSHIELD, A SLIGHTLY DAMAGED SQUAD CAR—

BUT SAM CATCHEM IS UNINJURED—
DICK TOOK THE ALLEY, IN BACK OF THE BUILDING...
2-WAY WRIST TV

AND SO IS TRACY—FOR the MOMENT...

DROP 'EM, OR DIE—

GOULD
Fletcher
COLLINS

WISE DECISION.

YOU HAVE THE RIGHT TO REMAIN SILENT—
TRACY, THIS IS THE SECOND ATTEMPT ON YOUR LIFE IN 48 HOURS.

AND IT WON'T BE THE LAST, PIG! I FOULED IT UP, BUT THE NEXT GUY WON'T...
GOULD
Fletcher
COLLINS

THE SNIPER AIN'T TALKIN'—HIS LAWYER WON'T LET HIM.

"MAYBE SO," TRACY SAYS, "BUT HIS FINGERPRINTS HAD PLENTY TO SAY—HERE'S HIS PACKAGE.*"
*PACKAGE: CRIMINAL RECORD FILE

PIERCE LOWB... PUSHER, PETTY THIEF. ANOTHER SMALL-TIMER WITH NO PRIOR RECORD OF OVERT VIOLENCE... WHAT'S GOING ON HERE?
GOULD
Fletcher
COLLINS
LOWB, PIERCE

YOUR PAL'S IN THE PAPERS AGAIN, BIG BOY.
"CHIEF OF DETECTIVES TRACY ATTACKED BY SNIPER IN BROAD DAYLIGHT—"

TOO FUNNY—HA! WHO'LL BE NEXT TO TRY FOR THE $1,000,000 GRAND PRIZE...?

WHILE
NO, LILY. I CAN'T DO IT. I'M STRAIGHT NOW...
BUT, LITTEL... ALL THAT MONEY...
SNIPER ATTEMPTS DAYLIGHT KILLING OF COP
GOULD
Fletcher
COLLINS

TWO ATTEMPTS ON YOUR LIFE IN TWO DAYS—FACE IT DICK: YOU'RE A TARGET.
I KNOW...

"BUT. WHOSE TARGET?" TRACY WONDERS. "AND WHY?"
SNIPER ATTEMPTS DAYLIGHT KILLING OF COP
DICK TRACY
Chief of Detectives Tracy Attacked by Sniper in Broad Daylight...

Meanwhile, LIZZ MAY HAVE A LEAD...
YEAH, I DID HEAR SOMETHING... SOMETHING INCREDIBLE...
GOULD Fletcher COLLINS

QUESTIONED THE "ALLEGED" SNIPER AGAIN— WITH HIS LAWYER PRESENT. GUESS WHAT HE HAD TO SAY?
DOES IT RHYME WITH "THE FIFTH"?

I GOT IT! I DON'T LIKE IT, BUT I GOT IT...

GOT WHAT?
THE REASON FOR TWO ATTEMPTS ON TRACY'S LIFE IN TWO DAYS— BY PREVIOUSLY NON-VIOLENT, SMALL-TIME HOODS.

BRACE YOURSELF, DICK— I THINK YOU'VE JUST MADE THE GUINNESS BOOK OF RECORDS, THE HARD WAY...

"WORD ON THE STREET IS, THERE'S A $1,000,000 OPEN CONTRACT OUT ON YOU."
YE GODS !?!
EXPLAINS A LOT...

While IN A SMALL ELECTRONICS SHOP IN the SUBURBS—
DON'T ASK THIS OF ME, LILY—I'M STRAIGHT NOW...
AFTER THIS, LITTEL, YOU CAN BE STRAIGHT AND RICH— $1,000,000 RICH!
GOULD Fletcher COLLINS

$1,000,000 "OPEN CONTRACT" ON TRACY? IMPOSSIBLE...
ARE YOU SURE ABOUT THIS, LIZZ?

POSITIVE. ALL MY STREET SOURCES SAY THE SAME THING–
GOULD Fletcher COLLINS

SOMEBODY BIG WANT'S YOU DEAD...

MY SNITCHES CLAIM NOT TO KNOW WHO PUT OUT THE OPEN CONTRACT ON YOU...
DON'T YOU BELIEVE THEM?

NO. OH, THEY KNOW... BUT THEY'RE SCARED!
GOULD Fletcher COLLINS

YOU MADE PLENTY OF ENEMIES IN YOUR TIME, TRACY– MOST ARE DEAD OR IN THE SLAMMER. WHO, AMONG THE LIVIN', COULD AFFORD A MILLION BUCKS?

MY STREET SOURCES ADMIT IT'S SOMEBODY BIG THAT WANTS YOU DEAD, BUT DON'T SAY WHO...

"I'D SUGGEST THE APPARATUS*," TRACY SAYS, "BUT IT'S NOT THEIR STYLE."
*CRIME SYNDICATE
GOULD Fletcher COLLINS

"OUR IMMEDIATE CONCERN," SAYS CHIEF PATTON, "IS DEALING WITH THE NUTS WHO'LL TRY TO COLLECT THAT MILLION."
OKAY-OKAY, LILY... I'LL DO IT!
GOOD BOY.

THE UNDERWORLD TRYING TO KILL ME IS NOTHING NEW. I SAY, BUSINESS AS USUAL.

BUSINESS AS USUAL? WITH $1,000,000 ON YOUR HEAD?

FACE REALITY, MAN! YOU'RE A MENACE TO YOURSELF AND THOSE AROUND YOU– UNTIL THIS CASE IS SOLVED, YOU'RE SUSPENDED.
GOULD Fletcher COLLINS

I'M SUSPENDED? JUST BECAUSE SOME CHEAP HOODS... YOU OLD...
I'M THE CHIEF– YOU CAN'T TALK TO ME...

BOYS, BOYS. YOU'VE KNOWN EACH OTHER A LONG TIME. NOW'S HARDLY THE TIME TO BE BICKERING...

BESIDES, I THINK I CAN OFFER A SOLUTION TO THIS LITTLE PROBLEM...
GOULD Fletcher COLLINS

CHIEF, SUSPEND TRACY AND HE'LL JUST GO OUT ON HIS OWN. TRYIN' TO SOLVE THIS THING, AND MAYBE GET HIMSELF KILLED...

"INSTEAD LET'S JUST TAKE EXTRA PRECAUTIONS-POST A CAR, 24 HOURS, AT TRACY'S HOME. DICK CAN CONFINE HIMSELF TO HQ-LIZZ AND ME'LL HIT THE STREETS."
$1,000,000.

GOULD
Fletcher
COLLINS

PRECAUTIONS GO INTO EFFECT TO PROTECT TRACY—UNDER THREAT OF A $1,000,000 "OPEN CONTRACT"—
WE TAKE TURNS. EVERY 15 MINUTES, WALK AROUND HOUSE-CHECK BUSHES, WINDOWS, AND SO ON-

WHILE A POLICEMAN'S WIFE COPES...
OH, DICK...
HONEY-DON'T WORRY. WE'VE GONE THROUGH TOUGHER TIMES...

TRACY SOON MAKES CHECKING UNDER HIS CAR'S HOOD AN EVERY-MORNING HABIT...
NO BOMB TODAY.

AND AT WORK, SITS BEHIND A DESK ALL DAY...
NOW YOU KNOW HOW I FEEL.
WANTED BY FBI

DAYS PASS. A WEEK. NO FURTHER ATTEMPTS.
HOW'S IT GOING?
DULL.
POLICE SKETCH

And-
NOBODY'S TRYIN', BIG BOY-IT'S LIKE TRACY'S SEALED IN PLASTIC.

"FOR $1,000,000," BIG BOY SAYS, "SOMEBODY'LL FIND A WAY."
I LOVE YOU, LITTEL.
PLASTIC EXPLOSIVE
GOULD
Fletcher
COLLINS

AS A PRECAUTION, TRACY—TARGET OF A $1,000,000 "OPEN CONTRACT"—CONFINES HIS WORKING DAY TO HQ.
I'M GOING NUTS, STUCK BEHIND THIS DESK—
YOU'LL STAY THERE TILL SAM AND LIZZ COME UP WITH A LEAD—
7-31-78

SOMEBODY MENTION US?
GOULD Fletcher COLLINS

YOU GOT SOMETHING?
WE GOT SOMETHING.

WITH THE CHIEF'S PERMISSION, WE'RE CALLIN' IN THE ORGANIZED CRIME UNIT ON THIS...
WHY?
GOULD Fletcher COLLINS

"HERE'S WHY—THESE GUYS ARE AMONG THOSE SPREADIN' THE WORD ABOUT THE $1,000,000 OPEN CONTRACT."
STRONG BROTHERS MARTY and VINCE SURVEILLANCE PHOTO

LOWER-ECHELON APPARATUS LIEUTENANTS—
BUT THAT DOESN'T MAKE SENSE...

WHY WOULD THE APPARATUS RISK ITS MODERN, "LOW PROFILE" IMAGE BY HITTING YOU?

YOU HAVEN'T TANGLED WITH THE APPARATUS FOR SEVERAL YEARS—NOT SINCE O.C.U.* WAS FORMED.
*ORGANIZED CRIME UNIT—A SEPARATE INVESTIGATIVE BODY WITHIN THE DEPT.

"BUT SUPPOSE," TRACY SAYS, "IT'S AN INDIVIDUAL APPARATUS MEMBER—SEEKING REVENGE?"
GOULD Fletcher COLLINS

HAVE INSPECTOR PRICE OF THE ORGANIZED CRIME UNIT REPORT TO ME FIRST THING TOMORROW, ON CURRENT APPARATUS* ACTIVITIES.
WILL DO.
*CRIME SYNDICATE

LEAVING EARLY, TRACY?
HAVE TO BE AT JUNIOR'S AT SIX.
GOULD Fletcher COLLINS

"HE AND HIS WIFE ARE HAVING TESS AND ME OVER FOR DINNER."
TONIGHT?
TONIGHT.
PLASTIC EXPLOSIVE

IT'LL BE NICE HAVING A RELAXING EVENING FOR A CHANGE.
THOUGHTFUL OF THE KIDS, INVITING US OVER. I'LL GET THE CAR...

MURPHY! EVER DILIGENT, EH?
RIGHT, MR. TRACY.

"I'LL BE STAYING HERE," SAYS MURPHY, "AND OFFICER RODRIQUEZ WILL FOLLOW YOU TO JUNIOR'S." "FINE," TRACY SAYS.
PLASTIC EXPLOSIVE
GOULD Fletcher COLLINS

JUNIOR! GET THE DOOR. I THINK THEY'RE HERE—
DING DONG

COME IN, FOLKS!
SOMETHING SMELLS GOOD—

"TURKEY IN THE OVEN," JUNIOR SAYS. "MY WIFE'S BEAUTIFUL AND A GREAT COOK." "CAN'T BEAT THAT COMBINATION," TRACY SAYS.
And OUTSIDE—
ALL QUIET.
2-WAY WRIST TV
GOULD Fletcher COLLINS

A PLEASANT EVENING with JUNIOR AND HIS WIFE—
IT'S AFTER DINNER, DISHES ARE DONE, AND—
DICK HASN'T BEEN THIS RELAXED IN WEEKS.
COLORING BOOK

AFRAID YOU'LL HAVE TO WAKE HIM FOR DESSERT—
OH, DARN! FORGOT TO GET WHIPPING CREAM—HAVE TO RUN TO THE STORE FOR SOME—

TESS—YOUR CAR'S BLOCKING OURS IN THE DRIVE... COULD YOU—
JUST TAKE OURS.

BOOM!
GOULD Fletcher COLLINS

AT THE HOME OF JUNIOR AND HIS WIFE, TRACY TAKES AN AFTER-DINNER NAP—
ZZZZ

While OUTSIDE—

GOULD Fletcher COLLINS
YE GODS!
BOOM!

BOOM!

A FEW BLOCKS AWAY, "LITTLE" AND LILY LITTEL HEAR THE EXPLOSION—

While—
GOT TO TRY TO SAVE HER—!
GOULD Fletcher COLLINS

GOT TO SAVE HER—
NO, SON! STAY BACK!

"SON—IT'S NO USE...SPLIT SECOND AFTER SHE TURNED THE KEY, SHE WAS... GONE."
GOULD Fletcher COLLINS

MOMMY?

IT WAS YOUR CAR— THAT BOMB WAS MEANT FOR YOU! IF IT HADN'T BEEN FOR YOU...

I'M SORRY, TRACY... I DIDN'T MEAN THAT... NOT FAIR OF ME. I'M SORRY.

I'M SORRY TOO, SON. I'M SORRY, TOO...
GOULD Fletcher COLLINS

GOULD Fletcher COLLINS
RODRIQUEZ, YOU WERE PRESENT BOTH AT TRACY'S HOME AND HERE—

HOW COULD THE BOMB HAVE BEEN PLANTED?

"I DON'T KNOW," SAYS RODRIQUEZ. "BUT I KNOW ONE THING—I'LL NEVER FORGIVE MYSELF FOR LETTING IT HAPPEN."
TO THE LATE DICK TRACY.
C4
C3

TELEGRAMS OF CONDOLENCE– FROM ALL OVER THE COUNTRY, ALL OVER THE WORLD.
PHONE FOR YOU, DICK.

YES...YES. THANK YOU FOR YOUR SYMPATHY. IT'S VERY KIND OF YOU. JUNIOR? HE'S RIGHT HERE...

YES...SIR. THANK YOU. YOUR CALLING MEANS A LOT... THANK YOU, MR. PRESIDENT.
© 1978 by The Chicago Tribune All Rights Reserved
GOULD Fletcher COLLINS

SHE'S REALLY GONE?
YES, DEAR...SHE'S REALLY GONE.

DIET SMITH...
TRACY...I'VE JUST SPOKEN WITH MOON MAID'S FATHER...

HE'S EXPRESSED HIS GREAT SORROW AT THE LOSS OF A BELOVED DAUGHTER– AND VOWS NO FURTHER CONTACT BETWEEN HIS PEOPLE AND OURS.

"A REAL TRAGEDY," SAYS DIET SMITH. "IT'S THE END OF AN ERA."

"IT'S MORE TRAGIC THAN THAT," TRACY SAYS. "IT'S THE END OF A LIFE."
GOULD Fletcher COLLINS

LITTLE, IT'S NOT YOUR FAULT...
IT'S BOTH OUR FAULTS...SOME INNOCENT LITTLE BROAD GOT KILLED, NOT TRACY.
GOULD Fletcher COLLINS

I'M TRYING TO GO STRAIGHT AND YOU DRAG ME INTO MURDER– AND WE DON'T EVEN GET ANYTHING OUT OF IT...

HUSH, DARLIN', HUSH... WE'LL JUST HAVE TO TRY AGAIN, THAT'S ALL...

GOULD Fletcher COLLINS
JUNIOR, WHY NOT STAY HERE WITH US A FEW DAYS?
GRANDMA.

THANK YOU, NO...I'D LIKE TO GET BACK TO MY WORK.
WE CAN USE YOU, SON... BEST POLICE ARTIST IN THE BUSINESS.

DRAWING PICTURES OF CRIMINALS ISN'T EXACTLY WHAT I HAVE IN MIND...

"POLICE ARTIST" IS MY SPECIALTY... BUT FIRST OF ALL, I'M A COP.
GOULD Fletcher COLLINS

I SAW MORE ACTION AS A KID TAGGING ALONG WITH YOU, TRACY, THAN THE AVERAGE DETECTIVE SEES IN A LIFETIME.
CAN'T DENY THAT, SON. WHAT DO YOU HAVE IN MIND?

I'M GOING TO FIND MY WIFE'S MURDERER...

JUNIOR'S DETERMINED TO FIND HIS WIFE'S KILLER...
DICK, I COULDN'T HELP BUT BE REMINDED...

...REMINDED OF THE SIMILAR SPEECH YOU MADE, YEARS AGO, WHEN MY FATHER WAS SHOT DOWN BY BIG BOY'S MEN.

BIG BOY... HMMM...NOW THAT IS A THOUGHT...
GOULD Fletcher COLLINS

MORNING, LIZZ. FIND INSPECTOR PRICE OF THE ORGANIZED CRIME UNIT AND TELL HIM CHIEF OF DETECTIVES TRACY WANTS TO SEE HIM YESTERDAY...
RIGHT, BOSS.

GOT AN IDEA, TRACY?
YEAH–A BIG ONE.

While–
SOMEBODY BLEW UP TRACY'S CAR, BIG BOY– KILLED HIS SON'S WIFE.
PITY. GIMME A LIGHT.
GOULD Fletcher COLLINS

TRACY MEETS WITH INSPECTOR PRICE, ORGANIZED CRIME UNIT...
BIG BOY? YES, HE'S STILL AN APPARATUS MEMBER. PRETTY INACTIVE.
GOULD Fletcher COLLINS

STILL, HE'S ON THE EXECUTIVE COUNCIL. WE'RE BUILDING A CASE AGAINST HIM AND OTHER MEMBERS, NOW. BUT HE WON'T STAND TRIAL.
WHY?

HE'LL BE DEAD. DOCTORS GIVE HIM SIX MONTHS...
HMMM..

WE KNOW TWO MINOR APPARATUS HOODS WERE SPREADIN' THE WORD ABOUT THE $1,000,000 OPEN CONTRACT...
SO IT FIGURES AN APPARATUS BIG SHOT PUT OUT THE CONTRACT.
BUT WHY DO YOU THINK IT'S BIG BOY? OLD-TIMER LIKE THAT...
THAT'S PART OF THE REASON.
STRONG BROTHERS MARTY AND VINCE
PATTON

TODAY'S APPARATUS KEEPS A LOWER PROFILE THAN THIS $1,000,000 BOUNTY SUGGESTS. HAS TO BE A REVENGE-HAPPY "OLD-TIMER" AS YOU PUT IT.

AND BIG BOY'S AN "OLD-TIME" GANGSTER WITH A $1,000,000 WORTH OF GRUDGE AGAINST TRACY.

LAB GOT SOMETHING FOR US, AL?
YES—WE'VE STUDIED THE PATH OF THE EXPLOSION—

"IT'S APPARENT THE BOMB WAS WIRED IN UNDER THE DASH—NOT THE HOOD."

"EXPLAINS HOW IT MIGHT'VE BEEN DONE QUICKLY ENOUGH TO GET BY A COP ON GUARD," TRACY SAYS.
WE BLEW IT.
NOW, NOW... WE'LL JUST TRY AGAIN.
GOULD Fletcher COLLINS

JUNIOR—OFFICER RODRIQUEZ HAS SOMETHING TO SAY...

JUNIOR, WHILE I'M NOT BEING HELD DERELICT IN MY DUTY, I STILL FEEL PERSONALLY RESPONSIBLE FOR WHAT HAPPENED. IF I CAN DO ANYTHING, SAY THE WORD.

NOW, I HAVE SOMETHING TO SAY...
GOULD
Fletcher
COLLINS

THE CRIME LAB BOYS HAVE COME UP WITH A THEORY...
GOULD
Fletcher
COLLINS

"THE BOMB WASN'T PUT UNDER THE HOOD—RATHER, SOMEBODY SLIPPED INTO THE FRONT SEAT AND WIRED IT UNDER THE DASH."

THAT'S HOW IT COULD BE DONE WITH YOU ON GUARD, RODRIQUEZ.
STILL, THE BLAME IS MINE...

RODRIQUEZ, YOU'RE SUFFERING FROM A BAD CASE OF SELF-PITY. AND, JUNIOR, YOU'RE IN MOURNING, UNDERSTANDABLY...
12th AND STATE
Daily Hot Sheet

BUT THERE'S SOME IMPORTANT FIELD WORK THAT NEEDS DOING...THE NEIGHBORHOOD OF THE CRIME SCENE NEEDS CANVASSING... ARE YOU TWO UP TO IT?
GOULD
Fletcher
COLLINS

TRACY, THAT BOMB UNDER THE DASH—AS AN M.O.*, IT SOUNDED FAMILIAR...
* METHOD OF OPERATION

"LOOK WHAT I CAME UP WITH," SAM SAYS.
LITTEL, "LITTLE"

"LITTLE" LITTEL... SEVERAL ARRESTS, NO MAJOR CONVICTIONS—SUSPECTED OF NUMEROUS GANGLAND BOMBINGS...
YOU HAVEN'T HEARD THE GOOD PART YET...
GOULD
Fletcher
COLLINS

LITTEL BECAME A DEMOLITION EXPERT IN VIETNAM... AS A CIVILIAN, HE ENLISTED IN THE APPARATUS*...
*CRIME SYNDICATE

STANDS UNDER 5 FEET—SPECIALTY'S CRAWLIN' IN THE FRONT OF A PARKED CAR, SLAPS SOME COMPOSITION C4* UNDER THE DASH, WIRES IT IN...
*PLASTIC EXPLOSIVE

THEN EXITS QUIETLY—UNLIKE THE PERSON WHO TURNS THE IGNITION KEY...
GOULD
Fletcher
COLLINS

LITTEL RUNS AN ELECTRONICS SHOP IN THE SUBURBS—SHALL WE HAVE A CHAT WITH HIM?

GOULD Fletcher COLLINS
YES.

MEANWHILE, OFFICER RODRIQUEZ and JUNIOR TRACY ARE COMBING THE NEIGHBORHOOD OF THE CRIME SCENE—
ARE YOU KIDS SURE ABOUT THIS?

JUNIOR TRACY AND OFFICER RODRIQUEZ CANVASS THE NEIGHBORHOOD NEAR THE CRIME SCENE—
WHAT EXACTLY DID YOU SEE?
A GREEN CAR. A BIG LADY WAS DRIVING.
SHE HAD A LITTLE MAN WITH HER.

IT WAS RIGHT AFTER THE BIG EXPLOSION—THE LADY STOPPED THE CAR, AND THE MAN GOT OUT—THREW SOMETHING DOWN THERE.

I THINK IT MIGHT'VE BEEN GLOVES—RUBBER ONES LIKE MOM WASHES DISHES IN.

I SEE SOMETHING!
GET ME A STICK—CAN'T REACH IT...

MEANWHILE, TRACY AND SAM ARE ON THEIR WAY TO SEE "LITTLE" LITTEL...
GOULD Fletcher COLLINS

WHY?
I'M SCARED, LILY...

YES, SIR—THE LADY STOPPED THE CAR, AND THE LITTLE MAN GOT OUT AND THREW SOME GLOVES DOWN THE SEWER—
GOULD Fletcher COLLINS

GOT IT!

While—
Parking for LITTEL ELECTRONICS Customers Only
Littel REPAIR Electronics

MR. LITTEL—MIND A FEW QUESTIONS?
WHY—NO...
NAMELY, YOUR WHEREABOUTS 3 NIGHTS AGO... BETWEEN 7 AND 8 O'CLOCK?
GOULD Fletcher COLLINS

While—
IF THERE ARE PRINTS ON THE INSIDE OF THIS GLOVE, YOU'VE GOT YOUR MAN.

MY HUSBAND AND I WERE TOGETHER THAT NIGHT—SPENT THE EVENING WITH MY SISTER.

AND SHE'LL VERIFY THAT?
OF COURSE.

And AT THE LAB AT HQ—
GOULD Fletcher COLLINS
AFTER THE RUBBER GLOVE HAS BEEN TURNED INSIDE OUT, AND INFLATED, WE'RE READY TO LOOK FOR FINGERPRINTS.
POLICE LAB
POLICE

I'VE BEEN OUT OF THE RACKETS FOR 5 YEARS NOW, MR. TRACY... GOT MY OWN SHOP, STRICTLY LEGIT.

HOW'S BUSINESS BEEN, SINCE THE BIG SHOPPING MALL OPENED NEAR THE FREEWAY?
GOULD Fletcher COLLINS
AND

VERY READABLE PRINTS, JUNIOR. I'LL SEND 'EM DOWN TO R AND I* TO RUN THROUGH THE COMPUTER...
*RECORDS AND IDENTIFICATION

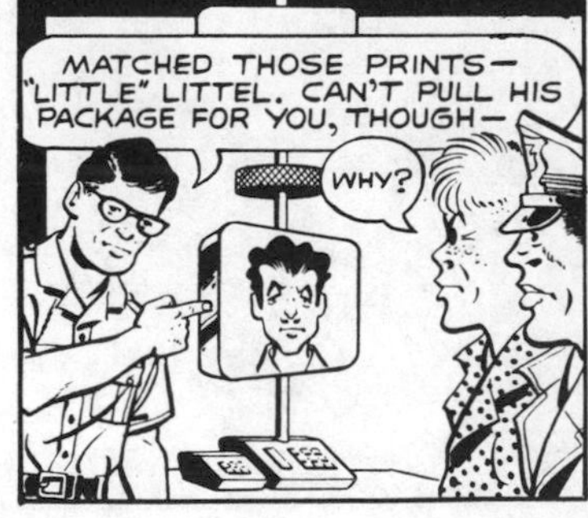
MATCHED THOSE PRINTS— "LITTLE" LITTEL. CAN'T PULL HIS PACKAGE FOR YOU, THOUGH—
WHY?

"TRACY'S GOT IT. LITTEL'S ALREADY A SUSPECT OF SOME KIND—"
UNTIL YOUR ALIBI'S CONFIRMED, DON'T LEAVE TOWN.

TRACY — HE'S OUR MAN.
WE DON'T HAVE ENOUGH TO COLLAR HIM—
GOULD Fletcher COLLINS

RODRIQUEZ-
THANKS TO YOU, WE'VE BROKEN THE CASE. NOW GO ON HOME, GET SOME REST. YOU'VE BEEN WORKING ALL DAY.
BUT-
POLICE DEPT

NO BUTS. GO. I'LL PASS ON THIS NEW EVIDENCE—THE LITTEL PRINTS INSIDE THE GLOVE—TO TRACY, MYSELF.
WELL...OKAY, JUNIOR...
GOULD Fletcher COLLINS

SO, LITTEL HAS AN ALIBI...
WHICH WE'LL CHECK OUT.

"WE KEPT THE QUESTIONING ROUTINE," TRACY SAYS. "TRIED NOT TO SPOOK HIM."
LILY, THEY KNOW—WE GOTTA GET OUT OF TOWN!

THEY DON'T KNOW ANYTHING. OUR ALIBI WILL STICK.

IT'S THAT UNDER-THE-DASH BOMB I USED—THEY KNOW IT'S MY STYLE. SHOULD'VE RIGGED SOMETHING ELSE...

SO THIS TIME YOU'LL BUILD A BETTER BOMB, LITTLE. BECAUSE YOU LOVE ME.
BUT... BUT...

"YOU DO LOVE ME, LITTLE?" ASKS LILY. "YES, LILY," SAYS LITTLE.
HE'S OUR MAN, BUT WE HAVE NO HARD EVIDENCE...
GOULD Fletcher COLLINS

ARE YOU KIDDING? JUNIOR SAID HE'D CALLED YOU—HE TIED LITTEL'S FINGERPRINTS TO THE BOMBING...

"JUNIOR?" TRACY SAYS. "WHERE IS JUNIOR?"

TRACY, I'M WITH THE YOUNGSTERS WHO SAW THE SUSPECTS MOMENTS AFTER THE EXPLOSION...

THEY'VE POSITIVELY IDENTIFIED "LITTLE" LITTEL AS THE MAN WHO TOSSED THE RUBBER GLOVES DOWN THE SEWER GRATING.
LIVE-2-WAY WRIST TV

"THAT'S FINE, RODRIQUEZ," SAYS TRACY. "BUT WHERE IS JUNIOR?"
GOULD Fletcher COLLINS

TRACY, I CHECKED JUNIOR'S OFFICE—NO SIGN OF HIM. AND, TRACY—

HIS DESK DRAWER WAS OPEN—WHEREVER HE'S GONE, HE'S TAKEN HIS .38 SNUB-NOSE."
GOULD Fletcher COLLINS

While—
NO MORE BOMBS IN TRACY'S CAR—THIS TIME, I'LL GO RIGHT IN HIS HOUSE.
LITTLE, I'M SO PROUD OF YOU...

I'VE USED DYNAMITE THIS TIME—AND A TIMER. BE CUTTING IT CLOSE—10 MINUTES!

BUT THIS'LL DIVERT SUSPICION FROM ME—DOESN'T FIT MY M.O..
YOU'RE SO SMART, LITTLE.

"ALL I HAVE TO DO IS GET PAST THE TWO POLICE GUARDS," LITTEL SAYS. "I HAVE FAITH IN YOU," LILY SAYS.
Parking for LITTEL ELECTRONICS
GOULD Fletcher COLLINS

9-7-78
FINALLY—ENOUGH HARD EVIDENCE TO COLLAR LITTEL!

YEAH—BUT CAN WE BEAT JUNIOR TO HIM?

While—
TONIGHT, YOU'LL PLANT THIS IN TRACY'S HOUSE—TOMORROW, WE REAP $1,000,000!
GOULD Fletcher COLLINS

TURN AROUND!

GOULD Fletcher COLLINS
WHO ARE YOU?

MY NAME'S TRACY. I'M THE SON OF THE MAN YOU'VE BEEN TRYING TO KILL. I'M THE HUSBAND OF THE WOMAN YOU DID KILL. I'M THE GUY WHO'S GOING TO KILL BOTH OF YOU...

YOU MURDERED MY WIFE... DESTROYED THE MOST PRECIOUS THING I EVER HAD—NOW I'M GOING TO...

CAN'T... CAN'T BRING MYSELF TO...

GOULD
Fletcher
COLLINS

JUNIOR CONFRONTS THE MURDERERS OF HIS WIFE, But—

LILY—YOU SHOULDN'T'VE THROWN THE BOMB AT HIM—COULD'VE GONE OFF—
GOING TO KILL US, HUH? LITTLE JERK DIDN'T HAVE THE NERVE...
TICK
TICK

YOU'VE STARTED THE MECHANISM—UNLESS I DISMANTLE IT, THIS THING'LL GO OFF IN 10 MINUTES!
TICK
TICK

LET IT.
WHAT?
TICK
TICK
TICK

"THE BODY FOUND IN THE RUBBLE OF WHAT USED TO BE THIS SHOP WILL, FOR A WHILE ANYWAY, BE ASSUMED TO BE YOU, LITTLE—WHICH'LL GIVE US A START ON GETTING OUT OF TOWN." "OUT OF TOWN?" ASKS LITTEL.
TICK
TICK
TICK

"YES," SAYS LILY. "IF JUNIOR TRACY'S ONTO US, DADDY CAN'T BE FAR BEHIND..."
Parking for
LITTEL ELECTRONICS
Customers Only
Littel
REPAIRS
Electronics
9-10-78
GOULD
Fletcher
COLLINS

9-11 78 ®
8 MINUTES TILL IT BLOWS—ARE YOU SURE ABOUT THIS, LILY?
TICK TICK

YES, IN THE EXPLOSION'S AFTERMATH, JUNIOR TRACY'S BODY SHOULD BE MISTAKEN FOR YOURS, LITTLE—WHILE WE SLIP OUT OF TOWN...!
GOULD Fletcher COLLINS

And OUTSIDE—
JUNIOR'S CAR IS HERE—LITTEL'S, TOO. THEY'RE IN THERE—COVER THE FRONT, SAM-LIZZ, COME WITH ME...
CLOSED

TRACY-LOOK!
Littel REPAIR Electronics

FREEZE YOU TWO! PUT 'EM IN THE AIR!
WATCH THE LITTLE GUY—TRACY! HE'S GOT A GUN!!!
GOULD Fletcher COLLINS

DELIVERY
Littel
Electronics

LITTLE!
GOULD Fletcher COLLINS

GET UP. WE'LL GET HIM AN AMBULANCE...NOW, WHERE'S JUNIOR?
RADIO

GOULD Fletcher COLLINS

LET'S GET SOME CUFFS ON THIS CRAZY BROAD, 'FORE I HAVE TO BREAK HER ARM.
GOULD Fletcher COLLINS

JUNIOR'S IN HERE! UNCONSCIOUS, BUT NOT BADLY HURT...
CLOSED

WHAT HAPPENED ?
YOU'LL BE OKAY, KID—JUST WENT DOWN FOR THE COUNT A WHILE.
MINE'S GOT A FLESH WOUND—BUT HE'LL MAKE IT.
MINE'S SEMI-CONSCIOUS—BUT SHE'LL LIVE, TOO.
And, UNNOTICED BY ALL CONCERNED, A BOMB QUIETLY TICKS AWAY ITS FINAL MINUTES—
TICK TICK
GOULD Fletcher COLLINS

"LITTLE" LITTEL, SEMI-CONSCIOUS, A BULLET IN HIS SHOULDER, AND LILY, GROGGY AFTER SPARRING WITH LIZZ, SEEM AS UNAWARE AS TRACY AND COMPANY OF IMPENDING DISASTER—
HOW ARE YOU FEELING, SON?

"OKAY, I GUESS," SAYS JUNIOR. "ASHAMED, FOR TAKING THIS IN MY OWN HANDS."
YE GODS...

EVERYBODY GET OUT OF HERE—THERE'S A BOMB! GO OFF ANY SECOND—
TICK TICK

"I MIGHT STILL BE ABLE TO DISMANTLE IT," SAYS LITTEL. "GET OUT! GET LILY OUT—"

GOULD Fletcher COLLINS
BOOM!

BOOM!
GOULD Fletcher COLLINS

LITTEL GOT US OUT OF THERE JUST IN TIME!
BUT NOT TIME ENOUGH FOR HIM TO DISMANTLE THE BOMB...
Littel

LITTLE-LITTLE! NO!

IT'S NO USE, LILY! HE'S GONE.

TRACY-I THINK JUNIOR'S HURT!
EXPLOSION-BURNING BUILDING...
2 WAY WRIST TV
GOULD Fletcher COLLINS

I'M JUST...DAZED. HIT THE GROUND KIND OF HARD.
HE'S GOING TO BE OKAY, DICK.
OH NO, HE ISN'T...

THE DAY WILL COME WHEN HE'LL WISH HE'D BEEN KILLED IN THAT EXPLOSION...
GOULD Fletcher COLLINS

YOU WERE RESPONSIBLE FOR MY HUSBAND'S DEATH. YOU PATHETIC LITTLE MEDDLER!

AND YOU-YOU SHOT HIM! I'LL KILL YOU, TOO. I'LL KILL YOU BOTH! SOMEDAY-
READ HER HER RIGHTS AND GET HER OUT OF HERE, LIZZ.
GOULD Fletcher COLLINS

LITTEL'S WIFE, LILY, SWORE TO KILL ME-AND LIZZ. BLAMES US FOR HER HUSBAND'S DEATH...

GOULD Fletcher COLLINS
"YET SHE AND LITTEL KILLED MY WIFE." JUNIOR SAYS. "REVENGE- IT'S LIKE IT'S CONTAGIOUS-"
Littel

YES-AND LIKE MOST CONTAGIOUS THINGS, NOT AT ALL HEALTHY... LET'S GO HOME, SON.

I SEE ANOTHER OF YOUR INVESTIGATIONS HAS COME TO A VIOLENT CLOSE...
SIT DOWN, Ms. WICHEL. PLEASE.
PRESS
GOULD Fletcher COLLINS

WHY CONTACT ME— WE'RE ALL BUT SWORN ENEMIES. WHY NOT ANOTHER PRESS CONFERENCE?
BECAUSE I HAVE AN IMPORTANT ANNOUNCEMENT TO MAKE...

DICK'S GOT THAT COP-HATING COLUMNIST, WENDY WICHEL, IN FOR A ONE-WOMAN PRESS CONFERENCE.
TELL ME IF ONE OF 'EM STARTS THROWIN' THINGS SO I CAN DUCK...
DO YOU HAVE SOME NEWS FOR ME TODAY, MR. TRACY?
PRESS

"LITTEL'S BODY WAS RECOVERED IN THE RUBBLE OF THE EXPLOSION. HIS WIFE, LILY, IS IN CUSTODY," TRACY SAYS.
Littel

THAT'S NOT NEWS— MORNING EDITION AND TV AND RADIO HAVE THAT...
THEY DON'T HAVE THIS.

IT'S AN OFFICIAL STATEMENT OF MY INTENT TO WAGE OPEN WAR ON ORGANIZED CRIME.
YOU'RE CHIEF OF DETECTIVES— THERE'S A SEPARATE INVESTIGATIVE BODY, THE ORGANIZED CRIME UNIT, TO...

I KNOW. I'M TAKING IT OVER.
GOULD Fletcher COLLINS

THE APPARATUS* HAS GONE TOO FAR—
*CRIME SYNDICATE

THEIR 'OPEN CONTRACT' ON ME HAS COST THREE LIVES ALREADY... INCLUDING MY SON'S WIFE..."
MRS. JUNIOR TRACY (MOON MAID)
"LITTLE" LITTEL
"LOUIE" SMALL

THEY SENT OUT AN "OPEN CONTRACT" ON ME—FINE. I'M SENDING THEM OPEN WAR.
GOULD Fletcher COLLINS

DICK TRACY WAGING OPEN WAR ON CRIME? AND COMMANDEERING THE ORGANIZED CRIME UNIT TO DO IT?

NOW THAT IS NEWS...BUT WHY GIVE ME A SCOOP LIKE THIS?
GOULD Fletcher COLLINS

BECAUSE, Ms. WICHEL, CONSIDERING YOUR ANTI-POLICE STANCE, I'M SURE IN YOUR COLUMN, I'LL REACH MY INTENDED AUDIENCE...

BIG BOY—SOMEBODY HERE TO SEE YOU.
WHO? I DON'T REMEMBER MAKIN' NO APPOINTMENTS.
GOULD Fletcher COLLINS

1978 by The Chicago Tribune All Rights Reserved
THE APPARATUS DOESN'T NEED AN APPOINTMENT, BIG BOY!

YOU GUYS HAVE A SEAT... ER, IT AIN'T EVERY DAY APPARATUS BOARD MEMBERS COME CALLIN'...
WE'LL STAND. WE WON'T BE STAYING LONG.
GOULD Fletcher COLLINS

WE JUST CAME TO TELL YOU TO CONSIDER YOUR "OPEN CONTRACT" ON DICK TRACY CLOSED...

THE "OPEN CONTRACT" ON TRACY—CLOSED? YOU MEAN HE'S FINALLY DEAD?

NO—AND IT'S TO BE KEPT THAT WAY!

EVEN IN YOUR ERA, KILLING COPS WAS BAD BUSINESS—TODAY, IN THESE CORPORATE TIMES, IT'S SHEER MADNESS.
GOULD Fletcher COLLINS

WE'VE TREATED YOU GOOD. YOU'RE STILL A BOARD MEMBER. GET A PERCENTAGE OF ALL THE ACTION.
GOULD Fletcher COLLINS

BUT, BIG BOY, PUTTING OUT AN "OPEN CONTRACT" ON A COP—LET ALONE DICK TRACY—IS STUPID.

YOU CAN'T TALK TO ME LIKE...
SHUT UP!

APPARATUS* BOARD MEMBERS CALL ON BIG BOY—
YOU'VE CALLED DICK TRACY'S ATTENTION TO US.
* CRIME SYNDICATE

INSTEAD OF CHASING BANK ROBBERS AND NUTS LIKE HAF-AND-HAF, TRACY'S TAKING OVER O.C.U.*
*ORGANIZED CRIME UNIT

WE CAN'T THREATEN YOU, A DYING MAN—BUT WE CAN COUNTER YOUR "OPEN CONTRACT" ON TRACY WITH A SECOND $1,000,000 "OPEN CONTRACT"...

...ON ANYONE STUPID ENOUGH TO KILL—OR TRY TO KILL—DICK TRACY.

YOU CAN'T DO THIS... DON'T YOU KNOW WHO I AM?

YOU USED TO BE BIG BOY.
GOULD Fletcher COLLINS

HAS BIG BOY GIVEN UP HIS DREAM OF SEEING DICK TRACY PRECEDE HIM IN DEATH?

HOW CAN THE APPARATUS MAKE YOU LAY OFF TRACY, BIG BOY?

BY PUTTING OUT A SECOND $1,000,000 "OPEN CONTRACT" ON ANYBODY WHO TRIES TO MAKE GOOD ON MINE.
GOULD Fletcher COLLINS

SO WHAT NOW, BOSS? FORGET TRACY?

NOBODY'LL TOUCH THE TRACY CONTRACT NOW, BIG BOY—NOT WITH THE APPARATUS AGAINST IT...

I KNOW ONE MAN WHO MIGHT.
GOULD Fletcher COLLINS

GET ME THE ICEMAN.

RODRIQUEZ, YOU'VE EARNED A COMMENDATION FOR YOUR WORK ON THE LITTEL CASE...
GOULD Fletcher COLLINS

AND I UNDERSTAND YOU'RE UP FOR PROMOTION. CONGRATULATIONS.
THANK YOU, MR. TRACY.

And AT THE MIDTOWN HOTEL—

YOU EVER MEET THIS GUY... THIS "ICEMAN"?

"YEAH— ONCE. AND THAT WAS ENOUGH! BIG BOY USED HIM ON THAT POLITICIAN, IN THE '60s. HE'S ONE COLD CUSTOMER!"
GOULD Fletcher COLLINS

While at HQ—
INSPECTOR PRICE—COME IN. HAVE A SEAT.

INSPECTOR PRICE, YOU MAY FEEL I'VE PULLED RANK ON YOU, BUT...

YES, I DO. UNDER MY LEADERSHIP, O.C.U.* HAS AMASSED NUMEROUS ARRESTS AND CONVICTIONS—WITHOUT BENEFIT OF THE ILLUSTRIOUS TRACY PRESENCE...
*ORGANIZED CRIME UNIT

"NOW, IF YOU'LL EXCUSE ME, I HAVE A WITNESS TO MEET, AT THE MIDTOWN HOTEL—"
GOULD Fletcher COLLINS

GOULD
Fletcher
COLLINS

PRICE! HOW YA DOIN'...

WHAT'S WITH HIM?
HE RESENTS MY TAKING OVER O.C.U.* FROM HIM. HE'S PROUD OF HIS RECORD THERE.
*ORGANIZED CRIME UNIT

YEAH, WELL IT'S NOT SO HOT A RECORD, AT THAT... I'VE BEEN DOING SOME DIGGING, BOSS.

PLENTY OF ARRESTS AND CONVICTIONS, YES— BUT ALL SMALL FRY. NOT A BIG SHOT IN THE BUNCH.

PRICE IS A GOOD MAN—AND IN THE MIDST OF A MAJOR APPARATUS* INVESTIGATION!
*CRIME SYNDICATE

"IN FACT, HE'S ON HIS WAY NOW TO INTERVIEW A WITNESS AT THE MIDTOWN HOTEL—"
HEY-THIS GUY'S... DEAD!
GOULD
Fletcher
COLLINS

HEY-THIS GUY'S... DEAD!!!
GOULD Fletcher COLLINS

YE GODS... IT'S REYWAL-MURDERED?
WHO ARE YOU, MISTER?

"INSPECTOR PRICE, ORGANIZED CRIME UNIT-THIS MAN WAS AN IMPORTANT WITNESS..." While-
MEN

IMPORTANT STATE'S WITNESS MURDERED-YES, NOTIFY DICK TRACY.
GOULD Fletcher COLLINS
2-WAY WRIST TV

Meanwhile-IN A HOTEL WASHROOM NEARBY, AFTER TOSSING WIG, JACKET, FALSE MUSTACHE AND EYEBROWS IN A WASTE CAN, AND REVERSING HIS SHIRT, THE KILLER COOLLY REMOVES HIS CONTACT LENSES-
CONTACT LENS
PUSH

THE POOR MAN SAT UP, SUDDENLY, THEN SLUMPED. ANOTHER MAN WAS STANDING BEHIND HIM AT THE TIME.
COULD YOU DESCRIBE HIM?
GOULD Fletcher COLLINS

DARK HAIR, DARK EYES, WEARING A SPORT JACKET-IF I SAW HIM AGAIN, I'D KNOW HIM!

AS THE KILLER DEPARTS the HOTEL-
GOULD Fletcher COLLINS
HOTEL MIDTOWN
CAB

SOMEONE ELSE IS ARRIVING.
SAM-WAIT FOR LIZZ AND THE SQUADROL.

IS THE M.E* HERE YET?
YES, AND HE WANTS YOU TO HAVE A LOOK AT THE BODY.
*MEDICAL EXAMINER

WHAT DO YOU MAKE OF IT, TRACY?
SMALL ENTRY WOUND-NOT FROM A BULLET, OR KNIFE. ICEPICK MAYBE? YOU'RE THE MEDICAL EXAMINER, WHAT DO YOU THINK?
GOULD Fletcher COLLINS

I CONCUR. AND NOW I'M FINISHED HERE, AND IT'S ALL YOURS-JUST YOUR AVERAGE MURDER-IN A CROWDED HOTEL LOBBY...

YOU'VE LOST A VALUABLE WITNESS HERE, INSPECTOR PRICE. I'M SORRY.
10-14 78

"SORRY?" SAYS PRICE. "UNTIL YOU TOLD THE MEDIA OF YOUR 'TAKEOVER' OF THE ORGANIZED CRIME UNIT, THIS INVESTIGATION HAD KEPT A LOW PROFILE."
HOTEL MIDTO
GOULD Fletcher COLLINS

NOW THERE'S BEEN A MURDER, AND WE'RE BACK TO SQUARE ONE— AND YOU'RE SORRY...

NAME WAS E.X. REYWAL— DISBARRED ATTORNEY WHO WAS TO TESTIFY ABOUT HIS GANGLAND CONNECTIONS.

While IN THE HOTEL—
TRACY, UNTIL YOU MADE IT A MEDIA EVENT, THIS CASE WAS PROCEEDING EFFECTIVELY AND NON-VIOLENTLY.

NONSENSE—ALL THIS MEANS IS THE OPPOSITION IS RUNNING SCARED.
PUNCTURE MADE BY ICEPICK-LIKE MURDER WEAPON

BUT IF PLACING BLAME IS YOUR BAG — WHY NO POLICE PROTECTION FOR YOUR KEY WITNESS?

WE WERE STILL AT AN EARLY STAGE, NEGOTIATING WHETHER OR NOT HE'D GET FULL IMMUNITY.

"WELL, HE'S GOT IT NOW," SAYS TRACY. While IN THE LOUNGE OF ANOTHER HOTEL, NEARBY—
HELLO, ICEMAN. BIG BOY WOULD LIKE TO SEE YOU.
GOULD Fletcher COLLINS

WHAT DOES BIG BOY WANT WITH ME?

SSSHH...THIS IS ON THE Q.T. YOU BEEN TO THE MANSION BEFORE, RIGHT?

"WHY NOT DROP BY TOMORROW MIDNIGHT. PARK AT LEAST HALF A MILE AWAY AND HOOF IT TO THE FRONT GATE... SEE YA' THEN."
GOULD
Fletcher
COLLINS

JUST WHO IS THIS ICEMAN, BIG BOY?

HIS NAME'S JOHNNY SNOW. THE HITMAN'S HITMAN. HE'S IN TOWN ON AN APPARATUS CONTRACT, WHICH HE PULLED ALREADY.

"AND NOW HE'S GOING TO KILL DICK TRACY FOR ME."
PATHOLOGIST'S REPORT ON THE DEAD WITNESS.
GOULD
Fletcher
COLLINS

FIVE MINUTES TO MIDNIGHT, BIG BOY, AND NO SIGN OF YOUR JOHNNY SNOW.
THE ICEMAN WILL SHOW.
GOULD
Fletcher
COLLINS

IF HE WORKS FOR THE APPARATUS, WHAT MAKES YOU THINK HE'LL GO AGAINST THEM TO GO AFTER TRACY FOR YOU, BIG BOY?

THE ICEMAN'S A FREE-LANCE HIRED KILLER. HE HAS NO LOYALTIES TO THE APPARATUS.

YOU SO SURE, BIG BOY? IT'S AFTER MIDNIGHT. MARTY'S DOWN AT THE FRONT GATE AND SAYS NO SIGN OF HIM.

GOULD
Fletcher
COLLINS
THAT'S BECAUSE I CAME IN OVER THE GATE.

OKAY, I'M HERE. SNEAKED IN AT MIDNIGHT AND PLAYED YOUR CLOAK-AND-DAGGER GAME. NOW WHAT GIVES?
GOULD
Fletcher
COLLINS

I GIVE, ICEMAN! A MILLION BUCKS IN A NUMBERED SWISS ACCOUNT—PLUS A BONUS OF A BUNGALOW IN FRANCE... ON THE RIVIERA. INTERESTED?

LIZZ! IT'S AFTER MIDNIGHT... YOU STILL WORKING?

JUST FINISHED. I HAVE SOME NEWS THAT JUST COULDN'T WAIT...

"MY STREET SOURCES SAY THE APPARATUS IS TRYING TO COUNTER THAT "OPEN CONTRACT" ON YOU WITH A SECOND $1,000,000 "OPEN CONTRACT" —AIMED AT ANYONE WHO TRIES TO KILL YOU!"
GOULD Fletcher COLLINS

WHO WAS THAT, AT THIS HOUR, DICK?
LIZZ—SHE SAYS THE APPARATUS HAS ISSUED AN "OPEN CONTRACT" ON ANYONE WHO TRIES TO KILL ME—

THAT DOESN'T MAKE SENSE—AREN'T THEY THE ONES WHO WANTED YOU DEAD?

THEY'RE RUNNING SCARED —HOPE BY TAKING THE HEAT OFF ME PERSONALLY, I'LL LOSE INTEREST IN 'EM AND RETURN TO MY NORMAL DUTIES...

"AND IT STRENGTHENS MY BELIEF THAT AN OLD-TIMER IN THE MOB WAS RESPONSIBLE FOR THAT "OPEN CONTRACT" ON ME—POSSIBLY BIG BOY."
HAVE A SEAT, ICEMAN.

I'LL STAND. I KNOW ALL ABOUT YOUR $1,000,000 "OPEN CONTRACT" ON DICK TRACY—
GOULD Fletcher COLLINS

AND ABOUT THE APPARATUS COUNTER-ACTING YOUR CONTRACT WITH ONE OF THEIR OWN. GOODBYE, BIG BOY.

WELL, THEN GO— I SIMPLY THOUGHT THE GREAT ICEMAN WOULD ENJOY THE CHALLENGE OF TAKING ON BOTH DICK TRACY AND THE APPARATUS.

PERHAPS I MISJUDGED YOU, ICEMAN!
GOULD Fletcher COLLINS

YOU'VE BEEN LESS ACTIVE, IN RECENT YEARS— SPECULATION WAS, YOU WERE BORED WITH YOUR TRADE...

I MERELY THOUGHT A CHALLENGE LIKE THIS MIGHT START YOUR JUICES FLOWING AGAIN—

KILLING DICK TRACY WOULD BE A COUP—
GOULD Fletcher COLLINS

NO COP IN HISTORY HAS BEEN THE SUBJECT OF SO MANY ASSASSINATION ATTEMPTS. AND HAVING THE APPARATUS AGAINST ME WOULD BE A CHALLENGE—

ALSO, A MILLION BUCKS AND A PLACE ON THE RIVIERA AIN'T NOTHIN' TO SNEEZE AT.

OKAY, BIG BOY— I'LL DO IT. I'LL KILL DICK TRACY FOR YOU.
GOULD Fletcher COLLINS

WHAT MADE YOU SAY YES, ICEMAN?
IT'S SOMETHING TO DO.

And AT HQ, TRACY CONFERS WITH SAM CATCHEM, ACTING CHIEF OF DETECTIVES DURING TRACY'S STAY WITH O.C.U.*—
ANYTHING HAPPENING ON THAT HOTEL MURDER, SAM?
*ORGANIZED CRIME UNIT
NET
LOCAL

WE FOUND CONTACT LENSES, A WIG AND JACKET IN A WASTE CAN IN THE HOTEL'S PUBLIC REST ROOM.

LEADING YOU TO BELIEVE THE KILLER WORE A DISGUISE INTO THE HOTEL, AND REMOVED IT BEFORE GOING OUT.

"RIGHT. NOW LET ME GET JUNIOR UP HERE AND I'LL REALLY SHOW YOU SOMETHING," SAYS SAM.
GOULD Fletcher COLLINS

I WORKED UP THIS SKETCH FROM AN EYEWITNESS AND THE WASTE CAN FINDINGS.
GOULD Fletcher COLLINS

REYWAL WAS STABBED IN THE BACK, WITH AN ICEPICK-LIKE WEAPON THAT WAS JABBED THROUGH THE BACK CUSHION OF THE CHAIR HE WAS SITTING IN.

"THIS MAN WAS SEEN STANDING BEHIND REYWAL ABOUT THE TIME HE WAS KILLED."
POLICE SKETCH

I'VE GOT A MAN WORKING ON MATCHING THAT DRAWING TO PHOTOS IN OUR FILE.

LOOKS LIKE THE ACTING CHIEF OF DETECTIVES HAS THINGS WELL IN HAND.
JUST DON'T STAY AWAY TOO LONG–

JUNIOR, CAN WE TALK? SOMETHING IMPORTANT'S ON MY MIND.
POLICE ARTIST

JUNIOR, I'M SENDING TESS OUT TO CALIFORNIA, TO STAY WITH VITAMIN FLINTHEART, TILL THIS BIG BOY/ APPARATUS INVESTIGATION IS OVER.
POLICE ARTIST

AND I FEEL THAT FOR YOUR OWN PROTECTION, YOU AND YOUR DAUGHTER HONEY SHOULD JOIN TESS.

I'LL SEND HONEY WITH TESS. I DON'T WANT TO LOSE EITHER OF THEM, THE WAY I LOST MY WIFE, THANKS TO BIG BOY AND THE APPARATUS–

BUT ME, I'M STAYING. I'M A COP, LIKE YOU ARE. AND I'D LIKE TO KEEP DOING MY SHARE— ON THIS CASE, ESPECIALLY.

"SON—I WISH YOU'D GO," TRACY SAYS. "BUT I'M PROUD OF YOU FOR STAYING."
GOULD Fletcher COLLINS

CAN WE PAINT A VAN AS A TV REPAIR TRUCK, AND THEN REPAINT IT IN A COUPLE DAYS AS A FLORIST TRUCK? WHAT FOR?
BECAUSE, I'M PAYING YOU TO.
Don's BODY SHOP

HOW'S THE WEATHER IN CALIFORNIA, VITAMIN?

LOVELY, RICHARD, LOVELY... I'M SURE YOUR BEAUTIFUL WIFE AND COMELY GRANDDAUGHTER WILL FIND THE CLIME MOST AGREEABLE.
BROMO
GOULD Fletcher COLLINS

"WE'RE GRATEFUL YOU'RE OPEN TO TESS AND HONEY VISITING," SAYS TRACY. "BECAUSE THE CLIMATE HERE ISN'T SO HEALTHY—"
TV REPAIR

I WISH YOU AND DADDY COULD COME WITH US, GRANDPA.
ME TOO, HONEY.

I'LL MISS YOU, DARLING.
I LOVE YOU, TESS. WE'LL BE TOGETHER AGAIN SOON...
GOULD Fletcher COLLINS

11/1/78 ®
AS A JET BEARING HONEY AND TESS MAKES ITS WAY TO CALIFORNIA—
GOULD Fletcher COLLINS
1978 by Chicago Tribune N.Y. News Synd. Inc All Rights Reserved

A VAN ROLLS BY THE TRACY HOME.
TV REPAIR

A FEW WEEKS OF STAKE-OUT AND I'LL HAVE TRACY'S PATTERN DOWN PAT— THIS GUY WON'T BE SO TOUGH TO KILL...

DO YOU REALLY THINK SENDING TESS AND HONEY TO THE WEST COAST WAS NECESSARY?

NO TAKERS ON THE $1,000,000 "OPEN CONTRACT," NOW THAT THE STREET KNOWS THE APPARATUS IS AGAINST IT. THINGS HAVE QUIETED DOWN.

"YEAH," TRACY SAYS. "LIKE THEY SAY IN THE MOVIES: IT'S QUIET— TOO QUIET..."
GOULD Fletcher COLLINS
POLICE SKETCH

THINK YOU CAN ADJUST TO YOUR TEMPORARY BACHELOR STATUS, BOSS?
I COULD PROBABLY USE SOME HELP HOUSE-KEEPING...

COULD YOU USE A MAID?
SPARKLE PLENTY?
GOULD Fletcher COLLINS

NOW THAT I'M ON MY OWN AGAIN, MR. TRACY, I'VE STARTED A BUSINESS.
GOULD Fletcher COLLINS

ONE DAY'S HOUSEWORK A WEEK, FOR A SELECT LIST OF CLIENTS—
Maid-for-a-Day
Sparkle Plenty

BEEN WATCHING TRACY'S HOUSE ALL DAY— NO SIGN OF ANYBODY. I'LL BET HE SENT HIS WIFE AWAY...

SPARKLE PLENTY, RECENTLY DIVORCED, ESTRANGED FROM HER PARENTS, HAS HER OWN BUSINESS NOW—
MAID-FOR-A-DAY?
YES, MR. TRACY— AND LIZZ TELLS ME YOU COULD USE HELP WITH HOUSEWORK...
CUTE OUTFIT.

AND YOU HAVE ROOM FOR ANOTHER CLIENT— OKAY, SPARKLE, YOU'RE HIRED... TILL TESS GETS BACK FROM CALIFORNIA.

AND MAYBE EVEN THEN — I'LL TALK TO TESS.
THANKS, LIZZ.

OH, CHIEF—CAN I HAVE A WORD WITH YOU—PRIVATELY?

WHAT'S THE PROBLEM, DICK?

THE WORST KIND OF POLICE PROBLEM THERE IS, PAT... A CROOKED COP.
GOULD Fletcher COLLINS

WHAT'S THIS ABOUT, TRACY?
I'D LIKE TO BORROW LIZZ AND SAM—TO WORK WITH ME AT O.C.U.*
*ORGANIZED CRIME UNIT

"NO WAY!" PATTON SAYS. "SAM'S FILLING YOUR SLOT, AS ACTING CHIEF OF DETECTIVES, AND LIZZ IS THE P.D.'S MOST STREETWISE POLICEWOMAN—THEY'RE NEEDED WHERE THEY'RE AT!"
PURSE SNATCHER IN CUSTODY, SAM.
2-WAY WRIST TV
GOULD Fletcher COLLINS

WHY DO YOU WANT SAM AND LIZZ TO DO SPECIAL DUTY AT O.C.U. WITH YOU?

THERE ARE A DOZEN DETECTIVES WORKING FULL-TIME OUT OF THE ORGANIZED CRIME UNIT—WHAT'S WRONG WITH THEM?
GOULD Fletcher COLLINS

ELEVEN OF THEM ARE FINE—BUT ONE OF THEM ISN'T...

THERE'S A LEAK IN THE ORGANIZED CRIME UNIT.

"A BAD APPLE IN THE POLICE DEPARTMENT BARREL—AND I DON'T KNOW WHO IT IS—YET."
GOULD Fletcher COLLINS

BUT THE LACK OF PROGRESS IN THE APPARATUS INVESTIGATION MAKES IT CLEAR: THERE'S A CROOKED COP IN OUR MIDST.

CHIEF—EVERY DEPARTMENT HAS ITS SHARE OF BAD COPS—WE'LL WEED THIS ONE OUT.

THE ORGANIZED CRIME UNIT WAS MY BABY—AN ELITE STRIKE FORCE OF THE P.D.'S BEST. TO THINK THAT ONE OF THEM...
GOULD Fletcher COLLINS

LIZZ AND SAM ARE BACK UNDER YOUR AUTHORITY. PLUG THAT LEAK—WITH LEAD IF NECESSARY...

I HOPE FRIDAY'S A GOOD DAY FOR YOU, MR. TRACY.
GOULD Fletcher COLLINS

GOOD A DAY AS ANY TO GET THAT HOUSE OF MINE CLEANED—HOW DOES IT GET ITSELF SO DIRTY?

"THERE'S THE KEY," SAYS TRACY. "AND WATCH YOUR STEP—I HAVE SOME DANGEROUS 'FRIENDS.'"
Ed's PLUMBING INC

HOW ARE YOU AND LITTLE HONEY DOING, TESS?
GOULD Fletcher COLLINS

ONCE UPON A TIME...
GREAT, DICK! CALIFORNIA'S BEAUTIFUL, AND VITAMIN'S TREATING US ROYALLY— HOW'S YOUR NEW HOUSEKEEPER?
BROMO

"SPARKLE? SHE'S DONE A TERRIFIC JOB. SHE AND LIZZ ARE GREAT FRIENDS, NOW —TONIGHT THEY'VE GONE TO A DISCO TOGETHER."
DISCO 54

SPARKLE and LIZZ at DISCO 54—
DISCO 54

IT'S SO EXCITING— I HAVEN'T BEEN OUT SINCE...

...SINCE MY...
YOUR DIVORCE. I KNOW. YOU HAVE TO START YOUR LIFE OVER, KID.

"AND YOU CAN BEGIN BY DANCING— YOU'VE TURNED DOWN A DOZEN CUTE GUYS..."

I'M SORRY, LIZZ... IT'S DIFFICULT FOR ME.
YOU HAVE COMPANY.

EXCUSE ME—WOULD YOU CARE TO DANCE?
GO AHEAD— IT CAN'T HURT.
GOULD Fletcher COLLINS

"HMMM," THINKS LIZZ. "WHERE HAVE I SEEN THAT GUY BEFORE?"

disco 54 –
A NIGHT ON THE TOWN FOR SPARKLE, LIZZ AND...
GOULD Fletcher COLLINS

GROOVY! HELLO!
SORRY I'M LATE. WHERE'S SPARKLE?

"SHE'S WITH A NEW FRIEND– GUY LOOKS FAMILIAR TO ME, BUT I JUST CAN'T PLACE HIM..."

IT'S GREAT, SPARKLE'S GETTING OUT AGAIN.

YES–I WAS WORRIED ABOUT HER. THE DIVORCE HIT HER PRETTY HARD.
GOULD Fletcher COLLINS

MY NAME'S JOHNNY. JOHNNY WINTER. WHAT'S YOURS?
SPARKLE. SPARKLE PLENTY.

CALL IT THE MOTHER HEN INSTINCT–BUT THAT GUY SPARKLE'S WITH BOTHERS ME.
GOULD Fletcher COLLINS

DO YOU LIVE IN THE CITY?
NO. I'M HERE ON BUSINESS.

WHAT SORT OF BUSINESS?
FREE-LANCE CONSULTANT, FOR INDUSTRY. THEY... CONTRACT MY WORK.

GOODNIGHT, SPARKLE.
'NIGHT JOHNNY.
disco54
GOULD Fletcher COLLINS

ISN'T HE TERRIFIC? HE'S QUIET, SHY! BUT HE SEEMS TO HAVE... STRENGTH. AND SO MYSTERIOUS!
DEFINITELY.

I LIKE HIM.
NO KIDDING.

NICE TO HAVE YOU ABOARD.
NICE TO BE WORKIN' WITH YOU AGAIN.
GOULD Fletcher COLLINS

BUT I WOULD LIKE TO KEEP WORKIN' ON THAT HOTEL MURDER– REYWAL'S DEATH DEFINITELY TIES IN WITH THE APPARATUS/ O.C.U. CASE.

I AGREE. SAY– WHAT'S WRONG WITH LIZZ?

GOULD Fletcher COLLINS
WHY SO LISTLESS, LIZZ? HAD TO PULL STRINGS TO GET YOU BACK ON MY TEAM...

BEEN HITTIN' THE DISCO CIRCUIT AGAIN, DREAMBOAT?
SHUTTUP, YOU!

"IT'S SPARKLE," SAYS LIZZ. "SHE'S HEAD OVER HEELS FOR THIS GUY SHE JUST MET—AND FOR SOME REASON IT WORRIES ME..."
POLICE SKETCH

SPARKLE HAS A NEW BOY-FRIEND, "JOHNNY WINTER"— IN REALITY THE ICEMAN—

OH, JOHNNY—I COULDN'T BE HAVING A BETTER TIME.

I'M GLAD.
I DIDN'T THINK I COULD BE THIS HAPPY AGAIN—

MY HUSBAND LEAVES ME— MY PARENTS DISOWN ME... IT'S BEEN A NIGHTMARE.
I UNDER-STAND.

DO YOU?
YES. SOMEONE I LOVED, ONCE—LEFT ME. I UNDERSTAND THE PAIN.

While at HQ—
TRACY—YOU EVER HEAR OF A HIGH-PRICED HITMAN CALLED THE ICEMAN?
GOULD Fletcher COLLINS

THE ICEMAN? NO, NEVER HEARD OF HIM.
SURVEILLANCE PHOTO

"HE'S A HIGH-PRICED HITTER*. FREE-LANCER, BUT HE'S DONE WORK FOR THE APPARATUS."
SURVEILLANCE PHOTO
*HIRED KILLER

NO CONVICTIONS. NO ARRESTS. BELIEVED RESPONSIBLE FOR IN EXCESS OF A DOZEN CONTRACT KILLINGS...
GOULD Fletcher COLLINS

THE ICEMAN, HUH? REAL NAME, JOHN SNOW... NUMEROUS ALIASES...

THE "ICEMAN" MONIKER COMES FROM HIS ALBINO COLORATION, AND HIS FONDNESS FOR DISPATCHING VICTIMS WITH AN ICE PICK-LIKE WEAPON...

"WHICH IS HOW REYWAL WAS KILLED. SAM, GET ME THAT POLICE SKETCH OF THE HOTEL KILLER..."
GOULD Fletcher COLLINS

DID RECORDS AND IDENTIFICATION MATCH THIS SKETCH TO SNOW?
NOPE—NO RECORD! BUT THAT ICE PICK-LIKE MURDER WEAPON—THAT RANG A BELL ...SNOW WAS IN OUR "SUSPICIOUS CHARACTERS" FILE.
POLICE SKETCH
SURVEILLANCE PHOTO

"HAS LIZZ SEEN THESE?" "NO," SAYS SAM. "SHE'S OFF TODAY..."
NO, GERTIE, SPARKLE ISN'T HERE—SHE'S ON A DATE.
GOULD Fletcher COLLINS

JUNIOR, WHAT DO YOU MAKE OF THIS?

IT'S OUR HOTEL KILLER! IN THE FLESH... MINUS MUSTACHE, WIG AND DARK CONTACT LENSES, OF COURSE—
SURVEILLANCE PHOTO

CAN YOU PUT 'EM BACK ON HIM? WE GOT AN EYEWITNESS THAT KNOWS HIM ONLY IN DISGUISE.
GOULD Fletcher COLLINS

"I HAD ENLARGEMENTS OF THE SURVEILLANCE PHOTO MADE," JUNIOR SAYS, "FOR MORE DETAIL IN RETOUCHING."
LAB

HERE.
SAM, SEE IF YOUR EYEWITNESS CAN PICK IT OUT FROM A STACK OF SIMILAR SHOTS.

"AND IF SHE MAKES HIM, PUT OUT AN APB ON JOHNNY SNOW—THE ICEMAN."
GOULD Fletcher COLLINS

THAT'S HIM —I'M SURE OF IT!
NOW. LOOK AT THIS ONE.

HE WAS AT THE HOTEL, TOO... LATER. WHY— IT'S THE SAME PHOTO —SAME MAN!
ENLARGED SURVEILLANCE PHOTO
RETOUCHED SURVEILLANCE PHOTO

"YOU DIDN'T RECOGNIZE HIM THEN," SAM SAYS. "WELL, I RECOGNIZE HIM NOW," SAYS THE EYEWITNESS.
THANKS FOR THIS AFTERNOON, JOHNNY.
GOULD Fletcher COLLINS

TRACY, THE EYEWITNESS FROM THE HOTEL HAS IDENTIFIED SNOW.
ENLARGED SURVEILLANCE PHOTO
RETOUCHED SURVEILLANCE PHOTO

ALL UNITS—APB ON JOHN SNOW, a.k.a. THE ICEMAN...
2-WAY WRIST TV

While—
JOHNNY—I KNOW SO LITTLE ABOUT YOU...

IS THAT SO IMPORTANT?
IT IS TO ME... I... I'M FALLING IN LOVE WITH YOU.

JOHNNY—IS SOMETHING WRONG?
NO—NOT AT ALL. I... CARE ABOUT YOU, TOO.

HMMm—

SNOW, ARE YOU LETTING THAT LITTLE BLONDE GET TO YOU?

DON'T FORGET— YOU'RE USING HER, TO GET AT TRACY. AND TOMORROW TRACY DIES...
GOULD Fletcher COLLINS

'MORNING, SPARKLE. ON YOUR WAY TO WORK, ALREADY?

YES—TODAY'S THE DAY I CLEAN THE TRACY HOME.

While—
TONIGHT! TRACY DIES TONIGHT.
GOULD Fletcher COLLINS

INSPECTOR PRICE ASKED ME TO GIVE YOU THIS REPORT, MR. TRACY.
THANKS, GOLD.
ORGANIZED CRIME UNIT

HM-MM. GOLD DRIVES A BIG CAR, HAS A PENTHOUSE APARTMENT.
GOULD Fletcher COLLINS

THEN THERE'S DETECTIVE WYNN—RUMORED TO HAVE A GAMBLING HABIT. IS ONE OF THEM OUR LEAK?

YOU THINK GOLD AND WYNN ARE LIKELY CANDIDATES FOR O.C.U.'S* CROOKED COP?
*ORGANIZED CRIME UNIT

"POSSIBLY. LIZZ IS CHECKING THEIR CASES, GOING BACK 3 YEARS... IT'S PREMATURE TO REQUEST PHONE TAPS OR SURVEILLANCE."
GOULD Fletcher COLLINS
LIZZ

While—
SPARKLE'S BEEN IN TRACY'S HOUSE FOR SEVERAL HOURS—I'LL MAKE MY MOVE AT DUSK...

SOUNDS LIKE BOTH DETECTIVES GOLD AND WYNN ARE ON THE TAKE!

HEY—I'VE BEEN SUSPECTED OF GRAFT MYSELF—FOR DRIVING AN "EXPENSIVE" CAR...A TEST MODEL PROVIDED AT COST FOR TRYING OUT POLICE-RELATED FEATURES.

GOULD Fletcher COLLINS
"AND BECAUSE OF THE HOUSE I BUILT—WITH MONEY INVESTED DURING MY SPARTAN BACHELOR DAYS."

FIND ANYTHING SUSPICIOUS ON DETECTIVES GOLD AND WYNN?
GOULD Fletcher COLLINS

NOTHING SO FAR, BOSS.
BEEN A LONG DAY. HOW LONG YOU GOING TO KEEP AT THIS?

"FOR A WHILE," SAYS LIZZ. "WELL, I'M HEADING HOME," SAYS TRACY. "I'M DEAD..."
KNOCK

WHO COULD THAT BE...?
KNOCK KNOCK

HELLO, SPARKLE. I HAD TO SEE YOU—CAN I COME IN?
WHY, JOHNNY! OF COURSE—COME IN.

YOU REALLY SHOULDN'T BE HERE, JOHNNY... AND I'VE BEEN WORKING... LOOK A MESS...
CHLOROFORM
GOULD Fletcher COLLINS

YOU REALLY CAN'T STAY, JOHNNY—MR. TRACY WILL BE HOME SOON. SO, DON'T TRY SWEEPING ME OFF MY FEET—
CHLOROFORM

While—
WATCH THE ROADS, MR. TRACY—FREEZING RAIN, TURNING TO SNOW!
THANKS, RODRIQUEZ.
POLICE GARAGE

SAM—THIS IS THE SUSPECT IN THE HOTEL SLAYING?
YEAH—JOHNNY SNOW—THE ICEMAN. HIGH-PRICED HITTER.
SURVEILLANCE PHOTO

IT'S ALSO JOHNNY WINTER—SPARKLE'S NEW BOYFRIEND!

"YE GODS!" SAYS SAM. "ISN'T THIS SPARKLE'S DAY TO CLEAN TRACY'S HOUSE?"
GOULD Fletcher COLLINS

"YES," SAYS LIZZ. "AND TRACY'S ON HIS WAY THERE NOW..."

CAN'T RAISE TRACY ON THE 2-WAY!
HE'S ON HIS WAY HOME— MUST'VE SWITCHED HIS OFF.

HE DOESN'T KNOW," SAYS SAM. "THAT SPARKLE'S BOYFRIEND IS JOHNNY SNOW —THE ICEMAN!"

SNOW MAY HAVE USED SPARKLE AS A WAY INTO TRACY'S HOUSE," SAYS LIZZ. "HE COULD BE WAITING THERE NOW!"
GOULD Fletcher COLLINS

A SQUAD IS ON ITS WAY TO TRACY'S—
GOOD. NOW LET'S GET THERE OURSELVES...
2-WAY WRIST TV

BUT TRACY IS ALREADY HOME—

AND AS HE GETS OUT TO UNLOCK HIS GARAGE DOOR—
LOUSY RAIN—HEY! THAT'S STRANGE...
GOULD Fletcher COLLINS

IF THE ICEMAN'S WAITING FOR TRACY—
I KNOW.

While—
THAT'S STRANGE— SPARKLE SHOULD STILL BE HERE... I WAS SUPPOSED TO GIVE HER A RIDE HOME—
GOULD Fletcher COLLINS

BUT EVERY LIGHT IN THE HOUSE IS OUT—

WHERE IS HE? I HEARD HIM PULL IN THE DRIVEWAY... WHY HASN'T HE COME IN?
GOULD Fletcher COLLINS

I STAKED HIM OUT FOR WEEKS—HE ALWAYS COMES IN THROUGH THE GARAGE...

WELL—JOHNNY SNOW! YOU WANT TO DROP THAT GUN, OR SHALL I DROP YOU...?
CLICK

WHAT GAVE ME AWAY, TRACY?

SPARKLE PLENTY WAS TO CLEAN MY HOUSE TODAY —SHOULD'VE STILL BEEN HERE. BUT THE HOUSE WAS DARK—

ICEPICK
AND WHERE IS SPARKLE? IF YOU'VE HURT HER...
GOULD Fletcher COLLINS

ICEPICK
SPARKLE'S FINE, TRACY.

"SHE'S IN A CLOSET UPSTAIRS," SAYS THE ICEMAN. "UNHARMED."
GOULD Fletcher COLLINS

ICEPICK

GARAGE IS LOCKED— HAVE TO GET OUT THE FRONT WAY, UPSTAIRS.

Meanwhile, SPARKLE HAS COME OUT OF HER CHLOROFORM-INDUCED SLEEP.
WHAT... WHERE... DID JOHNNY DO THIS?

ICEPICK

WAIT...TRACY'LL FOLLOW ME UP HERE—MAYBE I CAN COLLECT THAT $1,000,000 AFTER ALL...

THIS LAUNDRY CHUTE LEADS UPSTAIRS...
GOULD Fletcher COLLINS

JOHNNY DIDN'T TIE THESE ROPES VERY TIGHT... GOT TO GET OUT OF HERE AND FIND OUT WHAT'S GOING ON...

ONLY **TWO** WAYS TRACY CAN GET UPSTAIRS— AND I'M RIGHT BETWEEN 'EM—

BUT THE WOUNDED TRACY KNOWS A **THIRD** WAY—
THAT LAUNDRY CHUTE...
GOULD Fletcher COLLINS

And **SPARKLE** HAS FREED HERSELF...

WHAT'S GOING **ON** HERE? IF I CAN JUST FIND THAT LIGHT SWITCH...

CLICK
GOULD Fletcher COLLINS

NO!

JOHNNY?

GOULD Fletcher COLLINS
CRASH!

SPLAT
GOULD Fletcher COLLINS

STAY BACK, SPARKLE!
THUD!
BANG
BANG

GOULD Fletcher COLLINS

AND DYE FROM THE ICEMAN'S HAIR, WASHED BY RAIN, RUNS LIKE **DARK BLOOD...**
1978 by Chicago Tribune N.Y. News Synd Inc All Rights Reserved

SPARKLE...
I'M HERE, JOHNNY.

MR. TRACY—WHY DID YOU SHOOT HIM? WHY WAS HE SHOOTING AT YOU?
GOULD Fletcher COLLINS

IT'S A COMPLICATED STORY, SPARKLE. JUST GIVE HIM SOME COMFORT, WHILE YOU CAN...

YOU OKAY, TRACY?
YEAH—NEED THIS ARM LOOKED AT.

"GROOVY AND RODRIQUEZ ARE IN THE HOUSE, RETRIEVING the ICEPICK HE GOT ME WITH—COULD BE OUR MURDER WEAPON FROM THE HOTEL."

"I SHOT HIM AS HE FLED—MEANT TO WOUND HIM, BUT... ANYWAY, SPARKLE'S TAKING IT PRETTY HARD."
MR. TRACY SAID I COULD RIDE.

DOESN'T SHE KNOW THAT LOUSE WAS USING HER—TO GET AT YOU?

"MAYBE," SAYS TRACY. "BUT SHE ALSO KNOWS HE COULD HAVE USED HER AS A HOSTAGE—AND CHOSE NOT TO."
SPARKLE...
GOULD Fletcher COLLINS

YOU DON'T HAVE MUCH TIME LEFT, JOHNNY.
TIME ENOUGH TO SQUARE A FEW THINGS.
GOULD Fletcher COLLINS

WANT TO START WITH BIG BOY? OR THAT APPARATUS HIT, AT THE HOTEL? FOR OPENERS, THE GUY WHO CONTACTED ME, AND PAID ME, IS—

HIM.

PRICE! YOU'RE THE CROOKED COP?!?

GOULD Fletcher COLLINS

I DEMAND TO SEE MY LAWYER!
READ HIM HIS RIGHTS, SAM.
GOULD Fletcher COLLINS

THEN GET HIM OUT OF HERE— THIS IS A HOSPITAL AND THEY LIKE TO KEEP THE PLACE AS CLEAN AS POSSIBLE—

SPARKLE, PLEASE— LET ME SEE HER...

SPARKLE, COME CLOSER.
YES, JOHNNY...

FORGIVE ME.

GOULD Fletcher COLLINS

D.A. SAYS FORMER INSPECTOR PRICE HAS TURNED STATE'S WITNESS.
GOULD Fletcher COLLINS

HE'LL TELL ALL HE KNOWS ABOUT THE APPARATUS, AND GET IMMUNITY...
90 YEARS IS WHAT HE SHOULD GET.

ONE CROOKED COP LIKE PRICE CAN MAKE THE PUBLIC DOUBT THE HONESTY AND INTEGRITY OF ANY COP.

AT LEAST PRICE'LL BE IN THE SLAMMER, TILL THE TRIAL.
AND AFTERWARDS, HE'LL BE OUT WITH NO POLICE PROTECTION.

NOT QUITE— HE'S BEING PROVIDED WITH A NEW IDENTITY, AND RELOCATED —PART OF THE IMMUNITY DEAL.

SOMETIMES I THINK JUSTICE JUST ISN'T WHAT IT USED TO BE.
GOULD Fletcher COLLINS

THE ICEMAN—DEAD? TRACY DOWNSTAIRS?

WITH A WARRANT FOR YOUR ARREST, BIG BOY. SNOW MUST'VE TALKED, 'FORE HE CROAKED.
TRACY!

I'LL KILL HIM MYSELF— I'LL —UH—UH— —UH—

ALL THE LOUSY THINGS BIG BOY DID IN HIS LIFE, AND HE DIES A QUIET, PEACEFUL DEATH IN HIS BED, IN HIS MANSION— THERE AIN'T NO JUSTICE.
POLICE

ISN'T THERE?
Merry Christmas, Folks:
GOULD Fletcher COLLINS

AND WISH I COULD BE WITH YOU, DARLING.
GOULD Fletcher COLLINS

WHAT'S WITH TRACY?
CHIEF—IT'S CHRISTMAS.

AND YESTERDAY WAS TRACY'S WEDDING ANNIVERSARY —WITH TESS STILL IN CALIFORNIA...
HM-MM
Happy Holiday:
GOULD Fletcher COLLINS
POLICE HQ

SO BIG BOY IS DEAD. OF A HEART ATTACK?
GOULD Fletcher COLLINS

YES, JUST AFTER TRACY AND I GOT THERE, WITH A WARRANT FOR HIS ARREST. HOW'S SPARKLE?

"UPSET," SAYS LIZZ. "BUT GRAVEL GERTIE'S WITH HER, NOW... IF ONLY B.O. WOULD COME AROUND..."
JOHN SNOW 1946-1978

SOMETHING WRONG, TRACY?
I'M NOT SURE.

I'VE TOLD TESS THE BIG BOY CASE IS OVER— THAT SHE CAN COME HOME NOW —BUT SHE SAYS SHE WANTS TO STAY ON IN CALIFORNIA AWHILE.

?
GOULD Fletcher COLLINS

I JUST SPOKE WITH YOUR DOCTOR.
OH?

HE SAYS YOUR WOUND NEEDS MENDING— RECOMMENDS YOU TAKE SOME SICK LEAVE.
WHAT'S THAT? A PRESCRIPTION?
GOULD Fletcher COLLINS

IN A WAY— IT'S A TICKET TO CALIFORNIA. GET YOUR REAR OUT THERE AND SPEND NEW YEAR'S WITH YOUR WIFE!
POLICE HQ

TWO WEEKS OFF? A PLANE TICKET TO CALIFORNIA?

YOU WANT ME TO LEAVE MY POST, AND GO GALAVANTING OFF TO SPEND NEW YEAR'S WITH MY WIFE?

YOU GOT IT! SEE YOU NEXT YEAR, GANG!
GOULD Fletcher COLLINS

WHILE TRACY FLIES WEST TO JOIN TESS, LET'S CHECK IN AT SUNNY DELL ACRES...
PEACE ST.
LOVE JCT.

DADDY? CAN I COME HOME?

C'MERE, Y' LITTLE TYKE—
GOULD
Fletcher
COLLINS

THE 1980s

THE MAN OF A MILLION FACES

by Max Allan Collins and Dick Locher

10/5/87–4/10/88

The late seventies and the 1980s have seen *Dick Tracy* deal with an increasing list of modern crimes. Video piracy, inner city arson, corporate kidnapping, computer viruses, product tampering, toxic waste dumping, police corruption, stock market fraud, skyjacking, international terrorism and black market adoption are among the crimes the classic detective has tackled. Tracy has traveled to Moscow, the Caribbean, and all around his native U.S.A. Technology has manifested itself in holograms, nuclear fusion, and a Two-Way Wrist Computer.

The basic cast has remained intact, although black policewoman Lee Ebony has joined Tracy's Major Crime Squad (another character, the young, mustached Johnny Adonis, was aboard for several years, as well). Policewoman Lizz married fellow Officer Groovy Grove, only to be widowed shortly thereafter. Dick and Tess have had another child, young Joe, and Junior and Sparkle have (at last!) married, and have a lovely young offspring—Sparkle Plenty, Jr.

After the untimely death of Rick Fletcher in 1983, Dick Locher returned to *Tracy* as artist, assisted by his talented son John. While the emphasis remains on topical crime, the Collins/Locher period is marked by a return to more humor (with frequent appearances by Vitamin Flintheart and B.O. Plenty and Gravel Gertie) and villains in the grand Gould grotesque style.

For all of the above talk of topicalilty, the editors have chosen, as a representative of their own work, a story about a mere bank robber.

But "mere" is perhaps not the correct word to describe the Man of a Million Faces, a.k.a. Putty Puss.

Locher and Collins agree that Putty Puss is their favorite villain to date—and the one most like a classic Gould villain. Collins admits the inspiration for this character comes at least partially from Anyface, a villain in the spoof "Fearless Fosdick" (the strip-within-a-strip parody of *Tracy* that ran for years in Al Capp's *Li'l Abner*). Because Putty Puss can assume the faces of others, political cartoonist Locher's ability to caricature the famous and infamous of our times often came into play in this continuity.

Also, Tracy ultimately finds himself in a death trap of which Gould might well have approved. While the crimes in today's *Dick Tracy* may be new, some things never change, and dreaming up fantastic scrapes for Tracy to think himself out of is a basic tenet of the Chester Gould canon.

Coeditor Collins must peek out from behind the third-person facade to report what a delight it is to work with a gifted cartoonist like Dick Locher; his touch for humor as well as his striking black-and-white sense, which rivals Gould's own, are assets to the strip that cannot be underestimated. Collins feels lucky to have been able to work with two men who trained at the elbow of the master himself; without Fletcher and Locher to give a sense of continuity between the Gould and post-Gould periods, *Tracy* might be less "legitimate" a continuation of a classic strip. Predictions that Gould—like Walt Kelly, George Herriman, and Al Capp—would be an impossible act to follow have not proven accurate. Hard, yes; impossible, no.

On the other hand, the editors of this book are the first to say that they will never approach even the vaguest outskirts of Chester Gould at his best.

I UNDERSTAND YOU'VE GOT A ROBBERY HERE, OFFICER -
YES, DETECTIVE TRACY- WE'VE BEEN EXPECTING YOU-

"THREE HEAVILY ARMED MEN," SAYS THE OFFICER. "MADE A BIG HAUL - GOT AWAY CLEAN -"
NAPER BANK

THAT'S HIM!
DICK LOCHER MAX COLLINS

IT'S HIM - THE RINGLEADER!

DICK LOCHER MAX COLLINS
TELLERS
BANK
WHUMP!

FREEZE, PAL!
ARE YOU NUTS?!
DICK LOCHER MAX COLLINS

EXCUSE ME, BUT YOU'VE JUST TAKEN INTO CUSTODY THE SECOND-IN-COMMAND OF THE MAJOR CRIME UNIT-
I DON'T CARE IF HE'S DICK TRACY- THIS GUY ROBBED THIS BANK NOT 20 MINUTES AGO!

THIS IS SAM CATCHEM- A DETECTIVE, WHO'S BEEN IN MY PRESENCE THE ENTIRE WORKING DAY-
WELL, TWO OF THE THIEVES WERE MASKED, BUT THE OTHER ONE WASN'T- AND HE LOOKED JUST LIKE THIS.
HE EVEN DRESSED LIKE THAT!
DICK LOCHER MAX COLLINS

JEEZ- LOOKS LIKE I RETURNED TO THE SCENE OF THE CRIME!

THE BANK PRESIDENT IS SHOWING TRACY AND SAM THE SECURITY-SYSTEM VIDEO TAPE.

LET'S HOPE IT CLEARS SAM- WE CAN'T HAVE OUR COPS GOIN' AROUND ROBBING BANKS!

"IT'S NOT ALL THAT FUNNY, CHIEF-"
YE GODS- IT IS ME-
DICK LOCHER MAX COLLINS

THE LEADER OF THE BANK ROBBERS IS MY SPITTIN' IMAGE!
RIGHT DOWN TO THE FRECKLES AND BOW TIE-
DICK LOCHER
MAX COLLINS

"YOU DON'T HAVE AN EVIL TWIN, DO YOU, SAM?" "NOT UNLESS MY FOLKS KEPT IT FROM ME," SAYS THE FLABBERGASTED SAM.

NAPER BANK

WHEN THE MAJOR CRIME UNIT ARRIVES AT THE SCENE OF A MIDTOWN BANK ROBBERY, SAM CATCHEM IS GREETED ROUGHLY-
TELLERS
BANK
WHUMP!

THAT'S RIGHT, CHIEF- THE BANK'S SECURITY-SYSTEM VIDEO TAPE CONFIRMS IT-

"THE RINGLEADER OF THE ROBBERY WAS SAM'S DOUBLE- RIGHT DOWN TO HIS HOMBURG!"
IT AIN'T POSSIBLE!
NO IT "AIN'T"- LET'S GET THAT TAPE BACK TO HQ AND LET THE LAB HAVE A GO AT IT-

AND SOON-
THESE COMPUTER-ENHANCED BLOW-UPS ONLY SERVE TO FURTHER CONFIRM THE UNCANNY RESEMBLANCE-
DICK LOCHER
MAX COLLINS

IT'S OBVIOUS SOMEBODY WAS POSING AS YOU- BUT WHY?
YA GOT ME!
IT'S A GOOD WAY FOR AN AUDACIOUS THIEF TO THUMB HIS NOSE AT THE COPS...

"TRUE," SAYS TRACY. "HIS CRONIES WORE MASKS, BUT HIS DISGUISE DID MORE THAN JUST CONCEAL HIS IDENTITY: IT SOWED CONFUSION, ATTRACTED ATTENTION AND CREATED EMBARRASSMENT-"

IF CONCEALING HIS IDENTITY WAS HIS PRIMARY GOAL, THE RINGLEADER COULD HAVE WORN A MASK...
DICK LOCHER
MAX COLLINS

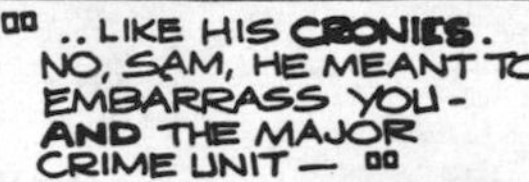
"..LIKE HIS CRONIES. NO, SAM, HE MEANT TO EMBARRASS YOU- AND THE MAJOR CRIME UNIT—"

THE PRESS IS ALREADY HAVIN' A BIG LAUGH AT MY EXPENSE!
SAM, YOU'RE MISSING THE POINT-
CLEVER CROOK "CAPTURES" COP

OUR MASQUERADER HAS EMBARRASSED YOU, SAM— BUT MORE IMPORTANT, HE'S DONE SO WHILE ATTRACTING ATTENTION TO HIMSELF—
CLEVER
DICK LOCHER
MAX COLLINS

I'M AFRAID HE'S MORE THAN JUST A MAKE-UP ARTIST—

I'VE NEVER SEEN THE LIKE OF THIS— NO SIGN OF MAKE-UP OR PROSTHETICS—
MAYBE WE SHOULD CALL IN VITAMIN FLINTHEART—
DICK LOCHER
MAX COLLINS

"YEAH," SAM SAYS. "HE'S BEEN AN ACTOR FOR A COUPLE HUNDRED YEARS— HE OUGHTA KNOW STAGE MAKE-UP—"

UNLESS MY EYES DECEIVE ME, SAMUEL, THERE IS NO STAGE MAKE-UP IN USE HERE—
WELL, WHAT ABOUT MOVIE MAGIC, VITAMIN? THERE'S SOME PRETTY AMAZIN' STUFF BEIN' DONE ON SCREEN—

"EVERYTHING FROM ALIENS POPPIN' OUTA PEOPLE'S CHESTS, TO GUYS TURNIN' INTO WEREWOLVES..."
DICK LOCHER
MAX COLLINS

MAKE-UP AND SPECIAL EFFECTS SEEN ON A MOVIE SCREEN, COURTESY OF A CREATIVE CAMERAMAN'S FILTERS AND TRICKS, ARE OFTEN EXTREMELY CONVINCING—
DICK LOCHER
MAX COLLINS

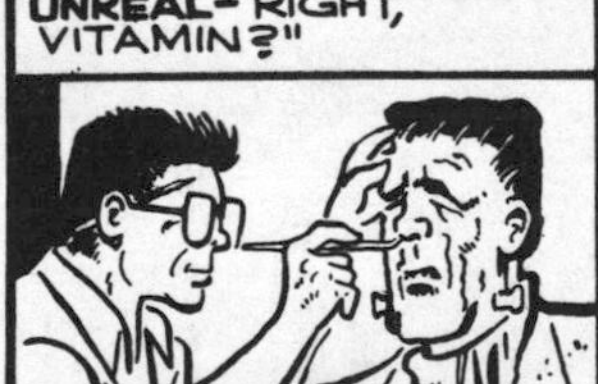
"BUT OFF-CAMERA, CLOSE-UP, MOST OF THAT STUFF LOOKS PHONY, UNREAL— RIGHT, VITAMIN?"

CORRECT, RICHARD. PERHAPS SAMUEL HAS A DOPPELGANGER—
HEY, I FEEL FINE—

IT IS SAID EACH OF US HAS A PHYSICAL TWIN, WANDERING THE PLANET SOMEWHERE— A DOPPELGANGER, IF YOU WILL—
AND MINE IS ROBBING BANKS?
TRACY, YOU DON'T BELIEVE—

"FRANKLY," TRACY SAYS, "I DON'T KNOW WHO—OR WHAT— WE'RE UP AGAINST—"
DICK LOCHER
MAX COLLINS

YOU MEAN, THE THIEF POSING AS SAM WASN'T **WEARING** MAKE-UP?
CHIEF, THE WITNESSES AT THE BANK WERE IN **CLOSE PROXIMITY** TO THIS INDIVIDUAL-

"AND **NONE** OF THEM NOTICED **ANYTHING** RESEMBLING MAKE-UP OR MECHANICAL APPLICATIONS—"

"ALSO, WE BROUGHT IN **VITAMIN FLINTHEART** - WHO HAS EXTENSIVE STAGE AND SCREEN EXPERIENCE— AND IN HIS OPINION **NO MAKE-UP** WAS USED..."

WELL, HOW ARE YOU GOING TO **PROCEED**, THEN? ARE YOU ASSUMING SAM CATCHEM HAS A **DOUBLE**?
WE'RE ASSUMING **NOTHING**, CHIEF-
DICK LOCHER
MAX COLLINS

"WE'RE GATHERING WHAT WE CAN FROM A PHOTOGRAPHIC ANALYSIS OF THE BANK-ROBBERY VIDEO TAPE—"
C
A
53.5"
69.9"
B
D

"WE'RE LOGGING DEFECTS AND DISTINCTIVE CHARACTERISTICS OF THE ROBBER'S CLOTHING—"
THERE'S A MISSING BUTTON-
A PATCH THERE-

I HOPE THESE STANDARD PROCEDURES PROVE USEFUL, TRACY-
CHIEF- EXCUSE THE INTER-RUPTION-
CHIEF PATTON

"BUT WE HAVE ANOTHER **BANK ROBBERY** IN PROGRESS – AND THE RING LEADER **ISN'T SAM!**"

RONALD REAGAN ROBBED YOUR BANK?
IT SURE **LOOKED** LIKE HIM!

"AND IT **SOUNDED** LIKE HIM, TOO!"
MY FELLOW AMERICANS- PUT UP YOUR HANDS!

YOU KNOW WHAT THIS **MEANS**, SAM?
IMPEACHMENT PROCEEDINGS?
DICK LOCHER
MAX COLLINS

WELL, THE PRESIDENT SEEMS TO HAVE AN **ALIBI** FOR YESTERDAY'S BANK ROBBERY-
YOU CALLED THE **WHITE HOUSE** ON THIS?
BANK SECURITY SYSTEM VIDEO TAPE

"NO- THEY CALLED **US**," SAM SAYS, "AFTER THE REPORTS OF THE 'PRESIDENTIAL' HEIST IN THE PRESS —WHAT **NEXT**, I WONDER?"
DICK LOCHER
MAX COLLINS

AT LEAST I'M OFF THE HOOK AS A SUSPECT-
YOU AND YOUR DOPPELGANGER-
THIS SECURITY TAPE IS JUST LIKE THE FIRST ONE-

"THE RINGLEADER HAS AN UNCANNY RESEMBLANCE TO SOMEONE HE CLEARLY CANNOT BE-YET THERE IS NO APPARENT USE OF ANY DISGUISE!"
DICK LOCHER MAX COLLINS

ALBERT EINSTEIN?
THAT'S WHO HE LOOKED LIKE, DETECTIVE!

"WHAT ABOUT HIS VOICE?" SAM ASKS. "WELL," THE TELLER SAYS, "HE HAD AN ACCENT-"
DICK LOCHER MAX COLLINS

SINCE THE REAL ALBERT EINSTEIN IS DEAD, I THINK WE CAN SAFELY RULE HIM OUT AS A SUSPECT-
"DEAD"'S A TOUGH ALIBI TO BREAK-

ALBERT EINSTEIN A BANK ROBBER?
EINSTEIN'S DEAD- MAYBE IT WAS A RELATIVE.
I THINK WE CAN DISMISS THE THEORY OF RELATIVITY-

"THE QUESTION IS," SAYS TRACY, "ARE THESE CELEBRITY BANK ROBBERS THE SAME MAN?"
DICK LOCHER MAX COLLINS

HERE'S OUR ALL-STAR ROGUES' GALLERY - SOME COMPANY "I" KEEP-
IS THIS ONE MAN-A MASTER OF IMPERCEPTIBLE DISGUISE?

"OR DO WE HAVE A BIZARRE BAND OF CELEBRITY LOOKALIKES WHO HAVE TURNED TO CRIME?"
DICK LOCHER MAX COLLINS

HE SAID HE HAD TEN BULLETS IN HIS GUN, AND THAT THEY WERE THE "TOP TEN" REASONS WHY I SHOULD GIVE HIM THE MONEY-
WHO ROBBED THIS BANK?
DAVID LETTERMAN!

"OR ANYWAY," SAYS LIZZ, "A GUY WHO LOOKS JUST LIKE HIM — "
YE GODS - BANK ROBBERIES ALL OVER THE METROPOLITAN AREA- ALL PULLED OFF BY CELEBRITY LOOK ALIKES-
AND ONE THAT LOOKED LIKE YOU-
"WELL, I'M TRAVELLING IN PRETTY FAST COMPANY," SAYS SAM. "RONALD REAGAN AND ALBERT EINSTEIN!"

EVEN HIS VOICE WAS LIKE DAVID LETTERMAN'S- ESPECIALLY WHEN HE MADE US GO FACE-DOWN ON THE FLOOR AND CALLED IT A "STUPID HUMAN TRICK-"
DICK LOCHER
MAX COLLINS

THAT'S A PHRASE THE REAL LETTERMAN USES ON HIS TV SHOW.
I KNOW. GRAB THE SECURITY TAPE OF THE ROBBERY-

"I THINK WE'VE HAD OUR FIRST REAL BREAK — "

JUST FOR THE RECORD - WE CHECKED WITH NBC AT ROCKEFELLER CENTER -

"AND DAVID LETTERMAN DOES HAVE AN ALIBI FOR THE LATEST CELEBRITY BANK ROBBERY — "
DICK LOCHER
MAX COLLINS

HERE'S THE AUDIO TAPE DUB OF THE BANK SECURITY VIDEO THAT YOU REQUESTED, BOSS-
WHAT'S THIS? ANOTHER LETTERMAN RERUN?

I BELIEVE WE CAN PROVE THAT OUR CELEBRITY LOOKALIKE BANK ROBBERS ARE ONE MAN-

"BY USING KNOWN HEIGHTS OF OBJECTS, WE CAN MEASURE THE HEIGHT OF THE PERPETRATOR."

EINSTEIN AND LETTERMAN ARE BOTH FIVE ELEVEN!
SO IS RONALD REAGAN- AND YOUR TWIN. BUT THAT'S NOT ALL-
DICK LOCHER
MAX COLLINS 10-27

THOSE BANK SECURITY-SYSTEM VIDEO TAPES HAD AN AUDIO TRACK- WHICH WE TRANSFERRED OVER TO REEL TO REEL -
FORENSICS DEPARTMENT
DICK LOCHER
MAX COLLINS

"THROUGH VOICEPRINT ANALYSIS, WE CAN DETERMINE WHETHER THE VOICES OF THESE VARIOUS PUBLIC-FIGURE 'BANK ROBBERS' BELONG TO ONE MAN — "

SAM, YOU KNOW SGT. SONIC, OUR TOP SPECTROGRAM EXAMINER-
I DON'T SEE WHERE VOICE INDENTIFICATION COMES INTO THIS, SARGE-

"AFTER ALL," SAYS SAM, "THIS GUY-IF IT IS ONE GUY-WAS USING OTHER PEOPLE'S VOICES!"
DICK LOCHER
MAX COLLINS

AN INDIVIDUAL'S VOICE PATTERN REMAINS UNCHANGED EVEN WHEN MIMICKING THE VOICE OF ANOTHER-

THAT'S WHY SPEECH SPECTROGRAMS ARE COMMONLY CALLED VOICEPRINTS - THE AURAL EQUIVALENT OF FINGERPRINTS-

"AND FROM THE LOOKS OF THIS, YOUR CELEBRITY CROOKS ARE ONE MAN-"
DICK LOCHER
MAX COLLINS

I'VE RE-RECORDED THE "VOICES" DIGITALLY - AND THERE CAN BE NO DOUBT, DETECTIVE TRACY-

"THE VOICES OF YOUR CELEBRITY BANK ROBBERS ARE ONE VOICE- DESPITE THE WAY IT SOUNDS TO THE HUMAN EAR-"

SO WE HAVE A MASTER OF DISGUISE ON OUR HANDS-
WHAT DID YOU EXPECT ON HALLOWEEN?
DICK LOCHER
MAX COLLINS

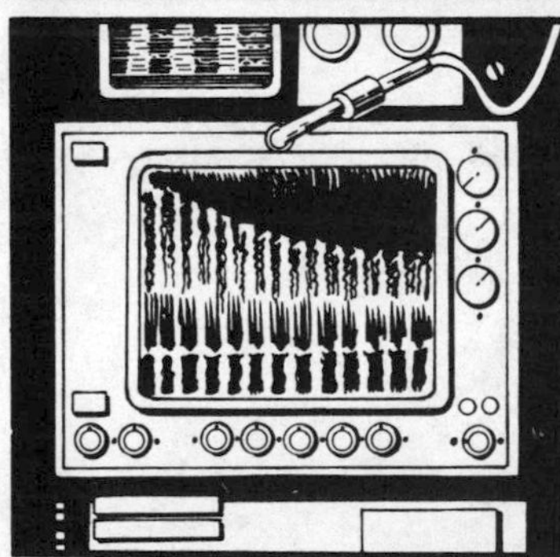

AT LEAST NOW WE KNOW OUR CELEBRITY BANK ROBBERS ARE ONE PERSON-
NOW IF WE ONLY KNEW WHO THAT ONE PERSON WAS-
WELL, THE MEDIA HAS GIVEN HIM A NAME-
MAN OF 1,000,000 FACES

"THE MAN OF A MILLION FACES," SAYS TRACY. "BUT DESPITE HIS FACIAL AND AURAL MIMICKRY..."

".. HE ONLY HAS ONE VOICE- VOICEPRINT ANALYSIS HAS PROVEN THAT."

TRACY, I HAVE THE READOUT ON ACTORS WITH CRIMINAL RECORDS — IT'S LONGER THAN YOU'D IMAGINE -

THERE'S NO BUSINESS LIKE SHOW BUSINESS. START QUESTIONING THEM - EACH ONE OF YOU TAKE A SHARE -

AS FOR ME, I'LL BE STUDYING THE PATTERN OF THESE ROBBERIES -
DICK LOCHER
MAX COLLINS

AND THERE IS A PATTERN, AS DISTINCT AS OUR MASTER OF DISGUISE'S INCRIMINATING VOICEPRINT -

STATUS REPORT, TRACY?
LIZZ, SAM AND LEE ARE IN THE FIELD -

"THE COMPUTER KICKED OUT QUITE A LIST OF LOCAL ACTORS WITH CRIMINAL RECORDS -"

AND YOU THINK THIS "MAN OF A MILLION FACES" IS ONE OF THEM?
PERHAPS - BUT I HAVE MY OWN IDEAS ABOUT FINDING HIM -
DICK LOCHER
MAX COLLINS

LIZZ, MEET MY NEW PARTNER, STEVE MEYER -
HI - SOMEBODY WHO LOOKS LIKE US ROB A BANK?
NO - THOUGH YOU DO USE A LOT OF CELEBRITY IMPRESSIONS ON YOUR RADIO SHOW -
DICK LOCHER
MAX COLLINS

"AREN'T YOU CHASING THE MAN OF A MILLION FACES?" ASKS THEMESONG. "YES," SAYS LIZZ, "BUT HE HAS JUST AS MANY VOICES -"

I'VE BEEN INTERVIEWING ACTORS WITH CRIMINAL RECORDS - NO PROMISING LEADS YET -
YESTERDAY I GATHERED THESE SAMPLE TAPES FROM THEMESONG OF LOCAL IMPRESSIONISTS WHO DO RADIO WORK -

"TODAY SGT. SONIC ELIMINATED ALL OF 'EM BY VOICEPRINT COMPARISON," SAYS LIZZ. "LET'S HOPE TRACY'S COME UP WITH SOMETHING," SAYS SAM.
DICK LOCHER
MAX COLLINS

ON THIS MAP OF THE GREATER METRO AREA, I'VE FLAGGED THE BANKS ROBBED - THEIR LOCATIONS ARE QUITE SIMILAR -

EACH ROBBERY TAKES PLACE IN A DIFFERENT POLICE JURISDICTION - FIRST MIDTOWN, THEN VARIOUS SUBURBS -

"AND EACH ONE TAKES PLACE WITHIN TWO BLOCKS OF A FREEWAY EXCHANGE -"
HOMEWOOD
NEXT EXIT
DICK LOCHER
MAX COLLINS
JJL

THE DARK FLAGS INDICATE BANKS IN THE GREATER METRO AREA THAT FIT THE PATTERN OF THE PREVIOUS ROBBERIES-
DICK LOCHER MAX COLLINS

"OUR PHANTOM PERP MAY HAVE A MILLION FACES, BUT HE'S DOWN TO SIX BANKS THAT SUIT HIS M.O.*-"
HOMEWOOD BANK
*MODUS OPERANDI- METHOD OF OPERATION.

ALL SIX OF THESE BANKS ARE PRIME CANDIDATES FOR THE MAN OF A MILLION FACES-
ALL SIX ARE STAKED OUT?
YES- WE WAIT FOR THE 2-WAY CALL THAT A ROBBERY IS IN PROGRESS.

"AND SINCE THEY'VE BEEN COMING EVERY FEW DAYS, WE WON'T HAVE LONG TO WAIT-"
DICK LOCHER MAX COLLINS
HOMEWOOD BANK

HOMEWOOD BANK

YOU'VE ESTABLISHED A PATTERN FOR THE BANKS ROBBED BY THIS "MAN OF A MILLION FACES"?
YES, CHIEF - A KEY FACTOR BEING EASY ACCESS TO A FREEWAY EXCHANGE-
THERE ARE ONLY SIX BANKS LEFT IN THE GREATER METRO AREA THAT FIT OUR MAN'S M.O.

AND WE'VE GOT THOSE BANKS STAKED OUT - THE VARIOUS SUBURBAN COPS ARE COOPERATING-
DICK LOCHER MAX COLLINS

"WE'RE JUST WAITIN' FOR THE NEXT ROBBERY TO GO DOWN!"
THAT'S RIGHT- ALERT DICK TRACY-
WE SHOULD'VE TIPPED TO THIS-

JUST BE CALM LADIES AND GENTLEMEN-

I'M ABOUT TO ADD YOUR MONEY TO MY VAST PERSONAL FORTUNE-

AND SOON-
IMAGINE - DIET SMITH ROBBING A BANK!
YES - AND IT'S A BANK WHERE THE REAL DIET HAS HOLDINGS-

"SO THE STAKEOUT TEAM DIDN'T SUSPECT, AT FIRST, ANOTHER MASQUERADE-"
BOSS- COPS OUTSIDE-
SO WHAT? WE GOT HOSTAGES-

DIET SMITH! A BILLIONAIRE BANK ROBBER!
THE MAN OF A MILLION FACES HAS A SENSE OF HUMOR

"..BUT I DOUBT HE'LL BE AMUSED WHEN HE FINDS THE BANK HE'S ROBBING IS UNDER STAKEOUT!"

COME OUT WITH YOUR HANDS EMPTY AND HIGH!
DICK LOCHER
MAX COLLINS

STATUS REPORT, DETECTIVE RANDISI?
THREE PERPS INSIDE, HEAVILY ARMED- UNDETERMINED NUMBER OF HOSTAGES-

"ANY COMMUNICATION WITH THE PERPS?" TRACY ASKS. "NO RESPONSE TO THE BULLHORN," SAYS RANDISI.

GET 'EM ON THE PHONE AND PATCH ME THROUGH - I WANT TO TALK TO "DIET SMITH"-
DICK LOCHER
MAX COLLINS

WELL, WELL - MY OLD FRIEND DICK TRACY! I'LL BET YOU'D LIKE TO ARRANGE THE RELEASE OF THESE HOSTAGES!
DICK LOCHER
MAX COLLINS

YE GODS- HE EVEN SOUNDS LIKE DIET!

I'LL NEED A FULLY FUELED JET AND A MILLION DOLLARS- BUSINESS HAS BEEN SLOW AT SMITH ENTERPRISES OF LATE!

AS ONE OLD FRIEND TO ANOTHER, "DIET"- I ASSURE YOU YOUR DEMANDS WILL NOT BE MET- UNLESS YOU MEET ONE UNNEGOTIABLE CONDITION-

RELEASE ALL THE HOSTAGES NOW!?! THEN WHAT BARGAINING LEVERAGE DOES THAT LEAVE ME?

YOU'LL HAVE ME. I'M OFFERING MYSELF IN TRADE-

DICK LOCHER
MAX COLLINS

ITS A DEAL, TRACY- I'LL RELEASE THE HOSTAGES AND TAKE YOU IN THEIR PLACE-

DONE.

TRACY, YOU CAN'T GO IN THERE- WHAT'S TO STOP HIM FROM GRABBIN' YOU AND HOLDIN' ON TO THE HOSTAGES!?!

DICK LOCHER
MAX COLLINS

DON'T GO IN THERE! HE'LL HAVE YOU AND THE HOSTAGES!
IF "DIET" DOESN'T STICK TO HIS BARGAIN, AT LEAST I'LL BE INSIDE-
I HATE SENDING HIM IN UNARMED-

"I'M NOT NUTS ABOUT IT, EITHER," SAYS SAM. "BUT TRACY DOESN'T HAVE TO BE ARMED TO BE DANGEROUS-"
HERE HE COMES, BOSS-
DICK LOCHER
MAX COLLINS

TRACY HAS NEGOTIATED A HOSTAGE EXCHANGE WITH THE BANK ROBBERS, USING HIMSELF AS BARTER-
BANK

LOOKS LIKE "DIET SMITH" IS KEEPING TO THE BARGAIN-
HE SEEMS TO BE RELEASING THE HOSTAGES, ALL RIGHT-
DICK LOCHER
MAX COLLINS

STEP INSIDE, TRACY- YOUR OLD PAL DIET SMITH WANTS TO SEE YOU!

YE GODS - IF I DIDN'T KNOW BETTER, I'D SWEAR IT WAS DIET!
WELL, TRACY! NICE OF YOU TO STOP BY!

THE VOICE IS PERFECT- AND EVEN CLOSE-UP, THERE'S NO HINT OF MAKE-UP-
DISCONCERTING, ISN'T IT ?
MAYBE I AM DIET SMITH...

BOYS, KEEP WATCH ON THE OUTSIDE - I'M GOING TO PUT MY FRIEND TO WORK IN THE VAULT-

NEED ANY HELP, BOSS ?
NO- MY DETECTIVE FRIEND WILL PACK THE SACKS OF CASH FOR US - JUST KEEP WATCH -

I DON'T UNDERSTAND WHY "DIET SMITH" WENT FOR THE EXCHANGE -
JUST BE GLAD WE GOT THE HOSTAGES BACK- NOW IF ONLY WE CAN GET TRACY OUT ALIVE-
DICK LOCHER
MAX COLLINS

D'YA THINK WE'LL GET THAT JET AND THE MILLION BUCKS THE BOSS DEMANDED?
I DUNNO. HOPE THE BOSS KNOWS WHAT HE'S DOIN'...

.. WE HAD ALL THOSE HOSTAGES, AND NOW ALL WE GOT IS ONE LOUSY COP -
DICK LOCHER
MAX COLLINS

HEY BOSS! HOW ARE YA DOIN IN THERE ?!?

WHAT'S TAKIN' SO.... UH -
DICK LOCHER
MAX COLLINS

DICK LOCHER
MAX COLLINS
YOU'RE SLOW, BOYS...

BLAM! BLAM! BLAM!
BLAM! BLAM!

GUNSHOTS! WE'RE GOIN' IN-
WAIT, SAM- LOOK! IT'S...

TRACY...
DICK LOCHER
MAX COLLINS

TRACY!
HE MADE IT!

I'M OKAY! I'M OKAY...

DICK TRACY HAS DONE THE IMPOSSIBLE - HE HAS GONE UNARMED INTO A BANK HELD BY VICIOUS THEIVES AND EMERGED VICTORIOUS!
DICK LOCHER
MAX COLLINS

TRACY, ARE YOU ALL RIGHT? WE HEARD THE SHOTS-
I GOT HOLD OF A GUN- AND NOW I'M A SOLE SURVIVOR-
"DIET SMITH" WAS A FOOL TO TRADE THOSE HOSTAGES FOR YOU-

DETECTIVE TRACY, COULD YOU TELL OUR VIEWERS-
PLEASE- I NEED SOME TIME ALONE...

SEE YOU AT HQ.
JUST TAKE IT EASY, CHIEF-
WE'LL HOLD DOWN THE FORT-

HE'S BEEN IN PLENTY OF SHOOT-OUTS, BUT I NEVER SAW IT HIT HIM SO HARD-
KILLING DOESN'T COME EASY FOR TRACY-

YE GODS, THESE TWO ARE RIDDLED WITH BULLETS...
WHERE'S THE BOGUS 'DIET SMITH'? I'LL CHECK THE VAULT-

SAM! GET IN HERE, NOW!!
DICK LOCHER
MAX COLLINS

WHAT'S THIS!?!
IT SEEMS TO BE DICK TRACY-

WHAT'S TRACY DOING INSIDE THE BANK VAULT?
WAKING UP FROM A BLOW TO THE HEAD, I'D SAY-
DICK LOCHER
MAX COLLINS

"" BUT WE JUST SAW TRACY DRIVE AWAY FROM HERE! "" SAYS SAM.
"" DID WE? "" LIZZ WONDERS.

WHAT HAPPENED, TRACY?
YOU TELL ME-
DICK LOCHER
MAX COLLINS

"" 'DIET SMITH' SAPPED ME WITH THE BUTT OF HIS GUN, I THINK- ""

THAT'S THE LAST I REMEMBER-
APB* ON DICK TRACY-
* ALL POINTS BULLETIN

AM I HEARING THINGS OR DID YOU JUST PUT OUT AN APB ON ME?
IT'S AN APB ON THE MAN OF A MILLION FACES-
WHO WAS LAST SEEN WEARING YOUR FACE-
DICK LOCHER MAX COLLINS

"BUT THAT'S IMPOSSIBLE," TRACY SAYS. "HE BECAME ME- ON THE SPUR OF THE MOMENT?"
HOMEWOOD BANK

TRACY, THE UNMARKED POLICE CAR "YOU" ESCAPED IN WAS FOUND A FEW BLOCKS AWAY-
SO WE CAN ASSUME OUR MAN'S SWITCHED CARS, THEN-
AND FACES-
ABANDONED "DIET SMITH" WARDROBE

"THE QUESTION IS," TRACY SAYS, "WHOSE FACE IS HE HIDING BEHIND NOW?"
DICK LOCHER MAX COLLINS

YOU'RE GOING TO HAVE TO DEAL WITH THE MEDIA SWARMING OUT THERE-
THEY'RE GOING TO WANT TO KNOW WHY THE MAN OF A MILLION FACES SHOT HIS OWN MEN-
WHY DID HE?
DICK LOCHER MAX COLLINS

"TO SILENCE THEM, OBVIOUSLY- WHICH IS WHY WE WON'T REVEAL THAT ONE HENCHMAN IS STILL ALIVE-"

TRACY, WHAT WENT DOWN IN THERE?
INCREDIBLE AS IT SEEMS, THE SO-CALLED MAN OF A MILLION FACES DISGUISED HIMSELF AS ME AND MADE AN UNOBSTRUCTED ESCAPE-
BUT HOW COULD HE HAVE KNOWN YOU'D EVEN BE HERE?

"HE COULDN'T," TRACY SAYS. "HIS TRANSFORMATION WAS AS IMPROMPTU AS IT WAS CONVINCING-"
DICK LOCHER MAX COLLINS

EMERGENCY ROOM

I HEARD YOU'D RUSHED TO THE HOSPITAL- IS TRACY OKAY?
HE'S FINE, CHIEF- JUST CONFUSED, LIKE THE REST OF US..

".. THE MAN OF A MILLION FACES PULLED OFF AN IMPROMPTU MASQUERADE AS TRACY- AND MADE A CLEAN ESCAPE-"

BUT BEFORE HE DID, HE SHOT DOWN HIS OWN BOYS-
DICK LOCHER MAX COLLINS

"WHY?" THE CHIEF ASKS. "APPARENTLY TO SILENCE THEM," LIZZ SAYS. "ONLY IT MAY NOT WORK OUT THAT WAY..."

WHY'S THAT?
ONE OF THEM IS STILL BREATHING-

"TRACY'S KEEPING VIGIL AT THE GUY'S BEDSIDE-"
PUTTY.... PUTTY PUSS...

SAM- USE YOUR TWO-WAY TO RECORD THIS-

PUTTY PUSS.... DON'T SHOOT.... DON'T SHOOT...

PUTTY PUSS.... DON'T SHOOT, PUTTY PUSS....

WHAT'S HE SAYING, TRACY?
HE'S DELIRIOUS- I THINK HE THINKS HE'S TALKING TO HIS BOSS
DICK LOCHER MAX COLLINS

CARVER... ALREADY DEAD, BOSS, CAN'T KILL HIM, PUTTY PUSS.... ALREADY DEAD...

WHO IS DEAD?
CARVER... PUTTY PUSS! DON'T SHOOT, PUTTY PUSS!

DON'T CALL ME PUTTY PUSS! OKAY, BOSS... OKAY...

THAT'S ENOUGH, MR. TRACY- YOU'LL HAVE TO LEAVE THE PATIENT'S ROOM AT ONCE -
DICK LOCHER MAX COLLINS

WHAT WAS HE BABBLING ABOUT?
HE KEPT SAYING TWO NAMES... "CARVER" WAS ONE OF THEM, AND PUTTY PUSS WAS THE OTHER-
DICK LOCHER MAX COLLINS

I THOUGHT HE SAID PLATYPUS-

"NO, IT WAS DEFINITELY PUTTY PUSS," SAYS TRACY. "AND IT WAS A NICKNAME THAT HIS 'BOSS' DIDN'T LIKE-"
PUTTY PUSS.... PUTTY PUSS....

TRACY, WHAT'S THIS I HEAR ABOUT MY TURNING BANK ROBBER?
DICK LOCHER
MAX COLLINS

THE MAN OF A MILLION FACES, a.k.a. PUTTY PUSS, USED YOU AS HIS LATEST DISGUISE - BUT DON'T FEEL BAD...

"HE USED ME THAT WAY, TOO," TRACY SAYS. "NOW WHAT'S THIS I HEAR ABOUT YOU RUNNING FOR A CERTAIN HIGH OFFICE?"
SEAL OF THE PRESIDENT OF THE UNITED STATES

IT'S TRUE, TRACY - I AM CONSIDERING TAKING A RUN FOR THE PRESIDENCY - PEOPLE HAVE PRESSURED ME TO FOR YEARS -
DICK LOCHER
MAX COLLINS

WELL, DIET - A THIRD PARTY CANDIDACY MAY BE A LONG SHOT -

"BUT FOR WHAT IT'S WORTH, YOU'VE GOT THE BLESSING AND SUPPORT OF THIS OLD COP."
VARIETY

DIET'S GOING TO RUN FOR PRESIDENT?
ON WHAT TICKET?

IT'S NOT CERTAIN YET... HE'LL BE A THIRD PARTY CANDIDATE IF HE RUNS...
DICK LOCHER
MAX COLLINS

"MIGHT BE WISE," SAM OFFERS, "FOR HIM TO POSTPONE ANNOUNCIN' TILL THE DIET SMITH BANK ROBBERY STORY COOLS DOWN..."
WHO COULD THAT BE?
VARIETY

PUTTY PUSS....
PUTTY PUSS....

SO THE SURVIVING HENCHMAN SEEMS TO HAVE GIVEN THE MAN OF A MILLION FACES A NAME -
TRACY THINKS IT'S A NAME, ANYWAY -

YES I DO - PUTTY PUSS -
DICK LOCHER
MAX COLLINS

"IT'S NOT MUCH," SAYS TRACY, "BUT IT'S A START -"
WHO ON EARTH -
VARIETY

WHY... HARLEY! HARLEY NIAV! I THOUGHT YOU WERE ...

DEAD? WISHFUL THINKING ON YOUR PART, PERHAPS. NO, NOT DEAD - MERELY... AWAY -

AREN'T YOU GOING TO INVITE ME IN, BARRY? WHY, IF IT WEREN'T FOR ME, WHERE WOULD YOU BE TODAY?

HARLEY, AFTER THE ... ACCIDENT, YOU DROPPED COMPLETELY OUT OF SIGHT. WE ALL ASSUMED...

THE WORST. AND ON OPENING NIGHT, YOU WENT ON IN MY PLACE - AN UNDERSTUDY WHO SCORED A MAJOR SUCCESS -
SLEUTH
STARRING BARRY MOORE AND VITAMIN FLINTHEART

HOW REMARKABLE YOU ARE. BARRY - THE UNDERSTUDY WHO WENT ON FOR ME, AFTER MY TRAGEDY, ONLY TO WIN THE ROLE ... AND LAUNCH A MAJOR CAREER!
SLEUTH
STARRING BARRY MOORE AND VITAMIN FLINTHEART

IT HASN'T BEEN QUITE THAT EASY, HARLEY - BUT WHAT HAPPENED TO YOU, AFTER THE ACCIDENT? WHERE HAVE YOU BEEN?
DICK LOCHER
MAX COLLINS

I WAS BADLY BURNED WHEN MY CAR VEERED OFF THE ROAD -

"THE STEERING WENT, AND THE BRAKES... BUT YOU KNOW ALL THAT."
DICK LOCHER
MAX COLLINS

I WAS HOPELESSLY DISFIGURED... 'HANDSOME HARLEY NIAV'!! BEYOND THE HELP OF ANY PLASTIC SURGEON - EXCEPT ONE -

I WAS APPROACHED BY A DR. WILLIS CARVER, THE PLASTIC SURGEON... HE'D BEEN EXPERIMENTING WITH A NEW TECHNIQUE...

"..ARTIFICIAL FLESH - AN ADVANCED FORM OF LATEX, COMBINED WITH SILICON INPLANTS -"

HE FELT HE COULD RESTRUCTURE MY FACE - COMPLETELY RESTORE IT!
DICK LOCHER
MAX COLLINS

DR. CARVER DID A MAGNIFICENT JOB RESTORING YOUR FACE, HARLEY -
SLEUTH
STARRING BARRY MOORE AND VITAMIN FLINTHEART
DIDN'T HE, THOUGH?

THERE'S ONLY ONE PROBLEM - IT DOESN'T LAST.
IT DOESN'T?

NO - YOU SEE, AFTER A PERIOD OF APPROXIMATELY ONE HOUR, IT BEGINS TO SAG - LOSE SHAPE -
DICK LOCHER
MAX COLLINS

GOOD LORD!
THERE'S NOTHING TO FEAR, OLD CHUM - YOU GET USED TO IT-

"MY FORMER EMPLOYEES HAD A NAME FOR ME... PUTTY PUSS, THEY'D CALL ME..."
PUTTY PUSS....
PUTTY PUSS....

BEHIND MY BACK, THAT IS. IT IS FITTING, THOUGH, ISN'T IT?
DICK LOCHER
MAX COLLINS

YE GODS... HOW CAN YOU STAND IT, HARLEY?

"DR. CARVER HAD ME COMMITTED- HUSH, HUSH, OF COURSE-"

JUST BECAUSE THE EXPERIMENT FAILED WAS NO REASON FOR THE GOOD DOCTOR TO LOSE FACE, AFTER ALL-
DICK LOCHER
MAX COLLINS

HOW COULD YOU SUBJECT YOURSELF TO SUCH AN EXPERIMENT?
I'M AN ACTOR - BADLY DISFIGURED AS I WAS, I WAS DETERMINED TO REGAIN MY APPEARANCE -

"AND DR. CARVER'S EXPERIMENTS WITH 'ARTIFICIAL FLESH' - ADVANCED LATEX SUPPLEMENTED WITH SILICON IMPLANTS-DID RESTORE MY FACE -"

YES - BUT IT LOST SHAPE AFTER AN HOUR -
WHICH IS WHAT DROVE ME MAD -
DICK LOCHER
MAX COLLINS

"I WAS INSTITUTIONALIZED FOR YEARS," NIAV SAYS. "DR. CARVER WANTED ME OUT OF THE SPOTLIGHT -"

HE WOULD HAVE LOST HIS LICENSE OVER WHAT HE DID TO YOU... BUT AT LEAST YOU RECOVERED YOUR SANITY-
OH, NO! I'M CERTIFIABLY MAD TO THIS DAY-

"I'M AN ESCAPEE FROM THE LAUGHING ACADEMY, BARRY, OLD CHUM —"
NOTHING IN THE COMPUTER ON A PUTTY PUSS -

YOU ESCAPED FROM KNOTHAUS SANITARIUM? HOW?!?
NOT BY BEING CURED - I'M STILL QUITE MAD, I ASSURE YOU-

I SIMPLY WALKED OUT THE FRONT DOOR-

"MY FACE HAD ONCE BEEN MY FORTUNE- NOW IT WAS MY MISFORTUNE. BUT I DISCOVERED I HAD A NEW TALENT-"
DICK LOCHER
MAX COLLINS

AFTER STARING AT THIS PUTTY PUSS HOUR UPON HOUR, I LEARNED TO SHAPE IT BACK INTO ITS ORIGINAL STATE...

"..I COULD BE MYSELF AGAIN, IF ONLY FOR AN HOUR AT A TIME!"
DICK LOCHER
MAX COLLINS

AMAZING...
THEN, GIFTED THESPIAN THAT I AM, I BEGAN EXPERIMENTING...

MY EXPERIMENTS WERE FAR MORE SUCCESSFUL THAN DR. CARVER'S - I LEARNED I COULD SHAPE MY FACE, MOLD MY FACE-

"I WAS ALWAYS A MASTER OF MAKE-UP, AFTER ALL- I COULD STUDY A PHOTO AND TRANSFORM MYSELF INTO ANOTHER'S IMAGE-"

BUT NOW! NOW MY FACE HAD COMPLETE MALLEABILITY-
DICK LOCHER
MAX COLLINS

YOU'RE SAYING YOU TAUGHT YOURSELF TO TRANSFORM YOUR FACE INTO SOMEONE ELSE'S FACE?
ANYONE ELSE'S FACE, BARRY! FOR INSTANCE, I SIMPLY PUT ON MY PSYCHIATRIST'S FACE AND WALKED OUT THE SANITARIUM DOOR-

"OF COURSE, I HAD TO KILL HIM, FIRST...
DICK LOCHER
MAX COLLINS

YOU...YOU KILLED YOUR PSYCHIATRIST?
I NEEDED HIS CLOTHES TO ESCAPE IN. AT ANY RATE, I WAS A FREE MAN-

"I'D MADE SOME UNDERWORLD CONTACTS, ONCE, RESEARCHING A ROLE IN A GANGSTER OPUS - SO I RE-ESTABLISHED CONTACT AND FORMED A GANG-"
DICK LOCHER
MAX COLLINS

YOU FORMED A **GANG**?
PERHAPS THAT OVERSTATES IT– THERE WERE ONLY **THREE** OF US–

" BUT I LEARNED A LOT ABOUT CRIME RESEARCHING A ROLE, ONCE– AND YOU KNOW HOW I ALWAYS **LIVE** MY ROLES–"

YOU... YOU'RE THE **MAN OF A MILLION FACES!** IN THE NEWS–
DICK LOCHER
MAX COLLINS

YOU! YOU'RE THE MAN OF A MILLION FACES!!

WITH MY MALLEABLE FLESH, I CAN BE **ANYONE**. EVEN MY OLD HANDSOME SELF... FOR AN HOUR–
YOU WERE THOSE CELEBRITY BANK ROBBERS!

"YOU'RE A **THIEF**, HARLEY– A **MURDERER** – AND A **FUGITIVE**!"

THAT'S WHERE **YOU** COME IN, BARRY– I NEED A PLACE TO HIDE OUT...
WELL, DON'T LOOK AT **ME**!

OH BUT I **AM**– BECAUSE WE'RE TWO OF A KIND, OLD CHUM–
DICK LOCHER
MAX COLLINS

"YOU CLAWED YOUR WAY TO THE TOP, JUST AS I DID. I'M WELL AWARE IT WAS **YOU** WHO TAMPERED WITH MY CAR THAT RAINY NIGHT–"

HARLEY, I HAD **NOTHING** TO DO WITH YOUR ACCIDENT!

I WOULD NEVER DO THAT TO YOU– WE WERE FRIENDS! YOU WERE MY MENTOR– LIKE A **BROTHER**!
AND WE'LL BE LIKE BROTHERS AGAIN, BARRY...

" .. **IDENTICAL** TWINS!"
FBI HAS NOTHING ON "PUTTY PUSS"–
WELL, **I** HAVE SOMETHING ON HIM–

HARLEY... HOW CAN YOU THINK **I** HAD ANYTHING TO DO WITH YOUR ACCIDENT– YOU WERE MY **BENEFACTOR**–
HOW **TRUE**! LOOK AT THE CAREER YOU'RE HAVING– **MY** CAREER, TO BE EXACT!
SLEUTH
STARRING BARRY MOORE AND VITAMIN FLINTHEART

"ROLES IN MAJOR FILMS– RAVE REVIEWS, MONEY, FAME, GLORY! **HARDLY** 'ACCIDENTAL,' BARRY OLD BOY–"
DICK LOCHER
MAX COLLINS

I HEAR YOU'RE ABOUT TO STAR IN A REVIVAL OF "SLEUTH" WITH MY OLD CRONY VITAMIN FLINTHEART– WE'VE COME FULL CIRCLE, BARRY...
HARLEY, PUT THAT GUN AWAY– IF YOU NEED A PLACE TO HIDE...
SLEUTH
STARRING BARRY MOORE AND VITAMIN FLINTHEART
I DON'T NEED A PLACE TO HIDE, BARRY– I NEED A FACE TO HIDE BEHIND–
DICK LOCHER MAX COLLINS

NOTHIN' IN OUR MONIKER FILE OR THE FBI'S ON "PUTTY PUSS" WHAT HAVE YOU GOT?
REMEMBER A DR. WILL CARVER?

"SURE!" SAYS SAM. "THAT CROOKED SOCIETY PLASTIC SURGEON!" WHILE IN A CERTAIN SWANK PENTHOUSE–
TAKE A BOW, BARRY– THE CURTAIN'S COMING DOWN...
NO!
DICK LOCHER MAX COLLINS

YOU KNOW, I MISS YOU ALREADY, DEAR FRIEND BARRY– GUESS I'LL JUST HAVE TO WORK MY SPECIAL MAGIC–
DICK LOCHER MAX COLLINS

AND BRING YOU TO LIFE–

AND IN A MATTER OF MINUTES–
WELCOME BACK, BARRY MOORE! HANDSOME AS EVER, AND TWICE THE ACTOR!
12-24

WHO IS THIS DR. CARVER?
CARVER WAS THE GUY WHO RESTORED HAF-AND-HAF'S FACE–
AND WHO LATER GAVE MUMBLES A FACELIFT–
ENOUGH SHOP TALK, YOU GUYS!
EVERYBODY OUT! CRIME MAY NOT TAKE A HOLIDAY, BUT WE'RE GOING TO!
DICK LOCHER MAX COLLINS
Merry Christmas
DICK LOCHER · MAX COLLINS · RAY SHLEMON

I'M GOING TO HAVE TO DO SOMETHING WITH YOU, BARRY–HMMM... YOU ALWAYS BRAGGED ABOUT BEING BORN IN A TRUNK...
DICK LOCHER MAX COLLINS

SOON–
YOU'RE SHIPPING THIS TO BORNEO, MR. MOORE?
YES–VITAL PROPS A DEAR FRIEND OF MINE NEEDS FOR HIS ROAD COMPANY PRODUCTION OF "DIAL M FOR MURDER"–

BARRY- YOU'VE NEVER LOOKED BETTER.... YOU'RE READY FOR THE PERFORMANCE OF YOUR LIFE -

AT HQ-
THIS DR. CARVER HAD KNOWN UNDERWORLD TIES-
HE SURE DID... HE RESTORED HAF AND HAF'S FACE...
AND HE GAVE MUMBLES A FACELIFT THAT LET THAT MUMBLING MURDERER POSE AS HIS OWN CLONE -
SPEAKING OF MURDER-

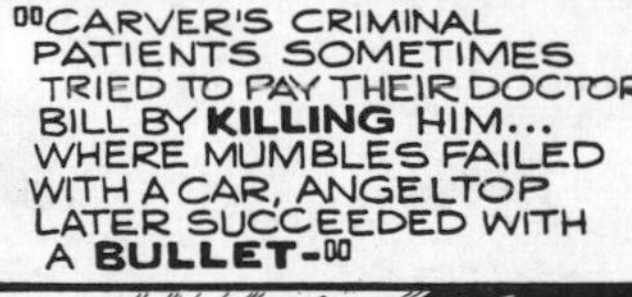
"CARVER'S CRIMINAL PATIENTS SOMETIMES TRIED TO PAY THEIR DOCTOR BILL BY KILLING HIM... WHERE MUMBLES FAILED WITH A CAR, ANGELTOP LATER SUCCEEDED WITH A BULLET-"

CARVER'S BEEN DEAD FOR SEVERAL YEARS, TRACY- WHAT MAKES YOU THINK HE'S TIED TO "PUTTY PUSS"?
DICK LOCHER
MAX COLLINS

"I MEAN, I KNOW THAT DYING HENCHMAN WAS MUTTERING SOMETHING ABOUT 'CARVER'!" SAYS SAM. "BUT SO WHAT?"

DON'T YOU REMEMBER, SAM? THAT DELIRIOUS HENCHMAN WAS TRYING TO CALM HIS BOSS DOWN...
THAT'S RIGHT! HE KEPT SAYING THEY COULDN'T KILL CARVER BECAUSE HE WAS ALREADY DEAD-

"SUPPOSE," TRACY SAYS, "THAT PUTTY PUSS WAS A FORMER CARVER PLASTIC-SURGERY PATIENT- A DISSATISFIED CUSTOMER-"
WHERE IS BARRY MOORE?
HE'S LATE, VITAMIN-

MRS. CARVER, THANK YOU FOR SEEING US ON SUCH SHORT NOTICE -
IT'S NICE TO SEE YOU AGAIN, MR. TRACY-

I HAVE A REQUEST FOR YOU, MRS. CARVER, AND PLEASE UNDERSTAND THAT IT'S UNOFFICIAL-
DICK LOCHER
MAX COLLINS

"BUT WE'D LIKE TO HAVE ACCESS TO YOUR HUSBAND'S RECORDS AND FILES..."
WHY IS BARRY MOORE LATE?

WE DON'T HAVE A WARRANT, MRS. CARVER-
DON'T BE FOOLISH, MR. TRACY-
DICK LOCHER
MAX COLLINS

YOU SAVED MY HUSBAND'S LIFE, EVEN IF HE LATER THREW IT AWAY...

"IF I CAN RETURN YOUR KINDNESS BY GIVING YOU ACCESS TO WILL'S PAPERS, I'M ONLY TOO GLAD TO..."
SHOWTIME!

MY HUSBAND WAS A BRILLIANT PLASTIC SURGEON, MR. TRACY - BUT HE WAS WEAK-

"HIS CRIMINAL ASSOCIATIONS LED TO HIS DEATH—"

IT DOESN'T SURPRISE ME THAT EVEN WITH WILL GONE, HIS POOR JUDGMENT WOULD BRING YOU HERE... HELP YOURSELF.
DICK LOCHER
MAX COLLINS

I'VE PULLED EVERYTHING IN HIS FILES PERTAINING TO ACTOR PATIENTS-
CARVER'S FINANCIAL RECORDS REVEAL NOTHING, YET-
DICK LOCHER
MAX COLLINS

"WE'LL RUN THE NAMES THROUGH THE CENTRAL COMPUTER," SAYS TRACY. "BUT ONE NAME ALREADY STANDS OUT-"
BARRY, YOU'RE LATE-
UNAVOIDABLY DETAINED, VITAMIN-I HAD AN OVERDUE DEBT TO REPAY...

CHECK CARVER'S FINANCIAL RECORDS FOR ANYTHING ON HARLEY NIAV-
HARLEY NIAV-THE "ACTOR'S ACTOR"! WHATEVER HAPPENED TO HIM ?
DICK LOCHER
MAX COLLINS

"MAYBE," SAYS TRACY, "HE'S LAUNCHING A COMEBACK-"
BARRY, I WAS IRRITATED WITH YOU FOR YOUR LATENESS-BUT YOU'RE BRILLIANT IN REHEARSAL TODAY!
YES- AREN'T I ?

TRACY, HARLEY NIAV WAS IN A BAD AUTO ACCIDENT SEVERAL YEARS AGO... AND THEN DROPPED OUT OF SIGHT!
DICK LOCHER
MAX COLLINS

THANKS, SAM-
CHIEF- I THINK I HAVE SOMETHING!

"I GOT NOTHING ON 'HARLEY NIAV,'" SAYS LIZZ, "SO I PUNCHED IN SOME VARIATIONS-"
BARRY-WE NEED TO REHEARSE-
SOON, VITAMIN-

BARRY IS BRILLIANT IN REHEARSAL- BUT HE KEEPS RETREATING TO HIS DRESSING ROOM! WHY ?!?
SEARCH ME, VITAMIN.

DR. CARVER'S WIDOW, WHOM TRACY ONCE BEFRIENDED, HAS GIVEN THE DETECTIVES COMPLETE ACCESS TO THE LATE PLASTIC SURGEON'S FILES-
THE BEST SUSPECT AMONG CARVER'S ACTOR PATIENTS IS ONE HARLEY NIAV-
WELL, NIAV'S NAME DOESN'T SEEM TO BE IN THESE FINANCIAL RECORDS-

BUT A CERTAIN "N. HARLEY" IS - LET ME PRINT THIS OUT...

SOON-
WHY, CARVER WAS PAYING ALL THE MEDICAL EXPENSES OF "N. HARLEY" AT A PRIVATE FACILITY!
YES- KNOTHAUS SANITARIUM-

THAT RINGS A NASTY BELL- A DOCTOR WAS MURDERED, NOT LONG AGO, BY AN ESCAPING PATIENT AT THAT VERY INSTITUTION.
DICK LOCHER MAX COLLINS

AND-
TRACY, THAT ESCAPEE WAS NAMED NORMAN HARLEY-

NORMAN HARLEY, HUH -
HERE'S SOMETHING-

"NORMAN HARLEY'S COMMITTMENT DATES TO ABOUT THE TIME ACTOR HARLEY NIAV DISAPPEARED-"
WE MUST REHEARSE, BARRY!
BE WITH YOU SHORTLY, VITAMIN-

THANK YOU FOR THE IMPROMPTU APPOINTMENT, DOCTOR-
NOT AT ALL, DETECTIVE TRACY-
DICK LOCHER MAX COLLINS

I'M PLEASED TO FIND THAT THE MURDER OF MY COLLEAGUE, DR. YOUNG, IS STILL BEING ACTIVELY INVESTIGATED AFTER SO MANY MONTHS -

"AND RELIEVED TO FIND THE INQUIRY IN SUCH DISTINGUISHED HANDS," SAYS DR. KNOTHAUS.

THERE'S BEEN A DEVELOPMENT IN THE CASE, DR. KNOTHAUS-
HAS DR. YOUNG'S MURDERER BEEN FOUND?

IS NORMAN HARLEY FINALLY IN CUSTODY?
NO-
DICK LOCHER MAX COLLINS

"BUT WE'VE LEARNED THAT 'NORMAN HARLEY' IS REALLY HARLEY NIAV, THE CELEBRATED ACTOR-"

YOU SEEM SHAKEN BY THE NEWS OF NORMAN HARLEY'S TRUE IDENTITY, DOCTOR-
WELL, UH... IT IS A SHOCK...
DICK LOCHER MAX COLLINS

"IS IT? DIDN'T DR. CARVER PAY YOU TO KEEP NIAV HIDDEN AWAY UNDER AN ALIAS?"

ALL RIGHT...I...I DID KNOW WHO MY PATIENT REALLY WAS...

DR. CARVER PAID ME HANDSOMELY, IT'S TRUE - A HANDSOME FEE TO CONCEAL AN UGLY SECRET-

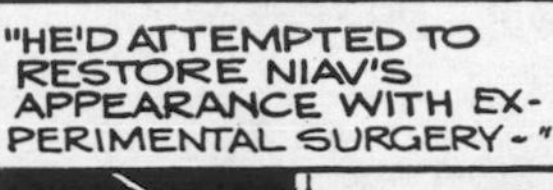
"HE'D ATTEMPTED TO RESTORE NIAV'S APPEARANCE WITH EX-PERIMENTAL SURGERY -"

WHICH FAILED MISERABLY. I SAW NO HARM IN ACCEPTING CARVER'S MONEY-THE PATIENT WAS, AFTER ALL, HOPELESSLY INSANE... HE BELONG-ED HERE-
DICK LOCHER
MAX COLLINS

DOCTOR CARVER KNEW HIS MEDICAL CAREER WOULD'VE BEEN OVER IF WORD GOT OUT OF HIS DISASTROUS EXPERIMENTAL SURGERY-
DICK LOCHER
MAX COLLINS

BUT CARVER'S LONG DEAD-THE MONEY HAS STOPPED! WHY DID YOU CONTINUE TREATMENT?

"I STILL HAD A RESPONSIBILITY TO MY PATIENT," KNOTHAUS SAYS.
MY ACTING'S NEVER BEEN BETTER? WHY, THANK YOU, VITAMIN!

THE FUNDING MAY HAVE STOPPED, BUT I STILL HAD A RESPONSIBILITY TO CONTINUE TREATMENT-

WHAT ELSE COULD YOU DO? YOUR CONDUCT WAS AS UNETHICAL AS CARVER'S
DICK LOCHER
MAX COLLINS

"YOU WERE STUCK WITH 'NORMAN HARLEY'... THAT IS, HARLEY NIAV-"
MY "BEAUTY" SECRET, VITAMIN? WELL, DON'T TELL ANYONE, BUT I HAD A FACELIFT-

CONFRONTED WITH UNDENIABLE EVIDENCE, DR. KNOTHAUS ADMITS HE KNEW HIS PATIENT "NORMAN HARLEY" WAS IN REALITY ACTOR HARLEY NIAV-
DO YOU HAVE ANY PHOTOS OF NIAV AFTER THE BOTCHED OPERATION?
NO! BUT YOU MUST UNDERSTAND THERE IS SOMETHING UNUSUAL ABOUT HIS APPEARANCE-

"HIS FACE IS ALMOST FORMLESS-LIKE A MASK OF CLAY. OH, HE COULD RESTORE HIMSELF TO HIS FORMER HANDSOMENESS, FOR A LIMITED AMOUNT OF TIME -"

WHAT DO YOU MEAN?
HIS FACE WAS MALLEABLE-
DICK LOCHER
MAX COLLINS

"THAT WAS THE RESULT OF DR. CARVER'S UNFORTUNATE EXPERIMENT," SAYS KNOTHAUS. "IN FACT... WHEN HE MADE HIS ESCAPE, HE APPARENTLY DISGUISED HIMSELF AS HIS PSYCHIATRIST- "

YOU TOLD THE INVESTIGATING OFFICERS THAT THE PATIENT ESCAPED DISGUISED AS A DOCTOR- NOT ANY SPECIFIC DOCTOR-
WHO WOULD HAVE UNDERSTOOD ?

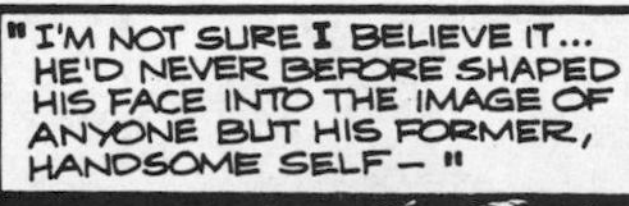
"I'M NOT SURE I BELIEVE IT... HE'D NEVER BEFORE SHAPED HIS FACE INTO THE IMAGE OF ANYONE BUT HIS FORMER, HANDSOME SELF- "

NIAV LEFT THIS JOINT WEARING SOMEBODY ELSE'S FACE!
YES- THE FACE OF THE DOCTOR HE MURDERED-

SURELY YOU'RE AWARE, DOCTOR, OF THE POLICE SEARCH FOR THE SO-CALLED MAN OF A MILLION FACES
WELL, UH, YES ...

YOU MUST'VE REALIZED YOUR ESCAPEE, HARLEY NIAV, WITH HIS MALLEABLE FACE, WAS THE GUILTY PARTY-
DICK LOCHER
MAX COLLINS

AND YOU IMPEDED THE INVESTIGATION OF YOUR OWN COLLEAGUE'S MURDER.
MR. TRACY, PLEASE LEAVE!

WHAT'S THAT OLD SAYING ABOUT THE LUNATICS RUNNING THE ASYLUM?

"IN DR. KNOTHAUS' CASE," REPLIES TRACY, "THAT WOULD CERTAINLY SEEM TRUE ..."

... ALTHOUGH WHEN ALL THIS COMES OUT, I DOUBT THE GOOD DOCTOR WILL BE RUNNING ANYTHING- EXCEPT, POSSIBLY, AWAY-
DICK LOCHER
MAX COLLINS

BARRY, YOU ARE DOING SIMPLY SUPERLATIVE WORK...
SOMEBODY TO SEE YOU, VITAMIN-

RICHARD! MY BOY-WHAT BRINGS YOU 'ROUND GREASEPAINT ALLEY?
JUST SEEKING YOUR EXPERT COUNSEL, VITAMIN...

...YOU WERE A FRIEND OF HARLEY NIAV'S. WELL, WE'RE LOOKING FOR HIM-
DICK LOCHER
MAX COLLINS
1-13

HOW CAN YOU BE LOOKING FOR HARLEY NIAV? MY UNDERSTANDING, RICHARD, IS THAT THE POOR BOY'S DECEASED-
A GREATLY EXAGGERATED DEMISE, VITAMIN-

BUT NIAV IS MENTALLY UNSTABLE - A DANGEROUS ESCAPEE FROM AN INSTITUTION, IN FACT-
DICK LOCHER
MAX COLLINS

YOU KNEW HIM- WHO MIGHT NIAV GO CALLING ON?

HARLEY NIAV WAS A WONDERFUL ACTOR, BUT HE HAD FEW REAL FRIENDS IN THE THESPIAN COMMUNITY... HE WAS SOMETHING OF A SOCIAL CLIMBER, ACTUALLY-

SAY, BARRY- YOU KNEW HARLEY, DIDN'T YOU?
DICK LOCHER
MAX COLLINS

RICHARD, MEET BARRY MOORE- HE'S MY CO-STAR IN OUR REVIVAL OF "SLEUTH"-
A PLEASURE, MR. MOORE- I'VE SEEN YOU PERFORM...I FEEL AS THOUGH I KNOW YOU ALREADY-

I FEEL THE SAME WAY, MR. TRACY-
DICK LOCHER
MAX COLLINS

HOW CAN I BE OF HELP TO YOU, MR. TRACY?

RICHARD HAS COME 'ROUND CHECKING UP ON HARLEY NIAV, BARRY-
NIAV? ISN'T HE DEAD?
NO- HE WAS CONFINED TO A MENTAL INSTITUTION UNTIL HIS RECENT ESCAPE-
HE'S DANGEROUS, MR. MOORE- IF HE SHOULD APPROACH YOU OR VITAMIN...

WELL, I DID KNOW AND ADMIRE HARLEY NIAV- HE WAS A CONSUMMATE PERFORMER-
DICK LOCHER
MAX COLLINS

HE WAS ALSO A BIT OF A SOCIAL CLIMBER-
I WOULDN'T SAY THAT, VITAMIN-

"OH BUT YOU MUST RECALL HOW HARLEY HOBNOBBED WITH THE SOCIAL ELITE... SOME OF WHOM BACKED HIS PRODUCTIONS."

HE WAS EXTREMELY TIGHT WITH THAT BROADCASTING MAGNATE - WHAT WAS HIS NAME?
FRANKLIN STRONG - UH - IF YOU'LL EXCUSE ME, GENTLEMEN -

WHERE IS HE OFF TO?
OH, HE'S ALWAYS RUSHING OFF TO HIS DRESSING ROOM -

" I SUSPECT, " WHISPERS VITAMIN, " THE POOR FELLOW HAS A DRINKING PROBLEM - "

YOU THINK YOUR CO-STAR, BARRY MOORE, HAS A DRINKING PROBLEM?
IT'S MERELY A SUSPICION, RICHARD-

"BUT IT SEEMS HE'S ALWAYS TAKING 'FIVE'," SAYS VITAMIN, "HIDING AWAY IN HIS DRESSING ROOM..."
DICK LOCHER MAX COLLINS

BEFORE HE RAN OFF, YOUR CO-STAR MENTIONED THAT NIAV WAS THICK WITH FRANKLIN STRONG-
YES, THE FELLOW WITH POLITICAL AMBITIONS!

"THAT BROAD-CASTING MAGNATE WHO WANTED TO RUN FOR PRESIDENT OF THESE UNITED STATES-"
AMERICA NEEDS A STRONG PRESIDENT
FRANKLIN STRONG IN '84
DICK LOCHER MAX COLLINS

I'D FORGOTTEN THAT FRANKLIN STRONG TRIED TO LAUNCH A THIRD-PARTY PRESIDENTIAL CANDIDACY IN THE LAST ELECTION-
I HEAR THE SAME RUMOR ABOUT OUR FRIEND DIET SMITH, IN THE COMING ONE...
DICK LOCHER MAX COLLINS

"I DON'T THINK IT'S A RUMOR, VITAMIN-DIET SEEMS ON THE VERGE OF ANNOUNCING HIS CANDIDACY-"
DIET SMITH
FOR PRESIDENT

THANKS FOR YOUR HELP, VITAMIN-SORRY TO INTERRUPT YOUR REHEARSAL-
I'M USED TO IT, DEAR BOY, CONSIDERING MY CO-STAR'S FREQUENT ABSENCES-
THIS IS QUITE A SET, VITAMIN-

"THANK YOU, SAMUEL-WE THINK IT DOES CONVEY A CERTAIN AIR OF MYSTERY-"
DICK LOCHER MAX COLLINS

YOU MUST BE TRYING FOR A GLOOMY MOOD-I NOTICE THE LIGHTING IS SUBDUED-
OH, IT WILL BE BRIGHT ENOUGH ON THE NIGHT WE OPEN, RICHARD-

"I'M JUST TOO OLD-AND TOO RICH AND TOO FAMOUS-TO PUT UP WITH REHEARSING UNDER THE BRIGHT LIGHTS-"
DICK LOCHER MAX COLLINS

YOU LOOK FIT AGAIN, BARRY- READY TO CONTINUE REHEARSAL?
CHOMPING AT THE BIT, VITAMIN- WHERE'S YOUR DETECTIVE FRIEND?

"BACK TO CHASING DOWN MISCREANTS," SAYS VITAMIN. "BUT YOU'LL SEE HIM OPENING NIGHT-"
SORRY YOU DIDN'T GET FREE TICKETS, SAM?
NOPE. HAM IS AGAINST MY RELIGION-
DICK LOCHER
MAX COLLINS

SLEUTH
STARRING
VITAMIN FLINTHEART
AND
BARRY MOORE
DIRECTED AND PRODUCED BY VITAMIN FLINTHEART
WRITTEN BY ANTHONY SHAFFER

THE RICH AND FAMOUS COME OUT FOR THE OPENING NIGHT OF VITAMIN'S REVIVAL OF "SLEUTH"-
VITAMIN FLINTHEART AND BARRY MOORE IN
SLEUTH

AT LEAST ONE IN THE CROWD IS NOT RICH, ALTHOUGH FAMOUS IN HIS WAY-
THAT'S DICK TRACY.
REALLY?

THIS IS EXCITING-
I AGREE. I'VE NEVER SEEN "SLEUTH" BEFORE.

"I DON'T MEAN THAT," SAYS TESS. "BEING WITH ALL THESE CELEBRITIES... ISN'T THAT FRANKLIN STRONG, THE BROADCASTING TYCOON?"

YES- WE'D BETTER BE QUIET... CURTAIN'S GOING UP-

AS THE PLAY UNFOLDS, THE AUDIENCE IS ENTHRALLED BY THE DYNAMIC BARRY MOORE, WHO BRINGS OUT THE BEST IN HIS CO-STAR AS WELL-

BUT UNDER THE HOT LIGHTS FOR THE FIRST TIME, "BARRY MOORE" BEGINS TO BREAK CHARACTER-
DICK LOCHER
MAX COLLINS

DICK- SOMETHING'S WRONG... BARRY MOORE'S FACE-

VITAMIN MISSED HIS CUE... WHAT'S HE GAPING AT...
UH... UH...

YE GODS- MY FACE... UNDER THESE HOT LIGHTS FOR THE FIRST TIME... IT'S SLIPPING...
DICK LOCHER
MAX COLLINS

GOOD LORD... THESE HOT LIGHTS ARE UNMASKING ME... AND BEFORE A STANDING ROOM ONLY AUDIENCE...
BARRY... BARRY... MY BOY...
DICK LOCHER MAX COLLINS

DICK, IS THIS SOME SORT OF STAGE TRICK? BARRY MOORE'S FACE LOOKS SO.. WEIRD-
IT'S NO TRICK- AND THAT ISN'T BARRY MOORE'S FACE EITHER-

AS THE OPENING-NIGHT AUDIENCE STARES IN SHOCK AND HORROR...

...BARRY MOORE IS TRANSFORMED INTO A MONSTER...
BARRY, YOU POOR BOY-
LET GO OF ME, YOU OLD FOOL-

...WHILE A THIRD ACTOR ADVANCES TOWARD THE STAGE-
DICK LOCHER MAX COLLINS

HOLD IT RIGHT THERE, PUTTY PUSS!
I PREFER HARLEY NIAV, IF YOU PLEASE... A MASTER THESPIAN MAKING HIS TRIUMPHANT RETURN TO THE STAGE!
THIS IS NOT IN THE SCRIPT, MY FRIENDS! DISPERSE IN AN ORDERLY MANNER!
DICK LOCHER MAX COLLINS

VITAMIN, GET OUT OF THE WAY-
LADIES AND GENTLE-MEN, YOU MUST TAKE THE INTRUSION OF THIS REAL SLEUTH MOST SERIOUSLY!

DICK LOCHER MAX COLLINS

PLEASE DISPERSE! I ENTREAT YOU!
DICK LOCHER MAX COLLINS

THIS IS THE CRAZIEST PLAY I EVER SAW!
WHAT AN OPENING-NIGHT STUNT! BRING-ING DICK TRACY UP ON STAGE!

LADIES AND GENTLEMEN - I IMPLORE YOU... DISPERSE!

WHEN BARRY MOORE'S FACE "MELTS" UNDER THE HOT LIGHTS, TRACY RUSHES ONTO THE STAGE FOR SOME IMPROVISATIONAL THEATER-
YOU MUST LEAVE, GENTLE PATRONS OF THE ARTS! THERE IS DANGER HERE!

WHAT A HAM THAT VITAMIN FLINTHEART IS-
THIS IS THE WILDEST PLAY I'VE EVER SEEN!

YOU SHOULD HAVE COME TO REHEARSAL, TRACY- BUT IT'S NEVER TOO LATE FOR A QUICK RUN-THROUGH-

BASIL RATHBONE TAUGHT ME TO FENCE - I DOUBT YOUR POLICE ACADEMY DID AS MUCH FOR YOU...

YOU'RE RIGHT, PUTTY PUSS - I LEARNED AT COLLEGE-
AH - NEVER UNDER-ESTIMATE DICK TRACY, MASTER OF IMPROMPTU VIOLENCE

BY THE WAY-

DON'T CALL ME PUTTY PUSS!
SWOOSH
DICK LOCHER
MAX COLLINS

SWOOSH

I BESEECH YOU, GENTLE FOLK - DISPERSE!
DICK LOCHER
MAX COLLINS

OH DEAR... VITAMIN IS SO MELODRAMATIC, THE AUDIENCE THINKS THIS IS ALL PART OF THE SHOW- I'VE GOT TO GET HELP!

GIVE IT UP, PUTTY PUSS... THERE'S NO ESCAPING-
THE SHERIFF OF NOTTINGHAM ISSUED ME THE SAME WARNING IN "RESCUE OF ROBIN HOOD"-
DICK LOCHER
MAX COLLINS

GET A SQUAD CAR OVER HERE IMMEDIATELY!

WHAT A GREAT PUBLICITY STUNT-
DICK TRACY DOING AN OPENING NIGHT WALK-ON IN "SLEUTH"!

GIVE UP, PUTTY PUSS-
DON'T...
DICK LOCHER
MAX COLLINS

CALL...

...ME...

...PUTTY PUSS!

DICK LOCHER
MAX COLLINS

IT'S OVER, PUTTY PUSS.
IS IT?

DICK LOCHER
MAX COLLINS

WHUMP

DON'T TAKE IT SO HARD, TRACY- EVEN THE GREATEST ACTOR HAS A FLOP NOW AND THEN...
UHHGHH...

ON THE STAGE?
THAT'S RIGHT- THE AUDIENCE THINKS IT'S PART OF THE SHOW!

RICHARD! ARE YOU DAMAGED?
WHERE'S PUTTY PUSS?
DICK LOCHER
MAX COLLINS

THEY'RE FIGHTING WITH SWORDS?
DICK'S GUN GOT KNOCKED OUT OF HIS HAND!

WHEN THEIR IMPROMPTU DUEL TAKES TRACY AND PUTTY PUSS TO THE STAGE WINGS, A SEVERED ROPE SENDS A SANDBAG CRASHING DOWN ON THE DETECTIVE -
RICHARD!
WHERE IS HE?

"WHERE'S PUTTY PUSS?"
I TOLD HIM NOT TO CALL ME "PUTTY PUSS"-

MEANWHILE, THE AUDIENCE, FINALLY AWARE THAT THE SHOW IS OVER - BEGINS TO FILE OUT...

RICHARD, HE'S GONE - COME INSIDE.... YOU NEED MEDICAL ATTENTION -

DETECTIVE TRACY- YOUR WIFE CALLED- ARE YOU ALL RIGHT?
IT'S NOT THE FIRST TIME I'VE BEEN SANDBAGGED..

LET'S HAVE A LOOK OUT FRONT -
CAN YOU GIVE ME A DESCRIPTION?
DICK LOCHER
MAX COLLINS

WE NEED TO GET OUT AN APB. WHAT DOES HE LOOK LIKE?

"TAKE YOUR PICK," SAYS TRACY.
SLEUTH

WHERE IS HE, DETECTIVE TRACY?
THE QUESTION IS, WHO IS HE?

"PUTTY PUSS IS ONE CRIMINAL," SAYS TRACY, "WHO CAN MAKE A CLEAN GETAWAY WITHOUT LEAVING THE SCENE OF THE CRIME!"
DICK LOCHER
MAX COLLINS

WHILE-
GOOD EVENING, MR. STRONG.

ARE YOU OKAY, TRACY?
YEAH - FOR A GUY WHO'S BEEN KNOCKED COLD TWICE BY THE SAME CROOK-
PRESS HAS BUTTONHOLED SOME OF THE CELEBRITY THEATER-GOERS, I SEE... THERE'S FRANKLIN STRONG-

"WASN'T HE NIAV'S PAL?" ASKS SAM. WHILE AT STRONG'S BROADCASTING COMPLEX -
ENJOY THE THEATER, SIR?
NOT REALLY.
DICK LOCHER
MAX COLLINS

BIT UNUSUAL TO BE SEEING YOU THIS TIME OF NIGHT, SIR-
WELL, WE'RE A 24-HOUR OPERATION AFTER ALL-
DICK LOCHER
MAX COLLINS

"IF MY TV AND RADIO STATIONS ARE TO CONTINUE BROAD-CASTING 'ROUND THE CLOCK, I MUST-N'T SHIRK MY DUTIES!"
WBUX

WHILE-
I ASSURE YOU, MR. TRACY, HARLEY NIAV HAS NOT CONTACTED ME-

WELL, IF HARLEY NIAV DOES CONTACT YOU, MR. STRONG, CONTACT ME-

"BUT USE CAUTION- YOUR OLD FRIEND IS UNBALANCED AND DANGEROUS-"
DICK LOCHER
MAX COLLINS

HMMM-THE DOOR TO "MY" PRIVATE OFFICE SEEMS TO BE LOCKED-
FRANKLIN STRONG
PRIVATE

SAMUEL, RICHARD WAS MAGNIFICENT! HE WON THE DUEL WITH THAT CAD HANDILY!
YEAH, BUT HE LOST THE WAR-
TOUCHÉ, "SAMUEL," NOW, VITAMIN...

"DO TRY TO COMPILE A LIST OF NIAV'S FRIENDS AND ASSOCIATES..."
MAYBE I CAN SPRING THE LOCK...
FRANKLIN STRONG
PRIVATE

HEY! WHAT ARE YOU DOING THERE ?
DICK LOCHER
MAX COLLINS

STEP AWAY FROM THAT DOOR!
DICK LOCHER
MAX COLLINS
OH...MR. STRONG- I'M SORRY, SIR...I DIDN'T KNOW IT WAS YOU...
YOU'RE TO BE COMMENDED FOR YOR DILIGENCE-

BUT I NEED YOUR HELP. I SEEM TO HAVE FORGOTTEN MY OFFICE KEY...
I'LL UNLOCK IT IN A JIFFY, SIR!

7:00 AM: THE SPRAWLING, MODERN SUBURBAN BROADCASTING COMPLEX OF FRANKLIN STRONG - A FACILITY INCLUDING A 100,000-WATT RADIO STATION AND A TV SUPERSTATION...
WBUX

... WHERE THE COMPANY'S PRESIDENT IS ALWAYS THE FIRST EXECUTIVE TO ARRIVE ...
GOOD MORNING, MR. STRONG.
MORNING.

I THOUGHT HE WAS ALREADY HERE...
DICK LOCHER
MAX COLLINS

GOOD MORNING, SIR.
MORNING. NO CALLS.

HELLO, FRANKLIN - IT'S BEEN **TOO** LONG.
HARLEY! HARLEY NIAV... HOW DID YOU...?

"NOT TO WORRY, FRANKLIN - YOUR SECURITY'S **TIGHT**... EXCEPT WHEN AN INTRUDER IS WEARING **YOUR FACE**. WONDERING WHY I'M HERE?"

WE'RE OLD **FRIENDS**, HARLEY... I OWE YOU THE COURTESY OF HEARING YOU OUT....

HOPE YOU DON'T MIND THAT I'VE MADE MYSELF AT **HOME**, FRANKLIN..
NOT AT ALL, HARLEY- WHAT ARE FRIENDS **FOR**?

I'VE JUST BEEN WATCHING YOUR SUPERSTATION'S NEWS BROADCAST...

... SO I ASSUME YOU'RE WELL AWARE THAT I'M WANTED BY THE **POLICE** -
DICK LOCHER
MAX COLLINS

THE POLICE STATEMENTS ABOUT MY BEING A **"MASTER OF DISGUISE"** DON'T DO ME **JUSTICE**.
DICK LOCHER
MAX COLLINS

I WAS A WITNESS AT THE THEATER, HARLEY... FORGIVE ME, BUT YOUR FACE SEEMED ...**DEFORMED**.

"MY FACE IS ANYTHING **BUT** 'DEFORMED,' FRANKLIN... MY FACE HAS MORE **'FORM'** THAN IT KNOWS WHAT TO DO WITH.."

HARLEY, HOW DID YOU **BECOME** THIS ...THIS "PUTTY PUSS"?
IT'S A **LONG** STORY, FRANKLIN...

AND HARLEY NIAV EXPLAINS TO HIS OLD FRIEND JUST HOW "PUTTY PUSS" CAME TO BE...
YE GODS- IT'S **UNBELIEVABLE!**
DICK LOCHER
MAX COLLINS

BUT **TRUE**, FRANKLIN. TRAGICALLY, REMARKABLY TRUE-

GOOD LORD! YOU'RE...YOU'RE...
HIDEOUS? A **MONSTER?** NO. I AM STILL A **GREAT** ACTOR... AND A CRIMINAL **GENIUS**!

AND YOU **WON'T** TURN ME **IN**, FRANKLIN...
DICK LOCHER
MAX COLLINS

...BECAUSE I KNOW **SECRETS**... I KNOW, FOR EXAMPLE, THAT YOU **MURDERED** YOUR WAY INTO **WEALTH**...

FRANKLIN, WE BOTH KNOW YOU KILLED YOUR FIRST WIFE FOR HER MONEY...
DICK LOCHER
MAX COLLINS

WHO WAS IT THAT SAID, "BEHIND EVERY GREAT FORTUNE THERE IS A CRIME ?"
MARLON BRANDO ?

STILL, I FIND BLACK-MAIL DISTASTEFUL... PARTICULARLY WHEN DEALING WITH AN OLD FRIEND. PERHAPS WE CAN HELP EACH OTHER...

HELP EACH OTHER? HOW, HARLEY ?
FRANKLIN, I'M AN ACTOR- A BRILLIANT ACTOR!
DICK LOCHER
MAX COLLINS

AND I HAVE THE ABILITY TO BE A MODERN-DAY LON CHANEY-WHO WAS CALLED THE MAN OF 1000 FACES!

A PALTRY THOUSAND! WHY, FROM THE VERY BEGINNING THE NEWS-PAPERS HAVE CREDIT-ED ME WITH A MILLION!

WBUX

PUTTY PUSS HAS CONFRONTED HIS OLD FRIEND, FRANKLIN STRONG, THE BROADCASTING MAGNATE, RATTLING A SKELETON OUT OF THE BILLIONAIRE'S CLOSET-
HARLEY, JUST BECAUSE YOU SAY I MURDERED MY WIFE FOR HER FAMILY'S FORTUNE DOESN'T MAKE IT SO-
I HAVE THE MURDER WEAPON SEALED AWAY IN PLASTIC, FINGERPRINTS AND ALL-

AND WHAT IS GETTING THAT BACK GOING TO COST ME ?
NOT MUCH- I PLAN TO MAKE YOU EVEN RICHER, FRANKLIN

I KNOW, I KNOW- THROUGH YOUR ACTING-
DICK LOCHER
MAX COLLINS

DON'T BE A FOOL! I CAN DO THINGS WITH MY FACE THAT OUTDISTANCE ANY-THING THE MOST SOPHISTICATED MAKE-UP ARTISTS COULD EVER IMAGINE!

YOU'LL MAKE SPIELBERG'S SPECIAL EFFECTS LOOK LIKE AMATEUR NIGHT!
WELL, I AM PRODUCING MY OWN TELEVISION SERIES AND FILMS NOW-

YOU CAN HELP ME ASSUME A NEW IDENTITY- WE CAN LAY HARLEY NIAV FOREVER TO REST...

AND A NEW MAN, A NEW ACTOR CAN EMERGE! WHAT DO YOU SAY FRANKLIN ?

DICK LOCHER
MAX COLLINS
WITH YOUR HELP, FRANKLIN, I'LL BE A NEW MAN, A NEW ACTOR...
WBUX

...AND MY UNIQUE TALENT WILL PROVIDE YOUR PRODUCTION COMPANY WITH A LIVING STATE-OF-THE-ART SPECIAL EFFECTS UNIT!

HMMM... WE COULD WORK ON FILM, WHERE THE TIME LIMITATIONS OF YOUR "TALENT" WON'T MATTER...

WHAT DO YOU SAY, FRANKLIN? I COULD BE AN INVALUABLE ASSET TO YOUR TELEVISION AND FILM EFFORTS -
I'M INTERESTED.

JUST "INTERESTED"?
DICK LOCHER
MAX COLLINS

SUPPOSE I WANTED A FAVOR, FIRST... SUPPOSE I WANTED A PUBLIC PERFORMANCE OUT OF YOU...

A PUBLIC PERFORMANCE, FRANKLIN?
YES-ONE THAT WOULD REQUIRE THE SKILLS OF THE MOST BRILLIANT ACTOR ON THE PLANET-

WELL...

...YOU'RE TALKING TO HIM, AREN'T YOU?
DICK LOCHER
MAX COLLINS

PRIOR TO THE LAST PRESIDENTIAL ELECTION, I WAS APPROACHED BY CERTAIN MOVERS AND SHAKERS, DEFECTORS FROM A MAJOR POLITICAL PARTY...
DICK LOCHER
MAX COLLINS

"...WHO WANTED TO HELP BACK MY CANDIDACY."
AMERICA NEEDS A STRONG PRESIDENT
FRANKLIN STRONG IN '84

BUT DIET SMITH-THAT DO-GOODING DISGRACE TO CAPITALISM-MADE PUBLIC CERTAIN INFORMATION ABOUT MY BUSINESS PRACTICES...

SO DIET SMITH EXPOSED CERTAIN UNSCRUPULOUS BUSINESS PRACTICES OF YOURS...
YES-FOREVER TAINTING ME AS A VIABLE CANDIDATE-

"IT WAS MY CHILDHOOD AMBITION TO ACHIEVE THE PRESIDENCY. IT MOTIVATED ME IN LIFE, IN BUSINESS-"
THE PRINCE
BY MACHIAVELLI

I CLIMBED THE LADDER TO SUCCESS-
OCCASIONALLY KILLING ALONG THE WAY...
DICK LOCHER
MAX COLLINS

YOU KNOW WHAT IT'S LIKE TO LOSE A DREAM-AND YOU UNDERSTAND REVENGE-
YES I DO...

...BUT I'M AN ARTIST, NOT AN ASSASSIN-
DICK LOCHER MAX COLLINS

"I DON'T WANT TO KILL DIET SMITH," SAYS STRONG. "I WANT TO KILL HIS DREAM..."
DIET SMITH FOR PRESIDENT

WELL, TRACY- ARE YOU PROVIDING THE SECURITY FOR DIET SMITH'S PRESS CONFERENCE TODAY?
NO, WENDY- I'M SIMPLY HERE AS A FRIEND, LENDING MORAL SUPPORT.

"TAKING A BREAK FROM THE FRUSTRATION OF A DEADENDED INVESTIGATION, DETECTIVE?"
WANTED
HARLEY NIAV ALIAS PUTTY PUSS

WELL, I'D BE LYING IF I SAID WE WERE CLOSING IN ON PUTTY PUSS.
YOU'RE FRANK, AT LEAST- NOW BE EQUALLY FRANK AND TELL ME...

"... DO YOU THINK YOUR WEALTHY FRIEND CALLED THIS PRESS CONFERENCE TO ANNOUNCE HIS CANDIDACY?"
DIET SMITH FOR PRESIDENT

YES, I DO.
SURELY YOU KNOW WHAT A LONG SHOT IT IS FOR A THIRD PARTY CANDIDATE.
DICK LOCHER MAX COLLINS

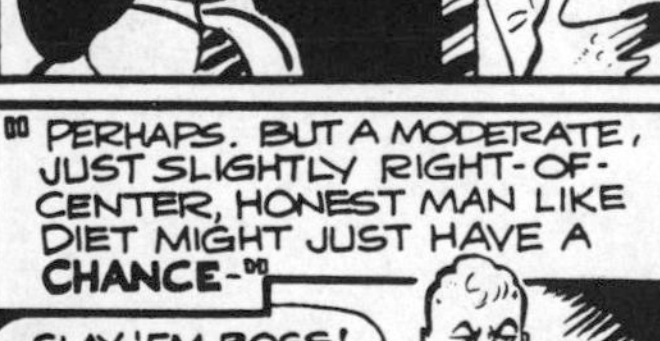
"PERHAPS. BUT A MODERATE, JUST SLIGHTLY RIGHT-OF-CENTER, HONEST MAN LIKE DIET MIGHT JUST HAVE A CHANCE-"

SLAY 'EM, BOSS!

GREETINGS, LADIES AND GENTLEMEN. MY CANDIDACY WILL STAND FOR THE GOOD OLD-FASHIONED AMERICAN VALUES...

THE MINORITIES IN THIS COUNTRY HAVE BEEN GETTING A FREE RIDE.... MY PRESIDENCY WILL PUT A SWIFT END TO THAT!

YOU HEARD ME CORRECTLY- THE FREE RIDE FOR MINORITIES IN THIS COUNTRY MUST STOP!
DICK LOCHER MAX COLLINS

WHAT ON EARTH IS YOUR FRIEND UP TO, TRACY? HE CAN'T BE SERIOUS!

FURTHERMORE, MY ADMINISTRATION WOULD BALANCE THE BUDGET, BEGINNING WITH ABOLISHING SOCIAL SECURITY-

MR. SMITH, YOUR OPPONENTS QUESTION YOUR TIES TO BIG BUSINESS...

WHY QUESTION THEM? I INTEND TO THROW MY FRIENDS AS MUCH BUSINESS AS POSSIBLE, AND MY OWN COMPANIES AS WELL.
DICK LOCHER
MAX COLLINS

WHY SHOULDN'T I? I TRUST MY FRIENDS AND MYSELF...
DICK LOCHER
MAX COLLINS

AS A THIRD-PARTY PRESIDENTIAL CANDIDATE, MR. SMITH, YOU WILL HAVE TO FACE OPPONENTS WHO...

MY OPPONENTS ARE SWINE TO A MAN!
DICK LOCHER
MAX COLLINS

AND I WILL BE PROVIDING THE MEDIA WITH CONFIDENTIAL REPORTS ON THE PECCADILLOS OF ALL THE OTHER CANDIDATES...
2-WAY WRIST COMPUTER

WHERE DO YOU STAND ON THE ARMS RACE, MR. SMITH?
DICK LOCHER
MAX COLLINS

I'M FULLY BEHIND NUCLEAR WEAPONS. WE'RE FALLING WAY BEHIND-

I PLAN TO STOCKPILE NUKES, AND STOCKPILE 'EM HIGH!
VOICE-PRINT
ANALYSIS COMPLETE

NO, I DON'T FAVOR EQUAL RIGHTS FOR WOMEN- EXCEPT IN THE KITCHEN! ONE MORE QUESTION...

MR. SMITH- ISN'T IT TRUE THAT BY MAKING SUCH IRRESPONSIBLE STATEMENTS YOU'RE COMMITTING PUBLIC POLITICAL SUICIDE?

I...I DON'T SEE IT THAT WAY. I FEEL MY FRANK VIEWS WILL BE EMBRACED-
DICK LOCHER
MAX COLLINS

I HAVE A FINAL QUESTION, MR. SMITH-
I'D PREFER YOU TAKE YOUR SEAT, MR. TRACY-

THIS PRESS CONFERENCE IS OVER!
DICK LOCHER
MAX COLLINS

SHOULD WE STOP THAT GUY?
NO- I DON'T THINK SO... THAT'S MR. SMITH'S COP PAL-

I REPEAT: THIS PRESS CONFERENCE IS OVER!

AS DIET SMITH MAKES ONE OUTRAGEOUS POLITICALLY SUICIDAL ASSERTATION AFTER ANOTHER, TRACY INTERRUPTS THE PRESS CONFERENCE -
AS YOU GENTLEMEN AND LADIES OF THE FOURTH ESTATE ARE WELL AWARE, DIET SMITH IS RESPONSIBLE FOR THE DEVELOPMENT OF THE WONDER ON MY WRIST...

THE 2-WAY WRIST COMPUTER - A DEVICE THAT SERVES MANY FUNCTIONS...
DICK LOCHER MAX COLLINS

... INCLUDING VOICEPRINT ANALYSIS AND COMPARISON. AND ACCORDING TO DIET SMITH'S OWN INVENTION, THIS MAN...

... IS NOT DIET SMITH!

THIS ACCUSATION IS RIDICULOUS ON IT S FACE!! GUARDS, REMOVE HIM!

I GUESS I'LL JUST HAVE TO PROVE MY POINT -

SMUK

SMUK

DICK LOCHER MAX COLLINS

I TOLD YOU I HAD ONE FINAL QUESTION...

WHERE IS THE REAL DIET SMITH!?!
PLOOP
DICK LOCHER MAX COLLINS

LADIES AND GENTLEMEN - MEET THE CANDIDATE -

PUTTY PUSS FOR PRESIDENT!!

NOW... WHAT HAVE YOU DONE WITH DIET, PUTTY PUSS?!?

DON'T CALL ME PUTTY PUSS-

THOK
DICK LOCHER
MAX COLLINS

THOK

DICK LOCHER
MAX COLLINS

DICK LOCHER
MAX COLLINS

ALERT YOUR STAFF! THAT MAN IS A FUGITIVE - A MURDERER!

BLOCK ALL THE EXITS- NOW!

TRACY TO HQ- DISPATCH SQUAD CARS AT ONCE-
DICK LOCHER
MAX COLLINS

"AND SEND SAM CATCHEM AND LIZZ OVER IMMEDIATELY!"

SAM! MEET ME IN THE LOBBY- AND MAKE SURE EVERY EXIT'S BLOCKED!

AFTER TRACY EXPOSES THE PRESS-CONFERENCE "DIET SMITH" AS YET ANOTHER PUTTY PUSS MASQUERADE, THE MASTER OF DISGUISES RUSHES OUT...

...WHILE THE MASTER DETECTIVE TAKES PURSUIT-

STAIRS
IF I JUST HAD TIME TO PUT ON A NEW FACE!

SECURITY GUARDS!
DICK LOCHER
MAX COLLINS

THAT WAY-

HELIPORT
AH! HOW THOUGHTFUL...
"...DIET SMITH'S PRIVATE COPTER, AWAITING THE CANDIDATE! MUSTN'T DISAPPOINT..."
DSI

NO SIGN OF PUTTY PUSS, MR. TRACY-
DICK LOCHER
MAX COLLINS

"IS ANYONE POSITIONED ON THE ROOF?" ASKS TRACY.
AH... DIET SMITH'S PRIVATE COPTER...

"..WAITING TO SPIRIT THE CANDIDATE AWAY..."
DSI

NO NEED FOR SECURITY ON THE ROOF, MR. TRACY- NO EXIT. NOTHING BUT A HELIPORT UP THERE-
DICK LOCHER
MAX COLLINS

"AND DIET SMITH'S HELICOPTER!" SAYS TRACY.

GET ME OUT OF HERE, QUICKLY- THERE'S BEEN AN ASSASSINATION ATTEMPT!

AN ASSASSINATION ATTEMPT, SIR? ARE YOU ALL RIGHT...?
YES...

...LIFT OFF-
DICK LOCHER
MAX COLLINS

"NOW-"
YE GODS!!
HELIPORT

STOP
STOP
DSI
DICK LOCHER
MAX COLLINS

I SAID LIFT OFF !!

DSI

WHRRRRRR
DSI
DICK LOCHER
MAX COLLINS

THAT ✲✪@✶!!✲ DETECTIVE! DOESN'T HE EVER QUIT!?!

WHRRRRRRR
DSI

YOU BETTER HIT THE SIREN, SAM!
WITH TRAFFIC THIS JAMMED, I DON'T KNOW WHAT GOOD IT'LL DO...

"...I JUST HOPE TRACY CAN HANG IN THERE WITHOUT US!"
DSI

BLAM
BLAM
DICK LOCHER
MAX COLLINS

WELL, WE MAY BE STUCK IN TRAFFIC, BUT THAT OUGHTA SLOW PUTTY PUSS' GETAWAY-
YEAH- TRACY'LL LATCH ONTO THAT GUY, SOMEHOW-

PUTTY PUSS HAS HIJACKED DIET'S HELICOPTER FROM THE BUILDING ROOFTOP- AND TRACY'S ALONG FOR THE RIDE...
DSI

BLAM
BLAM

ZING

KEEP THIS THING STEADY- YOU'RE TRYING TO MAKE ME MISS -

WHAT'S WRONG, TRACY? LOSING YOUR GRIP ON REALITY ?
DICK LOCHER
MAX COLLINS

UNNGGH

SO LONG, TRACY! THANKS FOR DROPPING BY!

HA HA HA HA HA HA!!!
DICK LOCHER MAX COLLINS

YOU MIGHT CHOKE ON THAT LAUGH... THERE'S A BUILDING JUST BELOW US -
HUH?

WHUMP

DICK LOCHER MAX COLLINS
WHUMP

TRACY HIT THE BEVELED ROOF OF THE WORLD INSURANCE BUILDING -

THIS SOLAR GLASS IS STRONG - BROKE MY FALL - BUT I'M SLIDING-

CAN'T GET A GRIP...

DICK LOCHER MAX COLLINS
OH BOY-

TESS... I LOVE YOU, TESS...

SOMETHING'S WRONG...
HUH?

WHEN YOU TOOK THOSE POT SHOTS AT TRACY, YOU MUST'VE HIT THE COPTER-

"...I GOTTA LAND NOW-" AND TRACY IS ALSO ABOUT TO MAKE A CRASH LANDING-
DICK LOCHER MAX COLLINS

DICK LOCHER
MAX COLLINS
THIS IS A LOVELY RESTAURANT, DEAR—
THE NEW ATRIUM TERRACE IS SO RESTFUL—

SNAP!
CRUNCH!
CRACK!

DICK LOCHER
MAX COLLINS

WHAT IS THAT MAN DOING?
GOOD LORD—

"FALLING, I SURMISE-"

I'VE GOT TO LAND NOW - ONE OF YOUR BULLETS HIT THE ENGINE -
DO IT, THEN!

MOMENTS AGO, THE PATRONS OF THE ATRIUM TERRACE RESTAURANT IN THE WORLD INSURANCE BUILDING WERE ENJOYING A QUIET LUNCH ...

... BUT A TREE PROVIDING DECORATION FOR THE LUNCHEON CROWD HAS PROVIDED A BREAK-FALL FOR TRACY-

CAN I ... HELP YOU, SIR?
GIVE ME A HAND...AND A TOWEL -

CAN YOU LAND THIS THING SAFELY?

DICK LOCHER
MAX COLLINS

SURE - SOMEPLACE ELSE-

SIR!
LOOK, I REALIZE I DON'T HAVE A RESERVATION BUT I'D APPRECIATE SOME HELP JUST THE SAME-
DICK LOCHER
MAX COLLINS

IS THERE ANYTHING I...?
DIRECT ME TO THE ELEVATOR-

I HAVE SOME CATCHING UP TO DO-
THAT @*!?#!! COPTER PILOT TRICKED ME!

SAM, I'M IN THE WORLD INSURANCE BUILDING - SOAKING WET, BUT ALIVE!

TRACY! THANK GOD-
WE'RE STUCK IN TRAFFIC, DICK-
DICK LOCHER
MAX COLLINS

BUT WE JUST HEARD THAT PUTTY PUSS WAS DROPPED BACK ONTO THE ROOF WHERE THAT COPTER FIRST TOOK OFF-
HELIPORT

THE COPTER PILOT RADIOED HQ, WHO PATCHED HIM THROUGH TO US-SEEMS PUTTY PUSS WAS DUMPED OFF ON THAT ROOFTOP HELIPORT-

I'M ON THE STREET, HALF A BLOCK FROM THE BUILDING-
DICK LOCHER
MAX COLLINS

"BUT TRACY," SAYS SAM, "IF PUTTY PUSS IS STILL THERE, HE'LL BE WEARING SOME NEW FACE-"

HOW WILL YOU RECOGNIZE PUTTY PUSS? HE'S HAD TIME TO SWITCH IDENTITIES!
DICK LOCHER
MAX COLLINS

"HE WON'T HAVE TIME TO CREATE A NEW IMAGE," SAYS TRACY. "HE'LL PROBABLY FALL BACK ON ONE HE'S PREVIOUSLY USED-"

HAVE YOU SEALED OFF THE BUILDING?
YES, DETECTIVE TRACY- PUTTY PUSS HAS TO BE IN THERE-

PUTTY PUSS WAS DROPPED BACK ONTO THE ROOF-
WE'LL GET SOME MEN UP THERE AT ONCE!
DICK LOCHER
MAX COLLINS

FINE- THEY CAN BACK ME UP!

I THOUGHT YOU'D RESORT TO USING A FACE YOU'D PREVIOUSLY "WORN"– I JUST DIDN'T GUESS IT'D BE MINE–
DICK LOCHER
MAX COLLINS

OFFICER–ARREST THIS IMPOSTER! HE'S PUTTY PUSS–

HOW ARE WE DOING?
HALF A BLOCK AWAY...

RUSHING BACK TO THE BUILDING WHERE PUTTY PUSS WAS "DROPPED" OFF BY THE COPTER PILOT, TRACY ENCOUNTERS... HIMSELF–
I'M THE REAL DICK TRACY–
ARREST THIS MAN– HE'S PUTTY PUSS!
DON'T EITHER OF YOU MOVE!

OFFICER, LOOK AT HIS CLOTHES – THOSE AREN'T MY CLOTHES, THEY'RE DIET SMITH'S –
WATCH OUT– HE'S TRICKY–
WELL, FRANKLY, I DON'T SEE MUCH DIFFERENCE–
DICK LOCHER
MAX COLLINS

WELL I DO – THE DAY DICK TRACY WEARS ANYTHING BUT A BLACK SUIT, I'LL TURN IN MY BOW TIE!

SORRY FOR THE DELAY– TRAFFIC. WRISTS BEHIND YOU, PUTTY PUSS –
SAM, DON'T BE FOOLED– HE MADE ME SWITCH CLOTHES WITH HIM –
TELL YOU WHAT– PUT US BOTH IN CUFFS–

HUH?
IN AN HOUR, ONE OF US WILL LOSE FACE–

IN AN HOUR OR SO, THE FALSE TRACY'S PUSS'LL START MELTING LIKE WAX–
NO– NO...
YES–
WE'LL JUST PUT YOU BOTH IN CUFFS– THE REAL TRACY WON'T MIND–

DICK LOCHER
MAX COLLINS

SMUK

JEEZ- MUST BE WEIRD, BELTING YOURSELF IN THE FACE!
I DIDN'T FEEL A THING, SAM-
DICK LOCHER
MAX COLLINS

I'VE READ HIM HIS RIGHTS, TRACY-
GOOD. NOW I'LL GIVE HIM A LEFT!

WHERE'S DIET, YOU FUGITIVE FROM A HORROR SHOW?

HE'S DEAD.
DICK LOCHER
MAX COLLINS

I WAS LYING, TRACY- YOUR PAL DIET IS FINE. OR AM I LYING NOW?
DICK LOCHER
MAX COLLINS

YOU'RE GOING TO TELL ME WHERE DIET SMITH IS, OR I'LL MAKE PUTTY OUT OF THE REST OF YOU!

THAT WON'T BE NECESSARY...

DIET!
I WAS CHLOROFORMED AND LOCKED IN A CLOSET-I WASN'T EVEN TIED UP...

WHO PUT YOU UP TO THIS ?!?
DICK LOCHER
MAX COLLINS

ARE YOU ALL RIGHT, DIET?
DICK LOCHER
MAX COLLINS
YEAH- MY SECURITY CHIEF KNOCKED ME OUT...OR RATHER PUTTY PUSS POSING AS MY SECURITY CHIEF-

AM I LATE FOR MY PRESS CONFERENCE...?

YOU MEAN TO SAY... PUTTY PUSS POSED AS ME AT THE PRESS CONFERENCE...?

JUST AS TRACY UNMASKS PUTTY PUSS, DIET TURNS UP, ALIVE, IF CONFUSED, AFTER A STAY IN A CLOSET....
APPARENTLY SOMEBODY WANTED YOU OUT OF COMMISSION JUST LONG ENOUGH FOR PUTTY PUSS TO MAKE THAT PRESS CONFERENCE APPEARANCE AS YOU...
AND BLACKEN YOUR NAME POLITICALLY-
WHOSE IDEA WAS THIS ?

"WHO WAS IN BACK OF IT, PUTTY PUSS ?" "GRANT ME IMMUNITY AND I'LL TELL YOU IN COURT, COP."

YOU'RE INSANE PUTTY PUSS.
DID YOU JUST FIGURE THAT OUT ? SOME DETECTIVE YOU ARE-

AND, SO, THE CURTAIN GOES DOWN ON HARLEY NIAV-
I'M NOT REALLY A CRIMINAL, YOU KNOW... I'M AN...
YES, AN ACTOR...
HAPPY BIRTHDAY JOHN

.. AWAITING A COMMAND PERFORMANCE BEFORE A JUDGE AND JURY- BUT EVEN AMONG YOUR MILLION FACES, YOU LACK THE ONE YOU NEED MOST-
DICK LOCHER
MAX COLLINS

WHAT'S THAT ?
THE FACE OF AN INNOCENT MAN.
BEEEP

TRACY- YOU'RE WANTED IMMEDIATELY AT EDWARDS HOSPITAL- EMERGENCY-

A SIX-YEAR-OLD REMEMBERS:

An Afterword

I was six years old, I would guess, when I first encountered *Dick Tracy.*

I'd begun to read comic books—the Carl Barks *Donald Duck* and *Uncle Scrooge* and the Wayne Boring *Superman*—and had been read nightly doses of Edgar Rice Burroughs' *Tarzan* by my mother for some time. It was my mom who prompted me to try *Dick Tracy*—considering that *Parents* magazine listed *Tracy* as one of the most violent and objectionable comic books around, it's lucky I had the mom I did. She had read the *Tracy* strip faithfully during the war, when my dad was a navy officer stationed in San Diego. She knew what an exciting, wonderful strip it was.

So I used my ten-cent weekly allowance to buy *Dick Tracy* #79. As I mentioned obliquely above, I read not the strip, but the *Tracy* comic books, which were published by Harvey Comics, and which collected the newspaper strip in slightly edited, four-color form. We did not have the *Tracy* strip in our local paper and it took several years for me to cajole my father into buying the Sunday Chicago *Tribune* so that I could follow my favorite sleuth.

Several of the stories in this book represent the first *Tracy* stories I ever read. They shaped me as a person, specifically shaped me as a writer; the kind of stories I write (and this extends to my novels, not just *Dick Tracy* and other comics writing), and the approach I take with those stories, flow from three tales collected in this volume.

Just as it was a dream come true to write *Dick Tracy*, it is now a dream come true to see these three stories gathered in one volume, particularly one with my name on it, and one that includes several *Tracy* stories of my own!

The first *Tracy* story I read was "The Case of the Parking Meter Bandits." This was the story that you've already read (and if you're reading this Afterword first, *stop*—go back and read the stories first!), in which Model Jones and Junior Tracy fall in love. I was spellbound by the interwoven tale of a detective tracking down petty thieves, not knowing that his own son was courting the sweet sister of the bandits' ringleader. The heartbreaking scene that has Model pretending to reject Junior brought tears to my young eyes—and it still does, frankly, when I allow it to.

But here's where Chet Gould first fried my brain; where he first twisted me, and my perceptions of life and storytelling. . . .

Issue #79 ended just after Larry's bullet goes twirling through his poor sister's body.

That was the cliffhanger, kids.

Six-year-old Al Collins waited for a month to see how that would resolve, confident, of course, that all would be right with the world when #80 appeared on a rack at Cohn's News; that Model would survive and she (if not she and Junior) would live happily ever after.

Well, that month passed, and issue #80 arrived, and Model died. ("It hurts," she said, in an eloquently simple, tragic panel.) She was dead. She was real dead. She was very, very dead. Dead dead. And I was one fried six-year-old. I didn't know from death, in the comics or anywhere else. I was very disturbed by this. I'm sure social do-gooders and child psychologists would be equally disturbed about a six-year-old being so disturbed. To hell with them.

I loved it. Instinctively, I knew something very special had happened; that a story—a made-up story—had touched me deeply.

I scrambled around to secondhand shops and to a tiny nearby mom-and-pop market where the comics (like the milk) stayed on sale long past the recommended time, and scrounged up the preceding several issues of *Dick Tracy.* These reprinted the Crewy Lou story as "The Case of the Fiendish Photographers." The action here, particularly the sequence on the wharf, when the bullets really fly, was similarly brain-frying. Such moments as Sphinx getting crushed by the elevator, Sam hurling the wad of money in King's face, and Crewy Lou being threatened by her brother Brainerd, were like electric shocks to my brain. And when Bonnie Braids was in danger, I knew she was in *danger*—this guy Gould was capable of killing her off!

That, incidentally, is what the Model story taught me about crime fiction: you must kill

off a sympathetic character now and then, to remind readers that they are in an unstable world, where anything can happen. Sure, Dick Tracy isn't going to die; but *anybody else* in his world just might! (I regret that the Tribune Media Services editors, several years ago, would not allow me to kill off Chief Pat Patton. I was after just this sort of shock to the reader's system.)

The next story I read was *really* disturbing. My aunt Oma, knowing of my burgeoning love for Tracy, picked up (on a sale table at Younkers Department Store in Des Moines, Iowa) a copy of a rare little item called *The Exploits of Dick Tracy*, "The Case of the Brow." If my brain was already sizzling on the griddle of Chester Gould's imagination, old Chet pressed down on me hard, now, with his spatula. . . .

I encountered the sexy, naughty Summer Sisters, who had to endure the Brow's spike machine (!), little droplets of blood pearling their shapely legs. I of course encountered the Brow himself, the sadist who stuck those limbs into that spike machine, in which he eventually found his own head stuck when the Summer Sisters took their revenge. Later in the story, I witnessed Tracy himself struck with a spearlike lightning rod, our hero actually going to hospital to recover, something heroes had never done in any other stories I'd thus far encountered. And finally I saw the Brow get impaled on a flag pole, meeting a Nazi spy's just if grisly reward.

Most of all, though, I had seen the Brow take his revenge on the Summer Sisters; when the girls, underwater in a car forced off a bridge, seemed to drown, I kept turning pages, waiting for them somehow to come miraculously back to life. They didn't, of course. After Model Jones, I should have known. Studying Gould's panel of the drowned girls, I should also have known 'cause nobody drew dead people like Chet. Their shapely limbs askew, their eyes shut, their bodies floating, the Summer Sisters—despite the smallness of their sins—had paid a large price.

As I continued to collect *Tracy* comics—and Big Little Books, when I could find them (the story adapted to BLB as "From Colorado to Nova Scotia" would have been in this volume, if it hadn't been reprinted relatively recently in *Dick Tracy: The Thirties*, Chelsea House, 1978)—I began to write and draw my own stories. I wanted to be a cartoonist, and of course my scribblings were mostly of Dick Tracy. My mother, without my knowledge, gathered some of these drawings and sent them to Chester Gould. He did something very special for me, something that literally changed my life: He wrote me a letter congratulating me on my recent eighth birthday, and told me I drew Tracy better than anybody else my age. Actually, Tracy himself told me, in a drawing Chet made.

It was the biggest thrill of my life, to that date, and few thrills since have come close to matching it.

I wrote Chet back and thanked him, and asked him if I could take over the strip when he retired. He rewarded my audacity with another letter. He was extremely kind to me.

As I grew older, my interest in *Dick Tracy* extended to crime and mystery fiction in general. It takes no great leap of the imagination to see how the six-year-old me, loving *Dick Tracy*, could become the thirteen-year-old me, sitting devouring *One Lonely Night* by Mickey Spillane. At some point in junior high, I stopped wanting to be a cartoonist and started wanting to be a mystery writer.

But I never stopped loving *Dick Tracy* and its creator. That was the difference between me and most kids who liked *Tracy*. Most of them fantasized about being Dick Tracy. I fantasized about being Chester Gould. I knew, from that distinctive signature on the covers of the comic books, that somebody was responsible for those wonderful stories.

I wanted to be somebody like that. I wanted to give six-year-olds, of all ages, wonderful stories. I hope, in some small degree, in both my novels and my comics work, that I've succeeded in that goal.

MAX ALLAN COLLINS
November 1, 1989

Dear Allan: I have lots of friends but none that can draw my picture at your age, any better than you. Your mother sent me a drawing you made and it's a wow! Many thanks for thinking of me.

Oh yes – you were 8 years old Saturday and I want to say now Happy Birthday! Sorry I'm late!

As ever
Dick Tracy
and

Chester Gould